Animal Stories

Animal
Stories

Cathay Books

First published in Great Britain in 1982 by Octopus Books Ltd

This edition published in 1984 by Cathay Books
59 Grosvenor Street
London W1

Reprinted 1985

Arrangement and illustrations © 1982 Hennerwood
Publications Ltd

Illustrated by Lesley Smith

ISBN 0 86178 240 2

All Rights Reserved

Printed in Czechoslovakia

50546/2

Contents

The Small Miracle

PAUL GALLICO

Approaching Assisi via the chalky, dusty road that twists its way up Monte Subasio, now revealing, now concealing the exquisite little town, as it winds its way through olive and cypress groves, you eventually reach a division where your choice lies between an upper and a lower route.

If you select the latter, you soon find yourself entering Assisi through the twelfth-century archway of the denticulated door of St Francis. But if, seduced by the clear air, the wish to mount even closer to the canopy of blue Italian sky and expose still more of the delectable view of the rich Umbrian valley below, you choose the upper way, you and your vehicle eventually become inextricably entangled in the welter of humanity, oxen, goats, bawling calves, mules, fowl, children, pigs, booths and carts gathered at the market place outside the walls.

It is here you would be most likely to encounter Pepino, with his donkey Violetta, hard at work, turning his hand to anything whereby a small boy and a strong, willing beast of burden could win for themselves the crumpled ten and twenty lira notes needed to buy food and pay for lodging in the barn of Niccolo the stableman.

Pepino and Violetta were everything to each other. They were

9

a familiar sight about Assisi and its immediate environs – the thin brown boy, ragged and barefooted, with the enormous dark eyes, large ears, and close-cropped, upstanding hair, and the dust-coloured little donkey with the Mona Lisa smile.

Pepino was ten years old and an orphan, his father, mother and near relatives having been killed in the war. In self-reliance, wisdom and demeanour he was, of course, much older, a circumstance aided by his independence, for Pepino was an unusual orphan in that having a heritage he need rely on no one. Pepino's heritage was Violetta.

She was a good, useful and docile donkey, alike as any other with friendly, gentle eyes, soft taupe-coloured muzzle, and long, pointed brown ears, with one exception that distinguished her. Violetta had a curious expression about the corners of her mouth, as though she were smiling gently over something that amused or pleased her. Thus, no matter what kind of work, or how much she was asked to do, she always appeared to be performing it with a smile of quiet satisfaction. The combination of Pepino's dark lustrous eyes and Violetta's smile was so harmonious that people favoured them and they were able not only to earn enough for their keep but, aided and advised by Father Damico, the priest of their parish, to save a little as well.

There were all kinds of things they could do – carry loads of wood or water, deliver purchases carried in the panniers that thumped against Violetta's sides, hire out to help pull a cart mired in the mud, aid in the olive harvest, and even, occasionally, help some citizen who was too encumbered with wine to reach his home on foot, by means of a four-footed taxi with Pepino walking beside to see that the drunkard did not fall off.

But this was not the only reason for the love that existed between boy and donkey, for Violetta was more than just the means of his livelihood. She was mother to him, and father, brother, playmate, companion, and comfort. At night, in the straw of Niccolo's stable, Pepino slept curled up close to her when it was cold, his head pillowed on her neck.

Since the mountainside was a rough world for a small boy, he was sometimes beaten or injured, and then he could creep to her for comfort and Violetta would gently nuzzle his bruises. When there was joy in his heart, he shouted songs into her waving ears; when he was lonely and hurt, he could lean his head against her soft, warm flank and cry out his tears.

On his part, he fed her, watered her, searched her for ticks and parasites, picked stones from her hoofs, scratched and groomed and curried her, lavished affection on her, particularly when they were alone, while in public he never beat her with the donkey stick more than was necessary. For this treatment Violetta made a god of Pepino, and repaid him with loyalty, obedience and affection.

Thus, when one day in the early spring Violetta fell ill, it was the most serious thing that had ever happened to Pepino. It began first with an unusual lethargy that would respond neither to stick nor caresses, nor the young, strident voice urging her on. Later Pepino observed other symptoms and a visible loss of weight. Her ribs, once so well padded, began to show through her sides. But most distressing, either through a change in the conformation of her head, due to growing thinner, or because of the distress of the illness, Violetta lost her enchanting and lovable smile.

Drawing upon his carefully hoarded reserves of lira notes and parting with several of the impressive denomination of a hundred, Pepino called in Dr Bartoli, the vet.

The vet examined her in good faith, dosed her, and tried his best; but she did not improve and, instead, continued to lose weight and grow weaker. He hummed and hawed then and said, 'Well, now, it is hard to say. It might be one thing, such as the bite of a fly new to this district, or another, such as a germ settling in the intestine.' Either way, how could one tell? There had been a similar case in Foligno and another in a far-away town. He recommended resting the beast and feeding her lightly. If the illness passed from her and God willed, she might live. Otherwise, she would surely die and there would be an end to her suffering.

After he had gone away, Pepino put his cropped head on Violetta's heaving flank and wept unrestrainedly. But then, when the storm, induced by the fear of losing his only companion in the world, had subsided, he knew what he must do. If there was no help for Violetta on earth, the appeal must be registered above. His plan was nothing less than to take Violetta into the crypt beneath the lower church of the Basilica of St Francis, where rested the remains of the Saint who had so dearly loved God's creations, including all the feathered and the four-footed brothers and sisters who served Him. There he would beg St Francis to heal her. Pepino had no doubt that the Saint would do so when he saw Violetta.

These things Pepino knew from Father Damico, who had a way of talking about St Francis as though he were a living person who might still be encountered in his frayed cowl, bound with a hemp cord at the middle, merely by turning a corner of the Main Square in Assisi or by walking down one of the narrow, cobbled streets.

And besides, there was a precedent. Giani, his friend, the son of Niccolo the stableman, had taken his sick kitten into the crypt and asked St Francis to heal her, and the cat had got well – at least half well, anyway, for her hind legs still dragged a little; but at least she had not died. Pepino felt that if Violetta were to die, it would be the end of everything for him.

Thereupon, with considerable difficulty, he persuaded the sick and shaky donkey to rise, and with urgings and caresses and minimum use of the stick drove her through the crooked streets of Assisi and up the hill to the Basilica of St Francis. At the beautiful twin portal of the lower church he respectfully asked Fra Bernard, who was on duty there, for permission to take Violetta down to St Francis, so that she might be made well again.

Fra Bernard was a new monk, and, calling Pepino a young and impious scoundrel, ordered him and his donkey to be off. It was strictly forbidden to bring livestock into the church, and even to think of taking an ass into the crypt of St Francis was a desecration. And besides, how did he imagine she would get down there when the narrow, winding staircase was barely wide enough to accommodate humans in single file, much less four-footed animals? Pepino must be a fool as well as a shiftless rascal.

As ordered, Pepino retreated from the portal, his arm about

Violetta's neck, and bethought himself of what he must do next to succeed in his purpose, for while he was disappointed at the rebuff he had received, he was not at all discouraged.

Despite the tragedy that had struck Pepino's early life and robbed him of his family, he really considered himself a most fortunate boy, compared with many, since he had acquired not only a heritage to aid him in earning a living but also an important precept by which to live.

This maxim, the golden key to success, had been left with Pepino, together with bars of chocolate, chewing gum, peanut brittle, soap, and other delights, by a corporal in the United States Army who had, in the six months he had been stationed in the vicinity of Assisi, been Pepino's demigod and hero. His name was Francis Xavier O'Halloran, and what he told Pepino before he departed out of his life for ever was, 'If you want to get ahead in this world, kid, don't never take no for an answer. Get it?' Pepino never forgot this important advice.

He thought now that his next step was clear; nevertheless, he went first to his friend and adviser, Father Damico, for confirmation.

Father Damico, who had a broad head, lustrous eyes, and shoulders shaped as though they had been especially designed to support the burdens laid upon them by his parishioners, said, 'You are within your rights, my son, in taking your request to the lay Supervisor and it lies within his power to grant or refuse it.'

There was no malice in the encouragement he thus gave Pepino, but it was also true that he was not loath to see the Supervisor brought face to face with an example of pure and innocent faith. For in his private opinion that worthy man was too much concerned with the twin churches that formed the Basilica and the crypt as a tourist attraction. He, Father Damico, could not see why the child should not have his wish, but, of course, it was out of his jurisdiction. He was, however, curious about how the Supervisor would react, even though he thought he knew in advance.

However, he did not impart his fears to Pepino and merely called after him as he was leaving, 'And if the little one cannot be got in from above, there is another entrance from below, through the old church, only it has been walled up for a hundred years. But it could be opened. You might remind the Supervisor when you see him. He knows where it is.'

Pepino thanked him and went back alone to the Basilica and the monastery attached to it and asked permission to see the Supervisor.

This personage was an accessible man, and even though he was engaged in a conversation with the Bishop, he sent for Pepino, who walked into the cloister gardens where he waited respectfully for the two great men to finish.

The two dignitaries were walking up and down, and Pepino wished it were the Bishop who was to say yea or nay to his request, as he looked the kindlier of the two, the Supervisor appearing to have more the expression of a merchant. The boy pricked up his ears, because, as it happened, so they were speaking of St Francis, and the Bishop was just remarking with a sigh, 'He has been gone too long from this earth. The lesson of his life is plain to all who can read. But who in these times will pause to do so?'

The Supervisor said, 'His tomb in the crypt attracts many to Assisi. But in a Holy Year, relics are even better. If we but had the tongue of the Saint, or a lock of his hair, or a fingernail.'

The Bishop had a far-away look in his eyes, and he was shaking his head gently. 'It is a message we are in need of, my dear Supervisor, a message from a great heart that would speak to us across the gap of seven centuries to remind us of The Way.' And here he paused and coughed, for he was a polite man and noticed that Pepino was waiting.

The Supervisor turned also and said, 'Ah yes, my son, what is it that I can do for you?'

Pepino said, 'Please, sir, my donkey Violetta is very sick. The Doctor Bartoli has said he can do nothing more and perhaps she will die. Please, I would like permission to take her into the tomb of Saint Francis and ask him to cure her. He loved all animals, and particularly little donkeys. I am sure he will make her well.'

The Supervisor looked shocked. 'A donkey. In the crypt. How-ever did you come to that idea?'

Pepino explained about Giani and his sick kitten, while the Bishop turned away to hide a smile.

But the Supervisor was not smiling. He asked, 'How did this Giani succeed in smuggling a kitten into the tomb?'

Since it was all over, Pepino saw no reason for not telling, and replied, 'Under his coat, sir.'

The Supervisor made a mental note to warn the brothers to keep a sharper eye out for small boys or other persons with suspicious-looking lumps under their outer clothing.

'Of course we can have no such goings on,' he said. 'The next thing you know, everyone would be coming, bringing a sick dog, or an ox, or a goat, or even a pig. And then where should we end up? A veritable sty.'

'But sir,' Pepino pleaded, 'no one need know. We would come and go so very quickly.'

The Supervisor's mind played. There was something touching about the boy – the bullet head, the enormous eyes, the jug-handle ears. And yet, what if he permitted it and the donkey then died, as seemed most likely if Dr Bartoli had said there was no further hope? Word was sure to get about, and the shrine would suffer from it. He wondered what the Bishop was thinking and how *he* would solve the problem.

He equivocated: 'And besides, even if we were to allow it, you would never be able to get your donkey around the turn at the bottom of the stairs. So, you see, it is quite impossible.'

'But there is another entrance,' Pepino said. 'From the old church. It has not been used for a long time, but it could be opened just this once – couldn't it?'

The Supervisor was indignant. 'What are you saying – destroy church property? The entrance has been walled up for over a century, ever since the new crypt was built.'

The Bishop thought he saw a way out and said gently to the boy, 'Why do you not go home and pray to Saint Francis to assist you?

If you open your heart to him and have faith, he will surely hear you.'

'But it wouldn't be the same,' Pepino cried, and his voice was shaking with the sobs that wanted to come. 'I must take her where Saint Francis can see her. She isn't like any other old donkey – Violetta has the sweetest smile. She does not smile any more since she has been so ill. But perhaps she would, just once more for Saint Francis. And when he saw it he would not be able to resist her, and he would make her well. I know he would!'

The Supervisor knew his ground now. He said, 'I am sorry, my son, but the answer is no.'

But even through his despair and the bitter tears he shed as he went away, Pepino knew that if Violetta was to live he must not take no for an answer.

'Who is there, then?' Pepino asked of Father Damico later. 'Who is above the Supervisor and my lord the Bishop who might tell them to let me take Violetta into the crypt?'

Father Damico's stomach felt cold as he thought of the dizzying hierarchy between Assisi and Rome. Nevertheless, he explained as best he could, concluding with, 'And at the top is His Holiness, the Pope himself. Surely his heart would be touched by what has happened if you were able to tell him, for he is a great and good man. But he is busy with important weighty affairs, Pepino, and it would be impossible for him to see you.'

Pepino went back to Niccolo's stable, where he ministered to Violetta, fed and watered her and rubbed her muzzle a hundred times. Then he withdrew his money from the stone jar buried under the straw and counted it. He had almost three hundred lire. A hundred of it he set aside and promised to his friend Giani if he would look after Violetta, while Pepino was gone, as if she were his own. Then he patted her once more, brushed away the tears that had started again at the sight of how thin she was, put on his jacket, and went out on the high road, where, using his thumb as he had learned from Corporal Francis Xavier O'Halloran, he got a lift in a lorry going to Foligno and the main road. He was on his way to Rome to see the Holy Father.

Never had any small boy looked quite so infinitesimal and forlorn as Pepino standing in the boundless and almost deserted,
since it was early in the morning, St Peter's Square. Everything
towered over him – the massive dome of St Peter's, the obelisk of
Caligula, the Bernini colonnades. Everything contrived to make
him look pinched and miserable in his bare feet, torn trousers, and
ragged jacket. Never was a boy more overpowered, lonely, and
frightened, or carried a greater burden of unhappiness in his
heart.

For now that he was at last in Rome, the gigantic proportions
of the buildings and monuments, their awe and majesty, began to
sap his courage, and he seemed to have a glimpse into the utter
futility and hopelessness of his mission. And then there would
arise in his mind a picture of the sad little donkey who did not
smile any more, her heaving flanks and clouded eyes, and who
would surely die unless he could find help for her. It was thoughts
like these that enabled him finally to cross the piazza and timidly
approach one of the smaller side entrances to the Vatican.

The Swiss guard, in his slashed red, yellow, and blue uniform,
with his long halberd, looked enormous and forbidding.
Nevertheless, Pepino edged up to him and said, 'Please, will you
take me to see the Pope? I wish to speak to him about my donkey
Violetta, who is very ill and may die unless the Pope will help me.'

The guard smiled, not unkindly, for he was used to these
ignorant and innocent requests, and the fact that it came from a
dirty, ragged little boy, with eyes like ink pools and a round head
from which the ears stood out like the handles on a cream jug,
made it all the more harmless. But, nevertheless, he was shaking
his head as he smiled, and then said that His Holiness was a very
busy man and could not be seen. And the guard grounded his
halberd with a thud and let it fall slantwise across the door to show
that he meant business.

Pepino backed away. What good was his precept in the face of
such power and majesty? And yet the memory of what Corporal
O'Halloran had said told him that he must return to the Vatican
yet once again.

At the side of the piazza he saw an old woman sitting under an umbrella, selling little bouquets and nosegays of spring flowers – daffodils and jonquils, snowdrops and white narcissus, Parma violets and lilies of the valley, vari-coloured carnations, pansies, and tiny sweetheart roses. Some of the people visiting St Peter's liked to place these on the altar of their favourite saint. The flowers were crisp and fresh from the market, and many of them had glistening drops of water still clinging to their petals.

Looking at them made Pepino think of home and Father Damico and what he had said of the love St Francis had for flowers. Father Damico had the gift of making everything he thought and said sound like poetry. And Pepino came to the conclusion that if St Francis, who had been a holy man, had been so fond of flowers, perhaps the Pope, who according to his position was even holier, would love them, too.

For fifty lire he bought a tiny bouquet in which a spray of lilies of the valley rose from a bed of dark violets and small red roses crowded next to yellow pansies all tied about with leaf and feather fern and paper lace.

From a stall where postcards and souvenirs were sold, he begged pencil and paper, and laboriously composed a note:

Dear and most sacred Holy Father: These flowers are for you. Please let me see you and tell you about my donkey Violetta who is dying and they will not let me take her to see Saint Francis so that he may cure her. I live in the town of Assisi, but I have come all the way here to see you.

Your loving Pepino.

Thereupon, he returned to the door, placed the bouquet and the note in the hand of the Swiss guard, and begged, 'Please take these up to the Pope. I am sure he will see me when he receives the flowers and reads what I have written.'

The guard had not expected this. The child and the flowers had suddenly placed him in a dilemma from which he could not extricate himself in the presence of those large and trusting eyes. However, he was not without experience in handling such matters. He had only to place a colleague at his post, go to the Guard Room, throw the flowers and the note into the wastepaper basket, absent himself for a sufficient length of time, and then return to tell the boy that His Holiness thanked him for the gift of the flowers and regretted that press of important business made it impossible for him to grant him an audience.

This little subterfuge the guard put into motion at once; but when he came to completing the next-to-last act in it, he found to his amazement that somehow he could not bring himself to do it. There was the wastepaper basket, yawning to receive the offering, but the little nosegay seemed to be glued to his fingers. How gay, sweet, and cool the flowers were. What thoughts they brought to his mind of spring in the green valleys of his far-off canton of Luzern. He saw again the snow-capped mountains of his youth, the little gingerbread houses, the grey, soft-eyed cattle grazing in the blossom-carpeted meadows, and he heard the heart-warming tinkling of their bells.

Dazed by what had happened to him, he left the Guard Room and wandered through the corridors, for he did not know where to go or what to do with his burden. He was eventually encountered by a busy little Monsignor, one of the vast army of clerks and secretaries employed in the Vatican, who paused, astonished at the sight of the burly guard helplessly contemplating a tiny posy.

And thus occurred the minor miracle whereby Pepino's plea and offering crossed the boundary in the palace that divided the mundane from the spiritual, the lay from the ecclesiastical.

For to the great relief of the guard, the Monsignor took over the burning articles that he had been unable to relinquish; and this priest they touched, too, as it is the peculiar power of flowers that while they are universal and spread their species over the world, they invoke in each beholder the dearest and most cherished memories.

In this manner, the little bouquet passed on and upward from hand to hand, pausing briefly in the possession of the clerk of the Apostolic Chamber, the Privy Almoner, the Papal Sacristan, the

Master of the Sacred Palaces, the Papal Chamberlain. The dew vanished from the flowers; they began to lose their freshness and to wilt, passing from hand to hand. And yet they retained their magic, the message of love and memories that rendered it impossible for any of these intermediaries to dispose of them.

Eventually, then, they were deposited with the missive that accompanied them on the desk of the man for whom they had been destined. He read the note and then sat there silently contemplating the blossoms. He closed his eyes for a moment, the better to entertain the picture that arose in his mind of himself as a small Roman boy taken on a Sunday into the Alban Hills, where for the first time he saw violets growing wild.

When he opened his eyes at last, he said to his secretary, 'Let the child be brought here. I will see him.'

Thus it was that Pepino at last came into the presence of the Pope, seated at his desk in his office. Perched on the edge of a chair next to him, Pepino told the whole story about Violetta, his need to take her into the tomb of St Francis, about the Supervisor who was preventing him, and all about Father Damico, too, and the second entrance to the crypt, Violetta's smile, and his love for her – everything, in fact, that was in his heart and that now poured forth to the sympathetic man sitting quietly behind the desk.

And when, at the end of half an hour, he was ushered from the presence, he was quite sure he was the happiest boy in the world. For he had not only the blessing of the Pope, but also, under his jacket, two letters, one addressed to the lay Supervisor of the Monastery of Assisi and the other to Father Damico. No longer did he feel small and overwhelmed when he stepped out on to the square again past the astonished but delighted Swiss guard. He felt as though he could give one leap and a bound and fly back to his Violetta's side.

Nevertheless, he had to give heed to the more practical side of transportation. He inquired his way to a bus that took him to where the Via Flaminia became a country road stretching to the north, then plied his thumb backed by his eloquent eyes, and before nightfall of that day, with good luck, was home in Assisi.

He rubbed her muzzle a hundred times

After a visit to Violetta she had assured him that she had been
well looked after and at least was no worse than she had been
before his departure, Pepino proudly went to Father Damico and
presented his letters as he had been instructed to do.

The Father fingered the envelope for the Supervisor and then,
with a great surge of warmth and happiness, read the one
addressed to himself. He said to Pepino, 'Tomorrow we will take
the Supervisor's letter to him. He will summon masons and the old
door will be broken down and you will be able to take Violetta into
the tomb and pray there for her recovery. The Pope himself has
approved it.'

The Pope, of course, had not written the letters personally.
They had been composed with considerable delight and satisfaction by the Cardinal-Secretary, backed by Papal authority, who
said in his missive to Father Damico:

> Surely the Supervisor must know that in his lifetime the
> blessed Saint Francis was accompanied to chapel by a little lamb
> that used to follow him about Assisi. Is an *asinus* any less created
> by God because his coat is rougher and his ears longer?

And he wrote also of another matter, which Father Damico imparted to Pepino in his own way.

He said, 'Pepino, there is something you must understand
before we go to see the Abbot. It is your hope that because of your
faith in St Francis he will help you and heal your donkey. But had
you thought, perhaps, that he who dearly cared for all of God's
creatures might come to love Violetta so greatly that he would
wish to have her at his side in Eternity?'

A cold terror gripped Pepino as he listened. He managed to say,
'No, Father, I had not thought –'

The priest continued: 'Will you go to the crypt only to ask,
Pepino, or will you also, if necessary, be prepared to give?'

Everything in Pepino cried out against the possibility of losing
Violetta, even to someone as beloved as St Francis. Yet when he
raised his stricken face and looked into the lustrous eyes of Father
Damico, there was something in their depths that gave him the

courage to whisper, 'I will give – if I must. But, oh, I hope he will let her stay with me just a little longer.'

The clink of the stonemason's pick rang again and again through the vaulted chamber of the lower church, where the walled-up door of the passageway leading to the crypt was being removed. Nearby waited the Supervisor and his friend the Bishop, Father Damico, and Pepino, large-eyed, pale, and silent. The boy kept his arms about the neck of Violetta and his face pressed to hers. The little donkey was very shaky on her legs and could barely stand.

The Supervisor watched humbly and impassively while broken bricks and clods of mortar fell as the breach widened and the freed current of air from the passage swirled the plaster dust in clouds. He was a just man for all his weakness, and had invited the Bishop to witness his rebuke.

A portion of the wall proved obstinate. The mason attacked the archway at the side to weaken its support. Then the loosened masonry began to tumble again. A narrow passageway was effected, and through the opening they could see the distant flicker of the candles placed at the altar wherein rested the remains of St Francis.

Pepino stirred towards the opening. Or was it Violetta who had moved nervously, frightened by the unaccustomed place and noises? Father Damico said, 'Wait,' and Pepino held her; but the donkey's uncertain feet slipped on the rubble and then lashed out in panic, striking at the side of the archway where it had been weakened. A brick fell out. A crack appeared.

Father Damico leaped and pulled boy and animal out of the way as, with a roar, the side of the arch collapsed, laying bare a piece of the old wall and the hollow behind it before everything vanished in a cloud of dust.

But when the dust settled, the Bishop, his eyes starting from his head, was pointing to something that rested in a niche of the hollow just revealed. It was a small, grey, leaden box. Even from there they could see the year 1226, when St Francis died, engraved on the side, and the large initial 'F.'

The Bishop's breath came out like a sigh. 'Ah, could it be? The legacy of Saint Francis! Fra Leo mentions it. It was hidden away centuries ago, and no one has ever been able to find it since.'

The Supervisor said hoarsely, 'The contents! Let us see what is inside – it may be valuable!'

The Bishop hesitated. 'Perhaps we had best wait. For this is in itself a miracle, this finding.'

But Father Damico, who was a poet and to whom St Francis was a living spirit, cried 'Open it, I beg of you! All who are here are humble. Surely Heaven's plan has guided us to it.'

The Abbot held the lantern. The mason with his careful, honest workman's hands deftly loosed the bindings and pried the lid of the airtight box. It opened with an ancient creaking of its hinge and revealed what had been placed there more than seven centuries before.

There was a piece of hempen cord, knotted as though, perhaps, once it had been worn about the waist. Caught in the knot, as fresh as though it had grown but yesterday, was a single sprig of wheat. Dried and preserved, there lay, too, the stem and starry flower of a mountain primrose and, next to it, one downy feather from a tiny meadow bird.

Silently the men stared at these objects from the past to try to read their meaning, and Father Damico wept, for to him they brought the vivid figure of the Saint, half-blinded, worn and fragile, the cord knotted at his waist, singing, striding through a field of wheat. The flower might have been the first discovered by him after a winter's snow, and addressed as 'Sister Cowslip,' and praised for her tenderness and beauty. As though he were transported there, Father Damico saw the little field bird fly trustingly to Francis' shoulder and chirrup and nestle there and leave a feather in his hand. His heart was so full he thought he could not bear it.

The Bishop, too, was close to tears as, in his own way, he

interpreted what they had found. 'Ah, what could be clearer than the message of the Saint? Poverty, love, and faith. This is his bequest to all of us.'

Pepino said, 'Please, lords and sirs, may Violetta and I go into the crypt now?'

They had forgotten him. Now they started up from their contemplation of the touching relics.

Father Damico cleared the tears from his eyes. The doorway was freed now, and there was room for boy and donkey to pass. 'Ah, yes,' he said. 'Yes, Pepino. You may enter now. And may God go with you.'

The hoofs of the donkey went sharply *clip-clop*, *clip-clop* on the ancient flagging of the passageway. Pepino did not support her now, but walked beside, hand just resting lightly and lovingly on her neck. His round, cropped head with the outstanding ears was held high, and his shoulders were bravely squared.

And to Father Damico it seemed, as they passed, whether because of the uneven light and the dancing shadows, or because he wished it so, that the ghost, the merest wisp, the barest suspicion of a smile had returned to the mouth of Violetta.

Thus the watchers saw boy and donkey silhouetted against the flickering oil lamps and altar candles of the crypt as they went forward to complete their pilgrimage of faith.

Bambi's Discovery

FELIX SALTEN

Bambi is a baby deer born in the wild. His mother sets about his education from a very early age . . .

In early summer the trees stood still under the blue sky, held their limbs outstretched and received the direct rays of the sun. On the shrubs and bushes in the undergrowth, the flowers unfolded their red, white and yellow stars. On some the seed pods had begun to appear again. They perched innumerable on the fine tips of the branches, tender and firm and resolute and seemed like small, clenched fists. Out of the earth came whole troops of flowers like motley stars, so that the soil of the twilit forest floor shone with a silent, ardent, colourful gladness. Everything smelled of fresh leaves, of blossoms, of moist clods and green wood. When morning broke, or when the sun went down, the whole woods resounded with a thousand voices and from morning till night, the bees hummed, wasps droned, and filled the fragrant stillness with their murmur.

These were the earliest days of Bambi's life. He walked behind his mother on a narrow track that ran through the midst of the bushes. How pleasant it was to walk there. The thick foliage stroked his flanks softly and bent supply aside. The track appeared to be barred and obstructed in a dozen places and yet they advanced with the greatest ease. There were tracks like this everywhere running criss-cross through the whole woods. His mother knew them all and, if Bambi sometimes stopped before a bush as if it were an impenetrable green wall, she always found where the path went through, without hesitation or searching.

Bambi questioned her. He loved to ask his mother questions. It was the pleasantest thing for him to ask a question and then to hear what answer his mother would give. Bambi was never surprised that question after question should come into his mind continually and without effort. He found it perfectly natural, and it delighted him very much. It was very delightful, too to wait expectantly till the answer came. If it turned out the way he wanted, he was satisfied. Sometimes, of course, he did not understand, but that was pleasant also because he was kept busy picturing what he had not understood, in his own way. Sometimes he felt very sure that his mother was not giving him a complete answer, was intentionally not telling him all she knew. And, at first, that was very pleasant, too. For then there would remain in him such a lively curiosity, such suspicion, mysteriously and joyously flashing through him, such anticipation, that he would become anxious and happy at the same time, and grow silent.

Once he asked, 'Whom does this trail belong to Mother?'

His mother answered, 'To us.'

Bambi asked again, 'To you and me?'

'Yes.'

'To us two?'

'Yes.'

'Only to us two?'

'No,' said his mother, 'to us deer.'

'What are deer?' Bambi asked, and laughed.

His mother looked at him from head to foot and laughed too. 'You are a deer and I am a deer. We're both deer,' she said. 'Do you understand?'

Bambi sprang into the air for joy. 'Yes, I understand,' he said. 'I'm a little deer and you're a big deer, aren't you?'

His mother nodded and said, 'Now you see.'

But Bambi grew serious again. 'Are there other deer besides you and me?' he asked.

'Certainly,' his mother said. 'Many of them.'

'Where are they?' cried Bambi.

'Here, everywhere.'

'But I don't see them.'

'You will soon,' she said.

'When?' Bambi stood still, wild with curiosity.

'Soon.' The mother walked on quietly. Bambi followed her. He kept silent, for he was wondering what 'soon' might mean. He came to the conclusion that 'soon' was certainly not 'now'. But he wasn't sure at what time 'soon' stopped being 'soon' and began to be a 'long while'. Suddenly he asked, 'Who made this trail?'

'We,' his mother answered.

Bambi was astonished 'We? You and I?'

The mother said, 'Well, we . . . we deer.'

Bambi asked, 'Which deer?'

'All of us,' his mother said sharply.

They walked on. Bambi was in high spirits and felt like leaping off the path, but he stayed close to his mother. Something rustled in front of them, close to the ground. The fern fronds and wood-lettuce concealed something that advanced in violent motion. A threadlike, little cry shrilled out piteously; then all was still. Only the leaves and the blades of grass shivered back into place. A ferret had caught a mouse. He came slinking by, slid sideways, and prepared to enjoy his meal.

'What was that?' asked Bambi excitedly.

'Nothing,' his mother soothed him.

'But,' Bambi trembled, 'but I saw it.'

'Yes, yes,' said mother. 'Don't be frightened. The ferret has killed a mouse.' But Bambi was dreadfully frightened. A vast, unknown horror clutched at his heart. It was long before he could speak again. The he asked, 'Why did he kill the mouse?'

'Because,' his mother hesitated. 'Let us walk faster,' she said as though something had just occurred to her and as though she had forgotten the question. She began to hurry. Bambi sprang after her.

A long pause ensued. They walked on quietly again. Finally Bambi asked anxiously, 'Shall we kill a mouse, too, some time?'

'No,' replied his mother.

'Never?' asked Bambi.

'Never,' came the answer.

'Why not?' asked Bambi, relieved.

'Because we never kill anything,' said his mother simply.

Bambi grew happy again.

Loud cries were coming from a young ash-tree which stood near their path. The mother went along without noticing them, but Bambi stopped inquisitively. Overhead two jays were quarrelling about a nest they had plundered.

'Get away, you murderer!' cried one.

'Keep cool, you fool,' the other answered, 'I'm not afraid of you.'

'Look for your own nests,' the first one shouted, 'or I'll break your head for you.' He was beside himself with rage. 'What vulgarity!' he chattered, 'What vulgarity!'

The other jay had spied Bambi and fluttered down a few branches to shout at him. 'What are you gawking at, you freak?' he screamed.

Bambi sprang away terrified. He reached his mother and walked behind her again, frightened and obedient, thinking she had not noticed his absence.

After a pause he asked, 'Mother, what is vulgarity?'

'I don't know,' said his mother.

Bambi thought a while; then he began again. 'Why were they both so angry with each other, Mother?' he asked.

'They were fighting over food,' his mother answered.

'Will we fight over food, too, some time?' Bambi asked.

'No,' said his mother.

Bambi asked, 'Why not?'

'Because there is enough for all of us,' his mother replied.

Bambi wanted to know something else. 'Mother,' he began.

'What is it?'

'Will we be angry with each other some time?' he asked.

'No, child,' said his mother, 'we don't do such things.'

They walked along again. Presently it grew light ahead of them. It grew very bright. The trail ended with the tangle of vines and bushes. A few steps more and they would be in the bright open space that spread out before them. Bambi wanted to bound forward, but his mother had stopped.

'What is it?' he asked impatiently, already delighted.

'It's the meadow,' his mother answered.

'What is a meadow?' asked Bambi insistently.

His mother cut him short. 'You'll soon find out for yourself,' she said. She had become very serious and watchful. She stood motionless, holding her head high and listening intently. She sucked in deep breathfuls of air and looked very severe.

'It's all right,' she said at last, 'we can go out.'

Bambi leaped forward, but his mother barred the way.

'Wait till I call you,' she said. Bambi obeyed at once and stood still. 'That's right,' said his mother, to encourage him, 'and now listen to what I am saying to you.' Bambi heard how seriously his mother spoke and felt terribly excited.

'Walking on the meadow is not so simple,' his mother went on. 'It's a difficult and dangerous business. Don't ask me why. You'll find that out later on. Now do exactly as I tell you to. Will you?'

'Yes,' Bambi promised.

'Good,' said his mother, 'I'm going out alone first. Stay here and wait. And don't take your eyes off me for a minute. If you see me run back here, turn round then and run as fast as you can. I'll catch up with you soon.' She grew silent and seemed to be thinking. Then she went on earnestly, 'Run even if something should happen ... even if you should see me fall to the ground ... Don't think of me, do you understand? No matter what you see or hear, start running at once and just as fast as you possibly can. Do you promise me to do that?'

'Yes,' said Bambi softly. His mother spoke so seriously.

She went on speaking. 'Out there if I should call you,' she said, 'there must be no looking around and no questions, but you must get behind me instantly. Understand that. Run without pausing or stopping to think. If I begin to run, that means for you to run too, and no stopping until we are back here again. You won't forget, will you?'

'No,' said Bambi in a troubled voice.

'Now I'm going ahead,' said his mother, and seemed to become calmer.

She walked out. Bambi, who never took his eyes off her, saw how she moved forward with slow, cautious steps. He stood there full of expectancy, full of fear and curiosity. He saw how his mother listened in all directions, saw her shrink together, and shrank together himself, ready to leap back into the thickets. Then his mother grew calm again. She stretched herself. Then she looked around satisfied and called, 'Come.'

Bambi bounded out. Joy seized him with such tremendous force that he forgot his worries in a flash. Through the thicket he could see only the green tree tops overhead. Once in a while he caught a glimpse of the blue sky.

Now he saw the whole heaven stretching far and wide and he rejoiced without knowing why. In the forest he had seen only a stray sunbeam now and then, or the tender, dappled light that played through the branches. Suddenly he was standing in the blinding hot sunlight whose boundless power was beaming upon him. He stood in the splendid warmth that made him shut his eyes but which opened his heart.

Bambi was as though bewitched. He was completely beside himself with pleasure. He was simply wild. He leaped into the air three, four, five times. He had to do it. He felt a terrible desire to leap and jump. He stretched his young limbs joyfully. His breath came deeply and easily. He drank in the air. The sweet smell of the meadow made him so wildly happy that he had to leap into the air.

Bambi was a child. If he had been a human child he would have shouted. But he was a young deer, and deer cannot shout, at least not the way human children do. So he rejoiced with his legs and with his whole body as he flung himself into the air. His mother stood by and was glad. She saw that Bambi was wild. She watched how he bounded into the air and fell again awkwardly, in one spot. She saw how he stared around him, dazed and bewildered, only to leap up over and over again. She understood that Bambi knew only the narrow deer tracks in the forest and how his brief life was used to the limits of the thicket. He did not move from one place because he did not understand how to run freely around the open meadow.

So she stretched out her forefeet and bent laughingly towards Bambi for a moment. Then she was off with one bound, racing around in a circle so that the tall grass stems swished.

Bambi was frightened and stood motionless. Was that a sign for him to run back to the thicket? His mother had said to him, 'Don't worry about me no matter what you see or hear. Just run as fast as you can.' He was going to turn around and run as she had commanded him to, but his mother came galloping up suddenly. She came up with a wonderful swishing sound and stopped two steps from him, and cried, 'Catch me.' And in a flash she was gone.

Bambi was puzzled. What did she mean? Then she came back again running so fast that it made him giddy. She pushed his flank with her nose and said quickly, 'Try and catch me,' and fled away.

Bambi started after her. He took a few steps. Then his steps became short bounds. He felt as if he were flying without any effort on his part. There was a space under his hoofs, space under his bounding feet, space and still more space. Bambi was beside himself with joy.

The swishing grass sounded wonderful to his ears. It was marvellously soft and as fine as silk where it brushed against him. He ran round in a circle. He turned and flew off in a new circle, turned around again and kept running.

His mother was standing still, getting her breath again. She kept following Bambi with her eyes. He was wild.

Suddenly the race was over. He stopped and came up to his

mother, lifting his hoofs elegantly. He looked joyfully at her. Then they strolled contentedly side by side.

Since he had been in the open, Bambi had felt the sky and the sun and the green meadow with his whole body. He took one blinding, giddy glance at the sun, and he felt its rays as they lay warmly on his back.

Presently he began to enjoy the meadow with his eyes also. Its wonders amazed him at every step he took. You could not see the tiniest speck of earth the way you could in the forest. Blade after blade of grass covered every inch of the ground. It tossed and waved luxuriantly. It bent softly aside under every footstep, only to rise up unharmed again. The broad green meadow was starred with white daisies, with the thick, round red and purple clover blossoms and bright, golden dandelion heads.

'Look, look, Mother,' Bambi exclaimed. 'There's a flower flying.'

'That's not a flower,' said his mother, 'that's a butterfly.'

Bambi stared at the butterfly, entranced. It had darted lightly from a blade of grass and was fluttering about in its giddy way. Then Bambi saw that there were many butterflies flying in the air above the meadow. They seemed to be in a hurry and yet moved slowly, fluttering up and down in a sort of game that delighted him. They really did look like gay flying flowers that would not stay on their stems but had unfastened themselves in order to dance a little. They looked, too, like flowers that come to rest at sundown but have no fixed places and have to hunt for them, dropping down and vanishing as if they really had settled somewhere, yet always flying up again, a little way at first, then higher and higher, and always searching farther and farther because all the good places have already been taken.

Bambi gazed at them all. He would have loved to see one close by. He wanted to see one face out continually. The air was aflutter with them.

When he looked down at the ground again, he was delighted with the thousands of living things he saw stirring under his hoofs. They ran and jumped in all directions. He would see a wild swarm of them, and the next moment they had disappeared in the grass again.

'Who are they, Mother?' he asked.

'Those are ants,' his mother answered.

'Look,' cried Bambi, 'see that piece of grass jumping. Look how high it can jump!'

'That's not grass,' his mother explained, 'that's a nice grasshopper.'

'Why does he jump like that?' asked Bambi.

'Because we're walking here,' his mother answered, 'he's afraid we'll step on him.'

'O,' said Bambi, turning to the grasshopper who was sitting on a daisy, 'O,' he said again politely, 'you don't have to be afraid; we won't hurt you.'

'I'm not afraid,' the grasshopper replied in a quavering voice, 'I was only frightened for a moment when I was talking to my wife.'

'Excuse us for disturbing you,' said Bambi shyly.

'Not at all,' the grasshopper quavered. 'Since it's you, it's perfectly all right. But you never know who's coming and you have to be careful.'

'This is the first time in my life that I've ever been on the meadow,' Bambi explained; 'my mother brought me. . . .'

The grasshopper was sitting with his head lowered as though he were going to butt. He put on a serious face and murmured, 'That doesn't interest me at all. I haven't time to stand here gossiping with you. I have to be looking for my wife. Hopp!' And he gave a jump.

'Hopp!' said Bambi in surprise at the high jump with which the grasshopper vanished.

Bambi ran to his mother. 'Mother, I spoke to him,' he cried.

'To whom?' his mother asked.

'To the grasshopper,' Bambi said, 'I spoke to him. He was very nice to me. And I like him so much. He's so wonderful and green and you can see through his sides. They look like leaves, but you can't see through a leaf.'

'Those are his wings,' said his mother.

'O,' Bambi went on, 'and his face is so serious and wise. But he was very nice to me anyhow. And how he can jump! "Hopp!" he said, and he jumped so high I couldn't see him any more.'

They walked on. The conversation with the grasshopper had excited Bambi and tired him a little, for it was the first time he had ever spoken to a stranger. He felt hungry and pressed close to his mother to be nursed.

Then he stood quietly and gazed dreamily into space for a little while with a sort of joyous ecstasy that came over him every time he was nursed by his mother. He noticed a bright flower moving in the tangled grasses. Bambi looked more closely at it. No, it wasn't a flower, but a butterfly. Bambi crept closer.

The butterfly hung heavily to a grass stem and fanned its wings slowly.

'Please sit still,' Bambi said.

'Why should I sit still? I'm a butterfly,' the insect answered in astonishment.

'O, please sit still, just for a minute,' Bambi pleaded, 'I've wanted so much to see you close to. Please.'

'Well,' said the butterfly, 'for your sake I will, but not for long.'

Bambi stood in front of him. 'How beautiful you are,' he cried, fascinated, 'how wonderfully beautiful, like a flower.'

'What?' cried the butterfly, fanning his wings, 'did you say like a flower? In my circle it's generally supposed that we're handsomer than flowers.'

Bambi was embarrassed. 'O, yes,' he stammered 'much handsomer, excuse me, I only meant . . .'

'What ever you meant is all one to me,' the butterfly replied. He arched his thin body affectedly and played with his delicate feelers.

Bambi looked at him enchanted. 'How elegant you are,' he said. 'How elegant and fine! And how splendid and white your wings are!'

The butterfly spread his wings wide apart, then raised them till they folded together like an upright sail.

'O,' cried Bambi, 'I know that you are handsomer than the flowers. Besides, you can fly and the flowers can't because they grow on stems, that's why.'

The butterfly spread his wings. 'It's enough,' he said, 'that I can fly.' He soared so lightly that Bambi could hardly see him or follow his flight. His wings moved gently and gracefully. Then he fluttered into the sunny air.

'I only sat still that long on your account,' he said, balancing in the air in front of Bambi. 'Now I'm going.'

That was how Bambi found the meadow.

Peter, The White Cat of Trenarren

A. L. ROWSE

The celebrated Oxford historian lives in an isolated Cornish cottage, alone apart from an elderly housekeeper and his most treasured companion, his white cat Peter ...

He was hardly ever scolded by me, for he never did anything that was reprehensible in my eyes. (Beryl was made of sterner stuff.) There was one exception. I have in the library a beautiful Louis xvi tapestry sofa – with panel of animal design by Oudry. Naturally no one is invited to sit on this precious piece of furniture.

But Peter took a fancy to it, in the curious way cats have of taking to different places for their pleasure. I would find him coiled up comfortably on the tapestry seat, looking up on my approach for the usual approbation. He did not get it.

Another fancied spot was the wide stool covered with malachite-green velvet – for which little claws opening and closing with pleasure, were not good. I had to shoo him off several times – and he was not pleased, could not understand my objection.

He was, however, allowed on the Louis Philippe tapestry chairs

– less valuable: poor little fellow couldn't distinguish between Louis Philippe and Louis Seize. So much in human behaviour must remain out of range, incomprehensible and possibly irrational to cats.

He did, however, appreciate the pussy-cat voice in which I talked to him, recognised that that was meant for him. And I think particularly liked being whispered to – no doubt that that was for him alone. He would respond with that gentle sizzling noise, not quite a purr, like a kettle singing on the hob. Perhaps it was his form of singing to me – it was certainly very soothing and welcome.

He hadn't much experience of dogs, since they were not allowed inside the grounds, scratching up the lawn, leaving scuffling footmarks on gravel, treading down flowers in the border. He must have known dear old Rover down at the farm, and his unfriendly successor Spot.

But once Peter was chased inside his own grounds – a great offence to dignity, most humiliating. And by a beautiful and friendly labrador, Apollo, belonging to my friends, the Hartleys. I was horrified and alarmed when I saw the big yellow dog gaining upon the little cat – and shouted furiously out of the window to get the bloody dog under control.

Harold replied peaceably that Apollo had only chased Peter because the cat ran away. And that the dog wouldn't know what to do with him if he caught him. I dare say. But instinct might tell him. And if he killed my Peter I could never speak to them again, etc.

When I came to know Apollo I found that he had an angelic disposition and that it was unlikely he would ever hurt a cat. But I was taking no risks.

Later that evening I went out to look for Peter, who had taken refuge in a remote part of the garden and wouldn't come in. He was sitting in a secluded patch, still swearing at the indignity of being chased in his own property and, when I approached, even raised his paw at me, for the only time in his life.

It was pure pretence, of course, and I was having no nonsense.

I picked him up still saying gr-r-, and gave him little smacks, saying 'Beryl', as if coming from the Boss, to behave himself.

That night he slept like a log for the whole night beside me, never making a movement, worn out with the excitement, apprehension and indignation.

While I was away in Oxford one summer term a really serious accident befell him.

In those days there were plenty of rabbits at Trenarren; today only one dinky, kittenish specimen has found its way there, heaven knows how (one rabbit, plus one squirrel, two green wood-peckers, a resplendent family of pheasants).

At Magdalen Bruce's cat had the Grove (where I have seen *A Midsummer Night's Dream* ending in the moonlight) to disport himself in; and the Master had the regular job of defleaing. I followed in his footsteps with the hunter at Trenarren. Fortunately animals' fleas are a different – and cleaner – variety than humans'. Peter would sit patiently while I went through his ears and head, myself saying Grr to express disapprobation, while he gave an occasional squeak of protest. However, he seemed to know that I was bent on his good, recognised the necessity of the operation, and never once attempted escape. He was an exceptionally docile, obedient cat.

One day he came back to the house with a foot more than half off: he had been caught in a rabbit-trap on the farm. Beryl's explanation was that the farm-boy (a pretty primitive type, handsome as Apollo, later drowned on the beach below) must have released the cat, to let him find his way home, where he arrived in a fainting condition.

Beryl laid him down on a rug in my study, gave him some warm milk, and summoned the vet, who put the fore-leg in a splint.

By the time I arrived home, Peter had recovered and was stumping about the house like a man with a crutch, and making almost as much noise. One could hear his approach, his movements about the house like another inhabitant.

Of course, he was a third inhabitant. When I called him a dear little thing (doo lil fing, in pussy-cat language) I used to correct myself: 'he's not a thing, but a person'. And when the form for the Register of Voters came – which one had to fill up under some penalty, which I much resented, never having wasted a minute of my time on voting since the decisive date 1945 – I had the greatest difficulty in resisting the temptation to add to

A.L.Rowse – householder
B.L.Cloke – housekeeper

the name

Peter Rowse – housemate.

After all, I would say, he knew as much about the issues at stake as the electorate.

It was some weeks before we called in the vet to take off Peter's splint. I found I couldn't do it. We used to sit at night in my armchair, he trying to gnaw at the tough linen bandage, while I tried to scissor it off. Both of us were defeated – but again, he recognised instinctively, as always, that I was trying to help and never made the least trouble.

The great day came when the vet was summoned, the splint removed, and Master Peter was able to leap about, a young cat active as ever.

The dreadful day came when Beryl went away for a holiday, and he had to go to the vet's for his. This became a regular summer routine – and how he hated it!

I was never here to see him go off, of course, and I longed to be the one to go into the town and bring him joyfully back.

Beryl told me he always cried all the way, uttering a loud wail at the gate, 'Ma', just like a child.

But once at the vet's he was patient and well-behaved – no fuming and cursing like some of the spoiled animals there. In fact the vet said he was the 'best behaved' cat of the lot. The only thing was that he went off his food, and always came back thin.

Jack tells me that he would cry all the way home in his box, then, when arrived and let out, he would take one look round, and recognise where he was with a sigh of satisfaction: 'Home again!'

I wish I could have been there: I was never there for this part of the routine of his life, which I dictated from a distance. Jack adds – what goes to my heart: 'he had a lonely life at times'. Alas! – that he was loved so much, and deserted so much: irreparable now.

Was he spoiled?

I don't think so, for all that he was petted, not pampered. The Professor, old sobersides, thought that he was, and that he used to take advantage of me. But then the Professor didn't like cats, the only defect in an otherwise perfect character.

I don't blame him for not liking the Wow-wow, for she once gave him a terrible fright in the night, in my upstairs guest room at Polmear, by jumping in through the window upon the recumbent and sleeping Professor. It must have been as much of a surprise to her as it was to him – a live full Professor too!

Nor was the great authority on railway engines, who had been mad about puff-puffs since his own boyhood, at all amused by the variety of names this simple Cornish cat enjoyed.

I rather think at this time I was calling him Fanty, Fanty-cat, or Fantigue-cat – all breakaways, as the etymologists put it, from the Cardinal Infant. Hence, too, Twenty, or Twenty-cat. I don't know how that arrived; but with me words have always had their own life and inner motion, and I have played games with them from first to second childhood.

I suppose the Professor was allergic to the religion of Trenarren: Peter-worship. At Oxford, when we wondered why Bruce McFarlane never produced a book, Richard Pares put forward the view that if one penetrated into Bruce's rooms at Magdalen one would find him on his knees before the cat.

Certainly Peter recognised at once, when Bruce came to stay, that he knew about cats – unlike the Professor. Peter would lie in his lap and allow himself to be fondled in the way Bruce well knew how, when Peter would not obtrude himself upon the Professor.

His differing attitude to people expressed what he thought of them. He took Beryl more seriously than he did me – after all the more serious concerns of life revolved around her. She was the regular provider of food – I fed him at times, particularly at my own meal-times, but that was only when I was at home during vacations.

He would go for walks with her around the grounds, but not with me. Sometimes all three of us would go – and delightful it was, with him scampering on ahead, occasionally dashing madly up a tree, or lagging behind with the curious discontinuity of a cat. Except in the chase, when hunting or watching prey, they have less concentration than dogs. Hence people find their habit of not attending maddening, when they are bent on making a cat do something it doesn't want to do. People-who-know-about-cats know that you can't *make* a cat do anything – a point Douglas Jay long ago made to me; you may not even be able to persuade or entice or lure. Cats have their own will and personality – as Colette understood so well; they do not reflect the personality of their masters, as dogs do – though they may reflect, or conform, to their habits.

Peter hated it when Beryl was away from the house. If she went into town of an afternoon, he would see her off at the gate, hardly ever going beyond, but taking up his post by the gate to wait for her. Often there he still would be in the evening to welcome her back. When I was away, he would be waiting for her down in the paddock in the mornings. He recognised her footstep as she came up the steep road outside. He never jumped over the hedge, but would follow her progress from inside, saying 'Ma-ma' the while.

By the time she had arrived at the big black gate – which he never climbed over and rarely went through – there would be a tiny white nose peeping under the gap.

He had, indeed, a hundred pretty ways.

Both of us hated Saturdays, when Beryl was away all afternoon and evening. When evening came Peter would come into the study and take refuge on my lap. I comforted him and he comforted me;

but when half-past nine came, it was no good – we both grew afraid, nerves and ears alert to every sound.

'Don't be late,' I would say; 'Peter doesn't like it.'

But I didn't like it either.

At last, he would receive the signal before me: he had heard the outside gate go, then the front door, and we would hear her steps in the hall.

'Beryl,' I would sing out, or more often, *'Béroul* – Peter wants to see you: he has been waiting and waiting.'

When Beryl came in, he would rouse himself to give her those two formal long licks the length of first and second fingers which represented the summit of his ritual of love – all with a lot of care and fuss and flurry. Never at other times, or in any other way.

'What about me?' I would say, sticking my first two fingers out, to receive the same ritual ablutions.

Once, in bed when my hand had got out over the coverlet, he woke me up with the same expressive gesture to tell me how much he loved me. Very endearing, and half asleep I responded by fondling head and ears as he liked.

At other times he has added to my nervousness. I have always been subject to night-terrors, and Cornish houses – if not precisely haunted – are distinctly atmospherical.

At a neighbouring old country house in mid-Cornwall, the squire was scribbling away in his study late at night, accompanied by his Esquimaux dog, window wide open. Suddenly the dog gave a loud howl and leaped through the window; nor did he return for three days.

Similarly with Peter; at one time he quite unnerved me two or three nights running by following something invisible along the cornice of the ceiling, right round the room.

Beryl said, 'Spiders.'

But one doesn't really know about extra-sensory perception, does one?

Later on, in his middle age, there came sickness. And in this he

He would come down covered with dust and . . . cobwebs

did follow his master (or servant), for he developed a stomach-ulcer and could keep nothing down.

Until this he had been a very healthy little creature, except for the tendency of cats to be chesty – one reason why the climate of Cornwall, warm and moist, is good for them, as with bronchial subjects.

When he had a cough, I used to smack him on the back or chest to help him – and again, he knew it was for his good and would stand patiently to be smacked. After all, he was never smacked in anger (by me): he never needed it, as horrid children do or those half-grown children, university students.

'If the cat has but a cough, you are worried' – Beryl would laugh at me (as I occasionally am laughing at my readers).

But his first illness was no laughing matter for us, for he went and hid himself away, in the way sick animals do. We thought he was lost, and couldn't think what had happened to him. Another trap? Over the cliff? (quite near on the road side of the house). Poisoned?

I got it in my head that he was poisoned. For, when we lived in the hateful Council houses at Robartes Place in the midst of the I.P., we had an exquisite marmalade kitten, whom I brought home in my pocket and buttered my fingers for him to lick, according to custom, so that he would stay with us. He was dinky when he came; so I called him Dinky.

I was an undergraduate at Oxford then; and, while I was away, an odious working-man up across the way, poisoned all the cats that belonged there.

Is it any wonder that I simply hated living there with the idiot people? – but I was then too poor, and later on too ill, to make a move.

Beryl and I raised the hue and cry for our white cat. The third day the farmboy told us that a white cat had been seen up at Lobb's Shop – what must have been a blacksmith's shop long before my time, kept by the vanished Lobb, at the four turnings: to Trenarren and Trevissick (beautiful Queen Anne house, with Jacobean hall-kitchen), with Penrice and Porthpean along the road; to

Pentewan, with haunted Sailor's Orchard on one side of the road, Polgaze of the Treleavens on the other; lastly, to Towan with its holy well, a rough track down through the King's Wood to Pentewan Valley.*

Beryl seized her stick and hurried up the lane, with me in hot pursuit. When we got up there, we discovered that the white cat seen there had been Farmer Yelland's from Castle Gotha.

No Peter!

Disconsolate we trudged back down Trenarren Lane, taking no notice of the wonderful views of the bay that open out along the road from Silvermine – right out to the Gribben on the other side from our Black Head.

Next morning I went out, and at the entrance to the back drive – there was Peter. Overjoyed, I took him up and covered him with kisses. He tried, but could hardly croak back in return.

I carried him down to my study, settled him in a warm rug in the chair by my desk and rang for the vet. There Peter remained, refusing food or milk, dozing, perfectly content to lie there beside me while I wrote.

The vet arrived – and waved aside my suggestion that he might have eaten something that poisoned him. Not a bit of it.

His temperature was taken – thermometer inserted in his rear without protest. His temperature was high – some fever, possibly pussy-cat flu.

The vet would give him a penicillin injection. I held him while the needle was inserted – a cry, but never a scratch or a bite.

By evening he was definitely better. I brought him a nice slice of chicken, which he consented to take rather coyly – then drank a whole saucer of water, which was what he liked.

*Trenarren means the hamlet or house of the ploughed land, Trevissick that of the cornfield; Penrice, the head of the ford; Pentewan, the head of the sands; Porthpean, the little beach; Polglaze, the green pool; Towan, sands or sandy place; Gribben, the crest; Castle Gotha, the old round-camp.

He descended somewhat unsteadily from the chair, where he had lain passive all day, and went out of doors gaining strength and assurance with every step.

He was completely recovered.

I think that, from the first, he liked the big house at Trenarren better than Polmear Mine – as we did. He didn't come into the house much there; but, after the move, he became more devoted to or dependent upon us, and lived with us far more. Trenarren became *his* place.

He explored all over the house and was more familiar with all its rooms that he had been at the smaller house. In the early days he would vanish upstairs for hours, we wondered where – and would come down covered with dust and blinking with cobwebs.

We thought he had been up a chimney. In fact he had discovered the exciting spaces, holes and corners, of the roof, haunt of bats, rafters festooned with spider's webs. (I preserve the spiders and encourage their campaign against flies.)

One day when he came down from his exploration in this state, Beryl gave him a bath and, much to his disgust, dusted his coat with scented powder. He thought this rather sissy – but he certainly looked beautiful, ivory-white, with the distinguished ruff he had then, like an Elizabethan.

Cat-like, he disliked water in general, and I could never induce him to keep me company while I had a bath. Bruce's cat had no such allergy, and one day – such was his devotion – came and sat on Bruce's chest *in* the bath. Peter would not come near, nor stay on a chair beside me while I splashed about: he regarded the spectacle as horrid, mewing the whole time with apprehension.

When we first came to the house I used to make morning-tea off the electric point in my bedroom. But he could not bear the sizzling noise of the kettle: it always disturbed him, probably affected his sensitive ears. Not all my wooing, or explaining, 'Make-a-tea, make-a-tea', persuaded him.

He knew the cellars better than I did, or have ever done. They continue all round under the house, excellent roomy compartments, cobbled or flagged, with at one point blocked-up stone steps that would arrive at the front door. At another a stone gives the date of the foundation, 1805, the year of Trafalgar.

They are quite big enough to stow away a regiment of soldiers. And must have stowed away many a cask of brandy, brought ashore from the cove on Black Head – Q. has a smuggling story of the lane out from the ledra to the headland and beach.

Then there are slate pans for brining the bacon, vaults for storing the wine, the coals that in old days were brought up over the cliff from Ropehawn,* where there was a little quay, now vanished. In fact, all the storage necessary for those days with family, servants, a household which, marooned out on this headland, needed to be self-sufficient.

In my time, a vast prowling place for Peter. Dr Johnson called the Codrington Library at All Souls a fine place to prance in. I never followed Peter on his prancing expeditions, keeping the mice down for us – but once, when he disappeared again for two or three days, found him with a cold nursing himself on the window-sill beside the stove down below that supplied central heating.

As for mice – if Beryl ever had a mouse in the kitchen, we simply shut Peter in for the night. There in the morning would be our mouse laid out for us on the mat. He well understood the approbation and praises he received: '*Good* cat! caught the *Mouse*', etc.

He hadn't the courage of a tom-cat and, naturally, having been neutered, was a bit sissy. Beryl used to say that he had 'a pretty face for a tom-cat'; I used to demur at this. Now I think she was right: he had a delicate, shapely head, with exquisite pink-transparent ears, like shell-whorls, nice whiskers and pale gentle eyes with a kind welcoming expression. For he had been loved into a state of perpetual seduction – I had only to put out a hand and he would purr. What a welcome always awaiting one!

I think that, among the small number of words he knew, was

*Ropehawn = Ropehaven.

the word 'love': he knew it not in the abstract sense but in the concrete meaning of being loved.

There was, for example, the chair in the dining room by the window, where he was accustomed to being loved. This meant kisses on the forehead, where were the diminutive pretty furrows; rubbing noses like Polynesians – a gesture of equality much appreciated by cats from humans; then nuzzling into his flank: an occasional squeak of protest and pleasure at being hugged too hard; then, subsidence into deep sleep. I would pull the curtain forward to protect him from the sun, and he would sleep there the whole morning.

The fact is that cats are mesmerisable. John Opie, the Cornish painter, would vary the occupation – for which he was scolded by his unresponsive, stupid parent – of 'for ever dra'in the cat', by mesmerising it.

What a subject! – the enchanting paintings of cats, by Hogarth, Gainsborough and other artists – and an exacting subject too, to catch their changing expressions and delicate gestures – that marvellous flick of the back leg, for example, to shake off a raindrop. Then there are the drawings of Beatrix Potter, or Louis Wain, who went off his head about cats. (I well understand that.)

To understand the mind, and world, of a cat would be a difficult and subtle task – beyond the barbarous methods of a physiologist like Pavlov – for, to begin with, there is their double life: their life with us, and their secret life to themselves, away from humans.

How many words did Peter know?

Not many – not so many as Barney (up in Trelawny Road), for he was not a clever cat; and no cats know as many words as dogs, for they are less dependent on humans, and dogs have larger brains.

I think all animals are not only responsive to the human voice but fascinated by it – for them the one marked difference between them and us, with our command of every variety of expresson: it is through the voice that we command them, direct them, entice them, scold them, make them love or fear us, teach them. I find very touching the effort the poor creatures make to follow our words, enter into our not always clear wishes, sometimes emitting a little squeak, like a question. They seem to be proud of themselves when they succeed in catching our meaning.

Peter knew the word Beryl; and Dinner; I think he knew the words Mouse, and Milk. Also No, and Out? He would go over to the door or window, while I said Out? It seems that it is more by tone of voice, and association that a cat will recognise a word, or a command.

Did he know the word Tea, or Cake? – I rather think he knew the latter; he had a special fondness for sponge-cake, which he would eat out of my hand, stickily licking up the crumbs left over. In fact, he was keen to pick up crumbs once pointed out.

Not having much courage was in itself a measure of defence. He never put himself in the way of danger and kept away from strangers. But he had the regular animal sense of his own territory and didn't like incursions into it – by the farm-cats for instance. When I have been shooing one off the lawn he would accompany me, making a pretence of courage and saying Gr-r – so long as I was beside him.

Once down in the orchard, when I was speaking kind words to a farm-cat that dared to approach me, Peter growled angrily, overcome by jealousy: I was *his* property. I told him that he was no better than a human – which made him look properly ashamed.

However, I did not put too great a strain on his good nature by praising another cat in his presence – as Dr Johnson did in front of his Hodge. Seeing the look of reproach on Hodge's face, the great bear of a Doctor with the tender heart, hastily added, 'But Hodge is a good cat, too' – and all was well.

The Call of Kind

JACK LONDON

White Fang, part dog, part wolf, has come from the wild, through a series of harsh and sometimes cruel adventures, to a serene and devoted existence with his beloved master, Weedon Scott, on his Southland ranch ...

The months came and went. There was plenty of food and no work in the Southland, and White Fang lived fat and prosperous and happy. Not alone was he in the geographical Southland, for he was in the Southland of life. Human kindness was like a sun shining upon him, and he flourished like a flower planted in good soil.

And yet he remained somehow different from other dogs. He knew the law even better than did the dogs that had known no other life, and he observed the law more punctiliously; but still there was about him a suggestion of lurking ferocity, as though the Wild still lingered in him and the wolf in him merely slept.

He never chummed with other dogs. Lonely he had lived, so far as his kind was concerned, and lonely he would continue to live. In his puppyhood, under the persecution of Lip-lip and the puppy-pack, and in his fighting days with Beauty Smith, he had acquired a fixed aversion for dogs. The natural course of his life had been diverted, and, recoiling from his kind, he had clung to the human.

Besides, all Southland dogs looked upon him with suspicion. He aroused in them their instinctive fear of the Wild, and they greeted him always with snarl and growl and belligerent hatred. He, on the other hand, learned that it was not necessary to use his teeth upon them. His naked fangs and writhing lips were uniformly efficacious, rarely failing to send a bellowing, on-rushing dog back on its haunches.

But there was one trial in White Fang's life – Collie. She never gave him a moment's peace. She was not so amenable to the law as he. She defied all efforts of the master to make her become friends with White Fang. Ever in his ears was sounding her sharp and nervous snarl. She had never forgiven him the chicken-killing episode, and persistently held to the belief that his intentions were bad. She found him guilty before the act, and treated him accordingly. She became a pest to him, like a policeman following him around the stable and the grounds, and, if he even so much as glanced curiously at a pigeon or chicken, bursting into an outcry of indignation and wrath. His favourite way of ignoring her was to lie down, with his head on his forepaws, and pretend sleep. This always dumbfounded and silenced her.

With the exception of Collie, all things went well with White Fang. He had learned control and poise, and he knew the law. He achieved a staidness, and calmness, and philosophic tolerance. He no longer lived in a hostile environment. Danger and hurt and death did not lurk everywhere about him. In time, the unknown, as a thing of terror and menace ever impending, faded away. Life was soft and easy. It flowed along smoothly, and neither fear nor foe lurked by the way.

He missed the snow without being aware of it. 'An unduly long summer,' would have been his thought, had he thought about it; as it was, he merely missed the snow in a vague, subconscious way. In the same fashion, especially in the heat of summer when he suffered from the sun, he experienced faint longings for the

Northland. Their only effect upon him, however, was to make him uneasy and restless without his knowing what was the matter.

White Fang had never been very demonstrative. Beyond his snuggling and the throwing of a crooning note into his love-growl, he had no way of expressing his love. Yet it was given him to discover a third way. He had always been susceptible to the laughter of the gods. Laughter had affected him with madness, made him frantic with rage. But he did not have it in him to be angry with the love-master, and when that god elected to laugh at him in a good-natured, bantering way, he was nonplussed. He could feel the pricking and stinging of the old anger as it strove to rise up in him, but it strove against love. He could not be angry; yet he had to do something. At first he was dignified, and the master laughed the harder. Then he tried to be more dignified, and the master laughed harder than before. In the end, the master laughed him out of his dignity. His jaws slightly parted, his lips lifted a little, and a quizzical expression that was more love than humour came into his eyes. He had learned to laugh.

Likewise he learned to romp with the master, to be tumbled down and rolled over, and be the victim of innumerable rough tricks. In return he feigned anger, bristling and growling ferociously, and clipping his teeth together in snaps that had all the seeming of deadly intention. But he never forgot himself. Those snaps were always delivered on the empty air. At the end of such a romp, when blow and cuff and snap and snarl were fast and furious, they would break off suddenly and stand several feet apart, glaring at each other. And then, just as suddenly, like the sun rising on a stormy sea, they would begin to laugh. This would always culminate with the master's arms going around White Fang's neck and shoulders, while the latter crooned and growled his love-song.

But nobody else ever romped with White Fang. He did not permit it. He stood on his dignity, and when they attempted it, his warning snarl and bristling mane were anything but playful. That he allowed the master these liberties was no reason that he should be a common dog, loving here and loving there, everybody's property for a romp and good time. He loved with single heart, and refused to cheapen himself or his love.

The master went out on horseback a great deal, and to accompany him was one of White Fang's chief duties in life. In the Northland he had evidenced his fealty by toiling in the harness; but there were no sleds in the Southland, nor did dogs pack burdens on their backs. So he rendered fealty in the new way by running with the master's horse. The longest day never played White Fang out. His was the gait of the wolf, smooth, tireless, and effortless, and at the end of fifty miles he would come in jauntily ahead of the horse.

It was in connection with the riding that White Fang achieved one other mode of expression – remarkable in that he did it but twice in all his life. The first time occurred when the master was trying to teach a spirited thoroughbred the method of opening and closing gates without the rider's dismounting. Time and again and many times he ranged the horse up to the gate in the effort to close it, and each time the horse became frightened, and backed and plunged away. It grew more nervous and excited every moment. When it reared, the master put the spurs to it and made it drop its forelegs back to earth, whereupon it would begin kicking with its hind-legs. White Fang watched the performance with increasing anxiety until he could contain himself no longer, when he sprang in front of the horse and barked savagely and warningly.

Though he often tried to bark thereafter, and the master encouraged him, he succeeded only once, and then it was not in the master's presence. A scamper across the pasture, a jackrabbit rising suddenly under the horse's feet, a violent sheer, a stumble, a fall to earth, and a broken leg for the master, was the cause of it. White Fang sprang in a rage at the throat of the offending horse, but was checked by the master's voice.

'Home! Go home!' the master commanded when he had ascertained his injury.

White Fang was disinclined to desert him. The master thought of writing a note, but searched his pockets vainly for pencil and paper. Again he commanded White Fang to go home.

The Call of Kind

The latter regarded him wistfully, started away, then returned and whined softly. The master talked to him gently but seriously, and he cocked his ears, and listened with painful intentness.

'That's all right, old fellow; you just run along home,' ran the talk. 'Go on home and tell them what's happened to me. Home with you, you wolf. Get along home!'

White Fang knew the meaning of 'home', and though he did not understand the remainder of the master's language, he knew it was his will that he should go home. He turned and trotted reluctantly away. Then he stopped, undecided, and looked back over his shoulder.

'Go home!' came the sharp command, and this time he obeyed.

The family was on the porch, taking the cool of the afternoon when White Fang arrived. He came in among them, panting, covered with dust.

'Weedon's back,' Weedon's mother announced.

The children welcomed White Fang with glad cries and ran to meet him. He avoided them and passed down the porch, but they cornered him against a rocking-chair and the railing. He growled and tried to push by them. Their mother looked apprehensively in their direction.

'I confess, he makes me nervous around the children,' she said. 'I have a dread that he will turn upon them unexpectedly some day.'

Growling savagely, White Fang sprang out of the corner, over-turning the boy and the girl. The mother called them to her and comforted them, telling them not to bother White Fang.

'A wolf is a wolf,' commented Judge Scott. 'There is no trusting one.'

'But he is not all wolf,' interposed Beth, standing for her brother in his absence.

'You have only Weedon's opinion for that,' rejoined the Judge. 'He merely surmises that there is some strain of dog in White Fang; but as he will tell you himself, he knows nothing about it. As for his appearance –'

He did not finish the sentence. White Fang stood before him, growling fiercely.

'Go away! Lie down, sir!' Judge Scott commanded.

White Fang turned to the love-master's wife. She screamed with fright as he seized her dress in his teeth and dragged on it till the frail fabric tore away. By this time he had become the centre of interest. He had ceased from his growling, and stood, head up looking into their faces. His throat worked spasmodically, but made no sound, while he struggled with all his body, convulsed with the effort to rid himself of the incommunicable something that strained for utterance.

'I hope he is not going mad,' said Weedon's mother. 'I told Weedon that I was afraid the warm climate would not agree with an Arctic animal.'

'He's trying to speak, I do believe,' Beth announced.

At this moment speech came to White Fang, rushing up in a great burst of barking.

'Something has happened to Weedon,' his wife said decisively.

They were all on their feet now, and White Fang ran down the steps, looking back for them to follow. For the second and last time in his life he had barked and made himself understood.

After this event he found a warmer place in the hearts of the Sierra Vista people, and even the groom whose arm he had slashed admitted that he was a wise dog, even if he was a wolf. Judge Scott still held to the same opinion, and proved it to everybody's dissatisfaction by measurements and descriptions taken from the encyclopaedia and various works on natural history.

The days came and went, streaming their unbroken sunshine over the Santa Clara Valley. But as they grew shorter, and White Fang's second winter in the Southland came on, he made a strange discovery. Collie's teeth were no longer sharp. There was a playfulness about her nips and a gentleness that prevented them from really hurting him. He forgot that she had made life a burden to him, and when she disported herself around him he responded solemnly, striving to be playful, and becoming no more than ridiculous.

One day she led him off on a long chase through the back-pasture and into the woods. It was the afternoon that the master was to ride, and White Fang knew it. The horse stood saddled and waiting at the door. White Fang hesitated. But there was that in him deeper than all the law he had learned, than the customs that had moulded him, than his love for the master, than the very will to live of himself; and when, in the moment of his indecision, Collie nipped him and scampered off, he turned and followed after. The master rode alone that day; and in the woods, side by side, White Fang ran with Collie, as his mother Kiche and old One Eye had run long years before in the silent Northland forest.

It was about this time that the newspapers were full of the daring escape of a convict from San Quentin prison. He was a ferocious man. He had been ill-made in the making. He had not been born right, and he had not been helped any by the moulding he had received at the hands of society. The hands of society are harsh, and this man was a striking sample of its handiwork. He was a beast – a human beast, it is true, but nevertheless so terrible a beast that he can best be characterised as carnivorous.

In San Quentin prison he had proved incorrigible. Punishment failed to break his spirit. He could die dumb-mad and fighting to the last, but he could not live and be beaten. The more fiercely he fought, the more harshly society handled him, and the only effect of harshness was to make him fiercer. Strait-jackets, starvation, and beatings and clubbings were the wrong treatment for Jim Hall; but it was the treatment he received. It was the treatment he had received from the time he was a little pulpy boy in a San Francisco slum – soft clay in the hands of society, and ready to be formed into something.

It was during Jim Hall's third term in prison that he encountered a guard that was almost as great a beast as he. The guard treated him unfairly, lied about him to the warden, lost him his credits, persecuted him. The difference between them was that the guard carried a bunch of keys and a revolver. Jim Hall had only his naked hands and his teeth. But he sprang upon the guard one day and used his teeth on the other's throat just like any jungle animal.

After this, Jim Hall went to live in the incorrigible cell. He lived there three years. The cell was of iron, the floor, the walls, the roof. He never left this cell. He never saw the sky nor the sunshine. Day was a twilight, and night was a black silence. He was in an iron tomb, buried alive. He saw no human face, spoke to no human thing. When his food was shoved into him, he growled like a wild animal. He hated all things. For days and nights he bellowed his rage at the universe. For weeks and months he never made a sound, in the black silence eating his very soul. He was a man and a monstrosity, as fearful a thing of fear as ever gibbered in the visions of a maddened brain.

And then, one night, he escaped. The warden said it was impossible, but nevertheless the cell was empty, and half in half out of it lay the body of a dead guard. Two other dead guards marked his trail through the prison to the outer walls, and he had killed with his hands to avoid noise.

He was armed with the weapons of the slain guards – a live arsenal that fled through the hills pursued by the organised might of society. A heavy price of gold was upon his head. Avaricious farmers hunted him with shotguns. His blood might pay off a mortgage or send a son to college. Public-spirited citizens took down their rifles and went out after him. A pack of bloodhounds followed the way of his bleeding feet. And the sleuth-hounds of the law, the paid fighting animals of society, with telephone and telegraph and special train, clung to his trail night and day.

Sometimes they came upon him, and men faced him like heroes, or stampeded through barbed-wire fences to the delight of the commonwealth reading the account at the breakfast-table. It was after such encounters that the dead and wounded were carted back to the towns, and their places filled by men eager for the man-hunt.

And then Jim Hall disappeared. The bloodhounds vainly quested on the lost trail. Inoffensive ranchers in remote valleys were held up by armed men and compelled to identify themselves.

While the remains of Jim Hall were discovered on a dozen mountain-sides by greedy claimants for blood-money.

In the meantime the newspapers were read at Sierra Vista, not so much with interest as with anxiety. The women were afraid. Judge Scott pooh-poohed and laughed, but not with reason, for it was in his last days on the bench that Jim Hall had stood before him and received sentence. And in open courtroom, before all men, Jim Hall had proclaimed that the day would come when he would wreak vengeance on the judge that sentenced him.

For once Jim Hall was right. He was innocent of the crime for which he was sentenced. It was a case, in the parlance of thieves and police, of 'railroading'. Jim Hall was being 'railroaded' to prison for a crime he had not committed. Because of the two prior convictions against him. Judge Scott imposed upon him a sentence of fifty years.

Judge Scott did not know all things, and he did not know that he was party to a police conspiracy, that the evidence was hatched and perjured, that Jim Hall was guiltless of the crime charged. And Jim Hall, on the other hand, did not know that Judge Scott was merely ignorant. Jim Hall believed that the Judge knew all about it, and was hand in glove with the police in the perpetration of the monstrous injustice. So it was, when the doom of fifty years of living death was uttered by Judge Scott, that Jim Hall, hating all things in the society that misused him, rose up and raged in the courtroom until dragged down by half a dozen of his blue-coated enemies. To him Judge Scott was the keystone in the arch of injustice, and upon Judge Scott he emptied the vials of his wrath and hurled the threats of his revenge yet to come. Then Jim Hall went to his living death . . . and escaped.

Of all this White Fang knew nothing. But between him and Alice, the master's wife, there existed a secret. Each night, after Sierra Vista had gone to bed, she rose and let in White Fang to sleep in the big hall. Now White Fang was not a house-dog, nor was he permitted to sleep in the house; so each morning, early, she slipped down and let him out before the family was awake.

On one such night, while all the house slept, White Fang awoke and lay very quietly. And very quietly he smelled the air and read the message it bore of a strange god's presence. And to his ears came sounds of the strange god's movements. White Fang burst into no furious outcry. It was not his way. The strange god walked softly, but more softly walked White Fang, for he had no clothes to rub against the flesh of his body. He followed silently. In the Wild he had hunted live meat that was infinitely timid, and he knew the advantage of surprise.

The strange god paused at the foot of the great staircase and listened, and White Fang was as dead, so without movement was he as he watched and waited. Up that staircase the way led to the love-master and to the love-master's dearest possessions. White Fang bristled, but waited. The strange god's foot lifted. He was beginning the ascent.

Then it was that White Fang struck. He gave no warning, with no snarl anticipated his own action. Into the air he lifted his body in the spring that landed him on the strange god's back. White Fang clung with his fore-paws to the man's shoulders, at the same time burying his fangs into the back of the man's neck. He clung on for a moment, long enough to drag the god over backward. Together they crashed to the floor. White Fang leaped clear, and, as the man struggled to rise, was in again with the slashing fangs.

Sierra Vista awoke in alarm. The noise from downstairs was as that of a score of battling fiends. There were revolver shots. A man's voice screamed once in horror and anguish. There was a great snarling and growling, and over all arose a smashing and crashing of furniture and glass.

But almost as quickly as it had arisen, the commotion died away. The struggle had not lasted more than three minutes. The frightened household clustered at the top of the stairway. From below, as from out an abyss of blackness, came up a gurgling sound, as of air bubbling through water. Sometimes this gurgle became sibilant, almost a whistle. But this, too, quickly died down and ceased. Then naught came up out of the blackness save a heavy panting of some creature struggling sorely for air.

Weedon Scott pressed a button, and the staircase and downstairs hall were flooded with light. Then he and Judge Scott, revolvers in hand, cautiously descended. There was no need for this caution. White Fang had done his work. In the midst of the wreckage of overthrown and smashed furniture, partly on his side, his face hidden by an arm, lay a man. Weedon Scott bent over, removed the arm, and turned the man's face upward. A gaping throat explained the manner of his death.

'Jim Hall,' said Judge Scott, and father and son looked significantly at each other.

Then they turned to White Fang. He too, was lying on his side. His eyes were closed, but the lids slightly lifted in an effort to look at them as they bent over him, and the tail was perceptibly agitated in a vain effort to wag. Weedon Scott patted him, and his throat rumbled an acknowledging growl. But it was a weak growl at best, and it quickly ceased. His eyelids drooped and went shut, and his whole body seemed to relax and flatten out upon the floor.

'He's all in, poor devil,' muttered the master.

'We'll see about that,' asserted the Judge, as he started for the telephone.

'Frankly, he has one chance in a thousand,' announced the surgeon, after he had worked an hour and half on White Fang.

Dawn was breaking through the windows and dimming the electric lights. With the exception of the children, the whole family was gathered about the surgeon to hear his verdict.

'One broken hind-leg,' he went on. 'Three broken ribs, one at least of which has pierced the lungs. He has lost nearly all the blood in his body. There is a large likelihood of internal injuries. He must have been jumped upon. To say nothing of three bulletholes clear through him. One chance in a thousand is really optimistic. He hasn't a chance in ten thousand.'

'But he mustn't lose any chance that might be of help to him.' Judge Scott exclaimed. 'Never mind expense. Put him under the X-ray – anything. – Weedon, telegraph at once to San Francisco for Doctor Nichols. – No reflection on you, doctor, you understand; but he must have the advantage of every chance.'

The surgeon smiled indulgently. 'Of course I understand. He deserves all that can be done for him. He must be nursed as you would nurse a human being, a sick child. And don't forget what I told you about temperature. I'll be back at ten o'clock again.'

White Fang received the nursing. Judge Scott's suggestion of a trained nurse was indignantly clamoured down by the girls, who themselves undertook the task. And White Fang won out on the one chance in ten thousand denied him by the surgeon.

The latter was not to be censured for his misjudgment. All his life he had tended and operated on the soft humans of civilisation, who lived sheltered lives and had descended out of many sheltered generations. Compared with White Fang, they were frail and flabby, and clutched life without any strength in their grip. White Fang had come straight from the Wild, where the weak perish early and shelter is vouchsafed to none. In neither his father nor his mother was there any weakness, nor in the generations before them. A constitution of iron and the vitality of the Wild were White Fang's inheritance, and he clung to life, the whole of him and every part of him, in spirit and in flesh, with the tenacity that of old belonged to all creatures.

Bound down a prisoner, denied even movement by the plaster casts and bandages, White Fang lingered out the weeks. He slept long hours and dreamed much, and through his mind passed an unending pageant of Northland visions. All the ghosts of the past arose and were with him. Once again he lived in the lair with Kiche, crept trembling to the knees of Grey Beaver to tender his allegiance, ran for his life before Lip-lip and all the howling bedlam of the puppy-pack.

He ran again through the silence, hunting his living food through the months of famine; and again he ran at the head of the team, the gutwhips of Mit-sah and Grey Beaver snapping behind, their voices crying 'Raa! Raa!' when they came to a narrow passage and the team closed together like a fan to go through. He lived again all his days with Beauty Smith and the fights he had fought. At such times he whimpered and snarled in his sleep, and they that looked on said that his dreams were bad.

But there was one particular nightmare from which he suffered – the clanking, clanging monsters of electric cars that were to him colossal screaming lynxes. He would lie in a screen of bushes, watching for a squirrel to venture far enough out on the ground from its tree-refuge. Then when he sprang out upon it, it would transform itself into an electric car, menacing and terrible, towering over him like a mountain, screaming and clanging and spitting fire at him. It was the same when he challenged the hawk down out of the sky. Down out of the blue it would rush, as it dropped upon him changing itself into the ubiquitous electric car. Or again, he would be in the pen of Beauty Smith. Outside the pen, men would be gathering, and he knew that a fight was on. He watched the door for his antagonist to enter. The door would open, and thrust in upon him would come the awful electric car. A thousand times this occurred, and each time the terror it inspired was as vivid and great as ever.

Then came the day when the last bandage and the last plaster cast were taken off. It was a gala day. All Sierra Vista was gathered around. The master rubbed his ears, and he crooned his love-growl. The master's wife called him the 'Blessed Wolf', which name was taken up with acclaim, and all the women called him the Blessed Wolf.

He tried to rise to his feet, and after several attempts fell down from weakness. He had lain so long that his muscles had lost their cunning, and all the strength had gone out of them. He felt a little shame because of his weakness, as though, forsooth, he were failing the gods in the service he owed them. Because of this he made heroic efforts to arise; and at last he stood on his four legs, tottering and swaying back and forth.

'The Blessed Wolf!' chorused the women.

Judge Scott surveyed them triumphantly.

'Out of your own mouths be it,' he said. 'Just as I contended right along. No mere dog could have done what he did. He's a wolf.'

'A Blessed Wolf,' amended the Judge's wife.

'Yes, Blessed Wolf,' agreed the Judge. 'And henceforth that shall be my name for him.'

'He'll have to learn to walk again,' said the surgeon; 'so he might as well start in right now. It won't hurt him. Take him outside.'

And outside he went, like a king, with all Sierra Vista about him and tending on him. He was very weak, and when he reached the lawn he lay down and rested for a while.

Then the procession started on, little spurts of strength coming into White Fang's muscles as he used them and blood began to surge through them. The stables were reached, and there in the doorway lay Collie, a half-dozen pudgy puppies playing about her in the sun.

White Fang looked on with a wondering eye. Collie snarled warningly at him, and he was careful to keep his distance. The master with his toe helped one sprawling puppy toward him. He bristled suspiciously, but the master warned him that all was well. Collie, clasped in the arms of one of the women, watched him jealously, and with a snarl warned him that all was not well.

The puppy sprawled in front of him. He cocked his ears and watched it curiously. Then their noses touched, and he felt the warm tongue of the puppy on his jowl. White Fang's tongue went out, he knew not why, and he licked the puppy's face.

Hand-clapping and pleased cries from the gods greeted the performance. He was surprised, and looked at them in a puzzled way. Then his weakness asserted itself, and he lay down, his ears cocked, his head on one side, as he watched the puppy. The other puppies came sprawling toward him, to Collie's great disgust; and he gravely permitted them to clamber and tumble over him. At first, amid the applause of the gods, he betrayed a trifle of his old self-consciousness and awkwardness. This passed away as the puppies' antics and mauling continued, and he lay with half-shut patient eyes, drowsing in the sun.

Tucker's Life Savings

GEORGE SELDEN

**Chester the cricket arrived in Times Square, New
York, in somebody's picnic basket. Rescued by
Mario, his life is now spent in a matchbox on a news-
stand, accompanied by his friends, Harry Cat and
Tucker Mouse ...**

Chester Cricket was having a dream. In his dream he was sitting
on top of his stump back in Connecticut, eating a leaf from a
willow tree. He would bite off a piece of leaf, chew it up, and
swallow it, but for some reason it didn't taste as good as usual.
There was something dry and papery about it, and it had a bitter
flavour. Still Chester kept eating, hoping that it would begin to
taste better.

A storm came up in his dream. The wind blew clouds of dust
across the meadow. They swirled around his stump, and Chester
began to sneeze because the dust got in his nose. But he still held
on to the leaf. And then he sneezed such a big sneeze that it woke
him up.

Chester looked around him. He had been walking in his sleep
and he was sitting on the edge of the cash register. The storm had
been a gust of air that blew into the news-stand when the shuttle

pulled up to the station. He was still choking from the dirt that flew around him. Chester looked down at his two front legs, half expecting to find the willow leaf. But it was no leaf he was holding. It was a two dollar bill and he had already eaten half of it.

He dropped the bill and leaped over to the cricket cage, where Tucker Mouse was sleeping peacefully. Chester shook the silver bell furiously; it rang like a fire alarm. Tucker jumped out from under his blanket of dollar bills and ran around the cage shouting. 'Help! Fire! Murder! Police!'

Then he realized where he was and sat down panting. 'What is the matter with you, Chester?' he said. 'I could have died from fright.'

'I just ate half of a two dollar bill,' said Chester.

Tucker stared at him with disbelief. 'You did *what*?' he asked.

'Yes,' said Chester, 'look.' He fetched the ruined two dollar bill from the cash register. 'I dreamed it was a leaf and I ate it.'

'Oh oh oh oh,' moaned Tucker Mouse. 'Not a one dollar bill – not even a one dollar bill and a fifty cent piece – *two dollars* you had to eat! And from the Bellinis too – people who hardly make two dollars in two days.'

'What am I going to do?' asked Chester.

'Pack your bags and go to California,' said Tucker.

Chester shook his head. 'I can't,' he said. 'They've been so good to me – I can't run away.'

Tucker Mouse shrugged his shoulders. 'Then stay and take the rap,' he said. He crept out of the cage and examined the remains of the money. 'There's still half of it left. Maybe we could put scotch tape along the edge and pass it off as a one dollar bill.'

'No one would believe it,' said Chester. He sat down, still forlornly holding the bill. 'Oh dear – and things were going along so nicely.'

Tucker Mouse put his bed clothes back in the cash register drawer and came to sit beside Chester. 'Buck up,' he said. 'We could still figure something out, maybe.'

They both concentrated for a minute. Then Tucker clapped his paws and squeaked, 'I got it! Eat the rest of it and they'll never know what happened.'

'They'd accuse each other of losing it,' said Chester. 'I don't want to make any bad feeling between them.'

'Oh you're so honourable!' said Tucker. 'It's disgusting.'

'Besides, it tastes bad,' added Chester.

'Then how about this,' Tucker had a new idea. 'We frame the janitor who cleans the station. I'll take the evidence over and plant it in his water closet. He whopped me with a mop last week. I would be glad to see him go to jail for a few days.'

'No, no,' said Chester. 'We can't get somebody else into trouble.'

'Then a stranger,' said Tucker. 'We tip over the Kleenex, break the glass in the alarm clock, and throw all the small change on the floor. They'll think a thief came in the night. You could even put a bandage on and make out like a hero. I could see it all –'

'*No!*' Chester interrupted him. 'The damage we'd do would cost even more than the two dollars.'

Tucker had one more idea: he was going to volunteer to go over and swipe two dollars from the lunch counter. But before he could suggest that, the top of the stand was suddenly lifted off. They had forgotten what time it was. Mama Bellini, who was on duty in the morning, stood towering, frowning down on them. Tucker let out a squeak of fear and jumped to the floor.

'Catch the mouse!' shouted Mama. She picked up a *Fortune* magazine – very big and heavy – and heaved it after Tucker. It hit him on the left hind leg just as he vanished into the drain pipe.

Chester Cricket sat frozen to the spot. He was caught red handed, holding the chewed up two dollars in his front legs. Muttering with rage, Mama Bellini picked him up by his antennae, tossed him into the cricket cage, and locked the gate behind him. When she had put the news-stand in order, she pulled out her knitting and began to work furiously. But she was so angry she kept dropping stitches, and that made her angrier still.

Chester crouched in a far corner of the cage. Things had been going so well between Mama and him – but that was all ruined now. He half expected that she would pick him up, cage and all, and throw him onto the shuttle tracks.

At eight-thirty Mario and Papa arrived. Mario wanted to go to Coney Island for a swim today, but before he could even say 'Good morning', Mama Bellini stretched out her hand and pointed sternly at Chester. There he was, with the evidence beside him.

A three-cornered conversation began. Mama denounced Chester as a money eater and said further that she suspected him of inviting mice and other unsavoury characters into the news-stand at night. Papa said he didn't think Chester had eaten the two dollars on purpose, and what difference did it make if a mouse or two came in? Mama said he had to go. Papa said he could stay, but he'd have to be kept in the cage. And Mario knew that Chester, like all people who were used to freedom, would rather die than live his life behind bars.

Finally it was decided that since the cricket was Mario's pet, the boy would have to replace the money. And when he had, Chester could come out again. Until then – the cage.

By working part time delivering groceries, when he wasn't taking care of the news-stand, Mario thought he could earn enough in a couple of weeks to get Chester out of jail. Of course that would mean no swimming at Coney Island, and no movies, and no nothing, but it was worth it. He fed the cricket his breakfast – left over asparagus tips and a piece of cabbage leaf. Chester had practically no appetite after what had happened. Then, when the cricket was finished, Mario said, 'Good-bye,' and told him not to worry, and went off to the grocery store to see about his job.

That night, after Papa had shut up the news-stand, Chester was hanging through the gilded bars of his cage. Earlier in the evening Mario had come back to feed him his supper, but then he had to leave right away to get in a few more hours of work. Most of the day Chester had spent inventing hopping games to try to keep himself entertained, but they didn't work, really. He was bored and lonely. The funny thing was that although he had been sleepy and kept wishing it were night, now that it was, he couldn't fall asleep.

Chester heard the soft padding of feet beneath him. Harry Cat sprang up and landed on the shelf. In a moment Tucker Mouse followed him from the stool, groaning with pain. He was still limping in his left hind leg where the *Fortune* magazine had hit him.

'How long is the sentence?' asked Harry.

'Until Mario can pay back the money,' sighed Chester.

'Couldn't you get out on bail for the time being?' asked Tucker.

'No,' said Chester. 'And anyway, nobody has any bail. I'm surprised they let me off that easily.'

Harry Cat folded his front paws over each other and rested his head on them. 'Let me get this straight,' he said. 'Does Mario have to work for the money as punishment – or does he just have to get it somewhere?'

'He just has to get it,' said Chester. 'Why should he be punished? I'm the one who ate the money.'

Harry looked at Tucker – a long look, as if he expected the mouse to say something. Tucker began to fidget. 'Say Chester, you want to escape?' he asked. 'We can open the cage. You could come and live in the drain pipe.'

'No,' Chester shook his head. 'It wouldn't be fair to Mario. I'll just have to serve out the time.'

Harry looked at Tucker again and began tapping one of his paws. 'Well?' he said finally.

Tucker moaned and massaged his sore spot. 'Oh my poor leg! That Mama Bellini can sure heave a magazine. Feel the bump, Harry,' he offered.

'I felt it already,' said Harry. 'Now enough of the stalling. You have money.'

'Tucker has money?' said Chester Cricket.

Tucker looked nervously from one to the other. 'I have my life's savings,' he said in a pathetic voice.

'He's the richest mouse in New York,' said Harry. 'Old Money Bags Mouse, he's known as.'

'Now wait a minute, Harry,' said Tucker. 'Let's not make too much from a few nickels and dimes.'

'How did you get money?' asked Chester.

Tucker Mouse cleared his throat and began wringing his two front feet. When he spoke, his voice was all choked up with emotion. 'Years ago,' he said, 'when yet a little mouse I was, tender in age and lacking in experience, I moved from the sweet scenes of my childhood – Tenth Avenue, that is – into Times Square subway station. And it was here that I learned the value of economicness – which means saving. Many and many an old mouse did I see, crawling away unwanted to a poor mouse's grave, because he had not saved. And I resolved that such a fate would never come to me.'

'All of which means that you've got a pile of loot back there in the drain pipe,' said Harry Cat.

'Just a minute, please, if you wouldn't mind,' said Tucker. 'I'll tell it in my own way.' His voice became high and pitiful again. 'So for all the long years of my youth, when I could have been gamboling – which means playing – with the other mousies, I saved. I saved paper, I saved food, I saved clothing – '

'Save time and get to the point,' said Harry.

Tucker gave Harry a sour smile. 'And I also saved money,' he went on. 'In the course of many years of scrounging, it was only natural I should find a certain amount of loose change. Often – oh often, my friends,' Tucker put his hand over his heart, 'would I sit in the opening of my drain pipe, watching the human beings and waiting. And whenever one of them dropped a coin – *however small!* – pennies I love – I would dash out, at great peril to life and limb, and bring it back to my house. Ah, when I think of the tramping shoes and the dangerous galoshes – ! Many times have I had my toes stepped on and my whiskers torn off because of these labours. But it was worth it! Oh, it was worth it, my friends, on account of now I have two half dollars, five quarters, two dimes, six nickels, and eighteen pennies tucked away in the drain pipe!'

'Which makes two dollars and ninety-three cents,' said Harry Cat, after doing some quick addition.

'And proud I am of it!' said Tucker Mouse.

'If you've got all that, why did you want to sleep on the two dollar bills in the cricket cage?' asked Chester.

'No folding money yet,' said Tucker. 'It was a new sensation.'

'You can get Chester out and still have ninety-three cents left,' said Harry Cat.

'But I'll be ruined,' whimpered Tucker. 'I'll be wiped out. Who will take care of me in my old age?'

'I will!' said Harry. 'Now stop acting like a skinflint and let's get the money.'

Chester rang the silver bell to get their attention. 'I don't think Tucker should have to give up his life savings,' he said. 'It's his money and he can do what he wants with it.'

Tucker Mouse poked Harry in the ribs. 'Listen to the cricket,' he said. 'Acting noble and making me look like a bum. Of course I'll give the money! Wherever mice are spoken of, never let it be said that Tucker Mouse was stingy with his worldly goods. Besides, I could think of it as rent I pay for sleeping in the cage.'

In order that Tucker could keep at least one of each kind of coin, Harry Cat figured out that they should bring over one half dollar, four quarters, one dime, five nickels, and fifteen cents. That would leave the mouse with a half dollar, a quarter, a dime, a nickel, and three cents.

'It's not a bad beginning,' said Tucker. 'I could make up the losses in a year, maybe.'

The cat and the mouse had to make several trips back and forth between the drain pipe and the news-stand, carrying the money in their mouths. They passed the coins into the cage one by one, and Chester built them up in a column, starting with the half dollar on the bottom and ending with the dime, which was the smallest, on top. It was morning by the time they were finished. They had just time enough to share half of a hot dog before Mama Bellini was due to open the stand.

Mario came with her. He wanted to feed Chester early and then work all morning until he took over the news-stand at noon. When they lifted off the cover, Mama almost dropped her end. There was Chester, sitting on top of the column of change, chirping merrily.

Mama's first suspicion was that the cricket had sneaked out and smuggled all the money from the cash register into the cage. But when she looked in the drawer, the money from the night before was still there.

Mario had the idea that Papa might have left it as a surprise. Mama shook her head. She would certainly have known if he had two dollars to leave anybody.

They asked Paul, the conductor, if he'd seen anyone around the news-stand. He said no. The only thing he'd noticed was that that big cat who sometimes prowled through the station had seemed to be busier than usual last night. And of course they knew that he couldn't have had anything to do with replacing the money.

But whoever left it, Mama Bellini was good to her word. Chester was allowed out of the cage, and no further questions were asked. Although she wouldn't have admitted it for the world, Mama felt the same way about money that Tucker Mouse did. When you had it, you had it – and you didn't bother too much about where it came from.

The Maltese Cat

RUDYARD KIPLING

They had good reason to be proud, and better reason to be afraid, all twelve of them; for though they had fought their way, game by game, up the teams entered for the polo tournament, they were meeting the Archangels that afternoon in the final match; and the Archangels' men were playing with half-a-dozen ponies apiece. As the game was divided into six quarters of eight minutes each, that meant a fresh pony after every halt. The Skidars' team, even supposing there were no accidents, could only supply one pony for every other chance; and two to one is heavy odds. Again, as Shiraz, the gray Syrian, pointed out, they were meeting the pink and pick of the polo-ponies of Upper India; ponies that had cost from a thousand rupees each, while they themselves were a cheap lot gathered, often from country carts, by their masters, who belonged to a poor but honest native infantry regiment.

'Money means pace and weight,' said Shiraz, rubbing his black silk nose dolefully along his neat-fitting boot, 'and by the maxims of the game as I know it – '

'Ah, but we aren't playing the maxims,' said the Maltese Cat. 'We're playing the game, and we've the great advantage of knowing the game. Just think a stride, Shiraz. We've pulled up from bottom to second place in two weeks against all those fellows on the ground here; and that's because we play with our heads as well as with our feet.'

'It makes me feel undersized and unhappy all the same,' said Kittiwynk, a mouse-coloured mare with a red browband and the cleanest pair of legs that ever an aged pony owned. 'They've twice our size, these others.'

Kittiwynk looked at the gathering and sighed. The hard, dusty Umballa polo-ground was lined with thousands of soldiers, black and white, not counting hundreds and hundreds of carriages, and drags, and dog-carts, and ladies with brilliant-coloured parasols, and officers in uniform and out of it, and crowds of natives behind them; and orderlies on camels who had halted to watch the game, instead of carrying letters up and down the station, and native horse-dealers running about on thin-eared Biluchi mares, looking for a chance to sell a few first-class polo-ponies. Then there were the ponies of thirty teams that had entered for the Upper India Free-for-All Cup – nearly every pony of worth and dignity from Mhow to Peshawur, from Allahabad to Multan; prize ponies, Arabs, Syrian, Barb, countrybred, Deccanee, Waziri, and Kabul ponies of every colour and shape and temper that you could imagine. Some of them were in mat-roofed stables close to the polo-ground, but most were under saddle while their masters, who had been defeated in the earlier games, trotted in and out and told each other exactly how the game should be played.

It was a glorious sight, and the come-and-go of the little quick hoofs, and the incessant salutations of ponies that had met before on other polo-grounds or racecourses, were enough to drive a four-footed thing wild.

But the Skidars' team were careful not to know their neighbours, though half the ponies on the ground were anxious to scrape acquaintance with the little fellows who had come from the North; and, so far, had swept the board.

'Let's see,' said a soft, golden-coloured Arab, who had been playing very badly the day before, to the Maltese Cat, 'didn't we meet in Abdul Rahman's stable in Bombay four seasons ago? I won the Paikpattan Cup next season, you may remember.'

'Not me,' said the Maltese Cat politely. 'I was at Malta then, pulling a vegetable cart. I don't race. I play the game.'

'O-oh!' said the Arab, cocking his tail and swaggering off.

'Keep yourselves to yourselves,' said the Maltese Cat to his companions. 'We don't want to rub noses with all those goose-rumped half-breeds of Upper India. When we've won this Cup they'll give their shoes to know us.'

'*We* shan't win the Cup,' said Shiraz. 'How do you feel?'

'Stale as last night's feed when a musk-rat has run over it,' said Polaris, a rather heavy-shouldered gray, and the rest of the team agreed with him.

'The sooner you forget that the better,' said the Maltese Cat cheerfully. 'They've finished tiffin in the big tent. We shall be wanted now. If your saddles are not comfy, kick. If your bits aren't easy, rear, and let the *saises* know whether your boots are tight.'

Each pony had his *sais*, his groom, who lived and ate and slept with the pony, and had betted a great deal more than he could afford on the result of the game. There was no chance of anything going wrong, and, to make sure, each *sais* was shampooing the legs of his pony to the last minute. Behind the *saises* sat as many of the Skidars' regiment as had leave to attend the match – about half the native officers, and a hundred or two dark, black-bearded men, with the regimental pipers nervously fingering the big be-ribboned bagpipes. The Skidars were what they call a Pioneer regiment; and the bagpipes made the national music of half the men. The native officers held bundles of polo-sticks, long cane-handled mallets, and as the grand-stand filled after lunch they arranged themselves by ones and twos at different points round the ground, so that if a stick were broken the player would not have far to ride for a new one. An impatient British cavalry band struck up 'If you want to know the time, ask a p'leeceman!' and the two umpires in light dust-coats danced out on two little excited ponies. The four players of the Archangels' team followed, and the sight of their beautiful mounts made Shiraz groan again.

'Wait till we know,' said the Maltese Cat. 'Two of 'em are

playing in blinkers, and that means they can't see to get out of the way of their own side, or they *may* shy at the umpires' ponies. They've *all* got white web reins that are sure to stretch or slip!'

'And,' said Kittiwynk, dancing to take the stiffness out of her, 'they carry their whips in their hands instead of on their wrists. Hah!'

'True enough. No man can manage his stick and his reins and his whip that way,' said the Maltese Cat. 'I've fallen over every square yard of the Malta ground, and *I* ought to know.' He quivered his little flea-bitten withers just to show how satisfied he felt; but his heart was not so light. Ever since he had drifted into India on a troopship, taken, with an old rifle, as part payment for a racing debt, the Maltese Cat had played and preached polo to the Skidars' team on the Skidars' stony polo-ground. Now, a polo-pony is like a poet. If he is born with a love for the game he can be made. The Maltese Cat knew that bamboos grew solely in order that polo-balls might be turned from their roots, that grain was given to ponies to keep them in hard condition, and that ponies were shod to prevent them slipping on a turn. But, besides all these things, he knew every trick and device of the finest game of the world, and for two seasons he had been teaching the others all he knew or guessed.

'Remember,' he said for the hundredth time as the riders came up, 'we *must* play together, and you *must* play with your heads. Whatever happens, follow the ball. Who goes out first?'

Kittiwynk, Shiraz, Polaris, and a short high little bay fellow with tremendous hocks and no withers worth speaking of (he was called Corks) were being girthed up, and the soldiers in the background stared with all their eyes.

'I want you men to keep quiet,' said Lutyens, the captain of the team, 'and especially *not* to blow your pipes.'

'Not if we win, Captain Sahib?' asked a piper.

'If we win, you can do what you please,' said Lutyens, with a smile, as he slipped the loop of his stick over his wrist, and wheeled to canter to his place. The Archangels' ponies were a little bit above themselves on account of the many-coloured crowd so close to the ground. Their riders were excellent players, but they were a team of crack players instead of a crack team; and that made all the difference in the world. They honestly meant to play together, but it is very hard for four men, each the best of the team he is picked from, to remember that in polo no brilliancy of hitting or riding makes up for playing alone. Their captain shouted his orders to them by name, and it is a curious thing that if you call his name aloud in public after an Englishman you make him hot and fretty. Lutyens said nothing to his men because it had all been said before. He pulled up Shiraz, for he was playing 'back,' to guard the goal. Powell on Polaris was half-back, and Macnamara and Hughes on Corks and Kittiwynk were forwards. The tough bamboo-root ball was put into the middle of the ground one hundred and fifty yards from the ends, and Hughes crossed sticks, heads-up, with the captain of the Archangels, who saw fit to play forward, and that is a place from which you cannot easily control the team. The little click as the cane-shafts met was heard all over the ground, and then Hughes made some sort of quick wrist-stroke that just dribbled the ball a few yards. Kittiwynk knew that stroke of old, and followed as a cat follows a mouse. While the captain of the Archangels was wrenching his pony round, Hughes struck with all his strength, and next instant Kittiwynk was away, Corks following close behind her, their little feet pattering like rain-drops on glass.

'Pull out to the left,' said Kittiwynk between her teeth, 'it's coming our way, Corks!'

The back and half-back of the Archangels were tearing down on her just as she was within reach of the ball. Hughes leaned forward with a loose rein, and cut it away to the left almost under Kittiwynk's feet, and it hopped and skipped off to Corks, who saw that, if he were not quick, it would run beyond the boundaries. That long bouncing drive gave the Archangels time to wheel and send three men across the ground to head off Corks. Kittiwynk stayed where she was, for she knew the game. Corks was on the ball half a fraction of a second before the others came up, and Macnamara, with a back-handed stroke, sent it back across the ground to Hughes, who saw the way clear to the Archangels' goal, and smacked the ball in before anyone quite knew what had happened.

'That's luck,' said Corks, as they changed ends. 'A goal in three minutes for three hits and no riding to speak of.'

'Don't know,' said Polaris. 'We've made 'em angry too soon. Shouldn't wonder if they try to rush us off our feet next time.'

'Keep the ball hanging then,' said Shiraz. 'That wears out every pony that isn't used to it.'

Next time there was no easy galloping across the ground. All the Archangels closed up as one man, but there they stayed, for Corks, Kittiwynk, and Polaris were somewhere on the top of the ball, marking time among the rattling sticks, while Shiraz circled about outside, waiting for a chance.

'*We* can do this all day,' said Polaris, ramming his quarters into the side of another pony. 'Where do you think you're shoving to?'

'I'll – I'll be driven in an *ekka* if I know,' was the gasping reply, 'and I'd give a week's feed to get my blinkers off. I can't see anything.'

'The dust *is* rather bad. Whew! That was one for my off hock. Where's the ball, Corks?'

'Under my tail. At least a man's looking for it there. This is beautiful. They can't use their sticks, and it's driving 'em wild. Give old Blinkers a push and he'll go over!'

'Here, don't touch me! I can't see. I'll – I'll back out, I think,' said the pony in blinkers, who knew that if you can't see all round your head you cannot prop yourself against a shock.

Corks was watching the ball where it lay in the dust close to his near fore with Macnamara's shortened stick tap-tapping it from time to time. Kittiwynk was edging her way out of the scrimmage, whisking her stump of a tail with nervous excitement.

'Ho! They've got it,' she snorted. 'Let me out!' and she galloped like a rifle-bullet just behind a tall lanky pony of the Archangels, whose rider was swinging up his stick for a stroke.

'Not to-day, thank you,' said Hughes, as the blow slid off his raised stick, and Kittiwynk laid her shoulder to the tall pony's quarters, and shoved him aside just as Lutyens on Shiraz sent the ball where it had come from, and the tall pony went skating and slipping away to the left. Kittiwynk, seeing that Polaris had joined Corks in the chase for the ball up the ground, dropped into Polaris's place, and then time was called.

The Skidars' ponies wasted no time in kicking or fuming. They knew each minute's rest meant so much gain, and trotted off to the rails and their *saises*, who began to scrape and blanket and rub them at once.

'Whew!' said Corks, stiffening up to get all the tickle out of the big vulcanite scraper. 'If we were playing pony for pony we'd bend those Archangels double in half an hour. But they'll bring out fresh ones and fresh ones, and fresh ones after that – you see.'

'Who cares?' said Polaris. 'We've drawn first blood. Is my hock swelling?'

'Looks puffy,' said Corks. 'You must have had rather a wipe. Don't let it stiffen. You'll be wanted again in half an hour.'

'What's the game like?' said the Maltese Cat.

'Ground's like your shoe, except where they've put too much water on it,' said Kittiwynk. 'Then it's slippery. Don't play in the centre. There's a bog there. I don't know how their next four are going to behave, but we kept the ball hanging and made 'em lather for nothing. Who goes out? Two Arabs and a couple of countrybreds! That's bad. What a comfort it is to wash your mouth out!'

Kitty was talking with the neck of a leather-covered soda-water bottle between her teeth and trying to look over her withers at the same time. This gave her a very coquettish air.

'What's bad?' said Gray Dawn, giving to the girth and admiring his well-set shoulders.

'You Arabs can't gallop fast enough to keep yourselves warm – that's what Kitty means,' said Polaris, limping to show that his hock needed attention. 'Are you playing "back," Gray Dawn?'

'Looks like it,' said Gray Dawn, as Lutyens swung himself up. Powell mounted the Rabbit, a plain bay countrybred much like Corks, but with mulish ears. Macnamara took Faiz Ullah, a handy short-backed little red Arab with a long tail, and Hughes mounted Benami, an old and sullen brown beast, who stood over in front more than a polo-pony should.

'Benami looks like business,' said Shiraz. 'How's your temper, Ben?' The old campaigner hobbled off without answering, and the Maltese Cat looked at the new Archangel ponies prancing about on the ground. They were four beautiful blacks, and they saddled big enough and strong enough to eat the Skidars' team and gallop away with the meal inside them.

'Blinkers again,' said the Maltese Cat. 'Good enough!'

'They're chargers – cavalry chargers!' said Kittiwynk indignantly. *'They'll* never see thirteen-three again.'

'They've all been fairly measured and they've all got their certificates,' said the Maltese Cat, 'or they wouldn't be here. We must take things as they come along, and keep our eyes on the ball.'

The game began, but this time the Skidars were penned to their own end of the ground, and the watching ponies did not approve of that.

'Faiz Ullah is shirking, as usual,' said Polaris, with a scornful grunt.

'Faiz Ullah is eating whip,' said Corks. They could hear the leather-thonged polo-quirt lacing the little fellow's well-rounded barrel. Then the Rabbit's shrill neigh came across the ground. 'I can't do all the work,' he cried.

'Play the game, don't talk,' the Maltese Cat whickered; and all the ponies wriggled with excitement, and the soldiers and the grooms gripped the railings and shouted. A black pony with blinkers had singled out old Benami, and was interfering with him in every possible way. They could see Benami shaking his head up and down and flapping his underlip.

'There'll be a fall in a minute,' said Polaris. 'Benami is getting stuffy.'

The game flickered up and down between goal-post and goalpost, and the black ponies were getting more confident as they felt they had the legs of the others. The ball was hit out of a little scrimmage, and Benami and the Rabbit followed it; Faiz Ullah only too glad to be quiet for an instant.

The blinkered black pony came up like a hawk, with two of his own side behind him, and Benami's eye glittered as he raced. The question was which pony should make way for the other; each rider was perfectly willing to risk a fall in a good cause. The black, who had been driven nearly crazy by his blinkers, trusted to his weight and his temper; but Benami knew how to apply his weight and how to keep his temper. They met, and there was a cloud of dust. The black was lying on his side with all the breath knocked out of his body. The Rabbit was a hundred yards up the ground with the ball, and Benami was sitting down. He had slid nearly ten yards, but he had had his revenge, and sat cracking his nostrils till the black pony rose.

'That's what you get for interfering. Do you want any more?' said Benami, and he plunged into the game. Nothing was done because Faiz Ullah would not gallop, though Macnamara beat him whenever he could spare a second. The fall of the black pony had impressed his companions tremendously, and so the Archangels could not profit by Faiz Ullah's bad behaviour.

But as the Maltese Cat said, when time was called and the four came back blowing and dripping, Faiz Ullah ought to have been kicked all round Umballa. If he did not behave better next time, the Maltese Cat promised to pull out his Arab tail by the root and eat it.

There was no time to talk, for the third four were ordered out.

The third quarter of a game is generally the hottest, for each side thinks that the others must be pumped; and most of the winning play in a game is made about that time.

Lutyens took over the Maltese Cat with a pat and a hug, for Lutyens valued him more than anything else in the world. Powell had Shikast, a little gray rat with no pedigree and no manners outside polo; Macnamara mounted Bamboo, the largest of the team, and Hughes took Who's Who, *alias* The Animal. He was supposed to have Australian blood in his veins, but he looked like a clothes-horse, and you could whack him on the legs with an iron crowbar without hurting him.

They went out to meet the very flower of the Archangels' team, and when Who's Who saw their elegantly booted legs and their beautiful satiny skins he grinned a grin through his light, well-worn bridle.

'My word!' said Who's Who. 'We must give 'em a little football. Those gentlemen need a rubbing down.'

'No biting,' said the Maltese Cat warningly, for once or twice in his career Who's Who had been known to forget himself in that way.

'Who said anything about biting? I'm not playing tiddlywinks. I'm playing the game.'

The Archangels came down like a wolf on the fold, for they were tired of football and they wanted polo. They got it more and more. Just after the game began, Lutyens hit a ball that was coming towards him rapidly, and it rose in the air, as a ball sometimes will, with the whirr of a frightened partridge. Shikast heard, but could not see it for the minute, though he looked everywhere and up into the air as the Maltese Cat had taught him. When he saw it ahead and overhead, he went forward with Powell as fast as he could put foot to ground. It was then that Powell, a quiet and level-headed man as a rule, became inspired and played a stroke that sometimes comes off successfully on a quiet afternoon of long practice. He took his stick in both hands, and, standing up in his stirrups, swiped at the ball in the air, Manipur fashion. There was one second of paralysed astonishment, and then all four sides of the ground went up in a yell of applause and delight as the ball flew true (you could see the amazed Archangels ducking in their saddles to get out of the line of flight, and looking at it with open mouths), and the regimental pipes of the Skidars squealed from the railings as long as the pipers had breath.

Shikast heard the stroke; but he heard the head of the stick fly off at the same time. Nine hundred and ninety-nine ponies out of a thousand would have gone tearing on after the ball with a useless player pulling at their heads, but Powell knew him, and he knew

Powell; and the instant he felt Powell's right leg shift a trifle on the saddle-flap he headed to the boundary, where a native officer was frantically waving a new stick. Before the shouts had ended Powell was armed again.

Once before in his life the Maltese Cat had heard that very same stroke played off his own back, and had profited by the confusion it made. This time he acted on experience, and, leaving Bamboo to guard the goal in case of accidents, came through the others like a flash, head and tail low, Lutyens standing up to ease him – swept on and on before the other side knew what was the matter, and nearly pitched on his head between the Archangels' goal-posts as Lutyens tipped the ball in after a straight scurry of a hundred and fifty yards. If there was one thing more than another upon which the Maltese Cat prided himself it was on this quick, streaking kind of run half across the ground. He did not believe in taking balls round the field unless you were clearly over-matched. After this they gave the Archangels five minutes' football, and an expensive fast pony hates football because it rumples his temper.

Who's Who showed himself even better than Polaris in this game. He did not permit any wriggling away, but bored joyfully into the scrimmage as if he had his nose in a feed-box, and were looking for something nice. Little Shikast jumped on the ball the minute it got clear, and every time an Archangel pony followed it he found Shikast standing over it asking what was the matter.

'If we can live through this quarter,' said the Maltese Cat, 'I shan't care. Don't take it out of yourselves. Let *them* do the lathering.'

So the ponies, as their riders explained afterwards, 'shut up.' The Archangels kept them tied fast in front of their goal, but it cost the Archangels' ponies all that was left of their tempers; and ponies began to kick, and men began to repeat compliments, and they chopped at the legs of Who's Who, and he set his teeth and stayed where he was, and the dust stood up like a tree over the scrimmage till that hot quarter ended.

They found the ponies very excited and confident when they

went to their *saises*; and the Maltese Cat had to warn them that the worst of the game was coming.

'Now *we* are all going in for the second time,' said he, 'and *they* are trotting out fresh ponies. You'll think you can gallop, but you'll find you can't; and then you'll be sorry.'

'But two goals to nothing is a halter-long lead,' said Kittiwynk, prancing.

'How long does it take to get a goal?' the Maltese Cat answered. 'For pity's sake, don't run away with the notion that the game is half won just because we happen to be in luck now. They'll ride you into the grand-stand if they can; you must *not* give 'em a chance. Follow the ball.'

'Football, as usual?' said Polaris. 'My hock's half as big as a nose-bag.'

'Don't let them have a look at the ball if you can help it. Now leave me alone. I must get all the rest I can before the last quarter.'

He hung down his head and let all his muscles go slack; Shikast, Bamboo, and Who's Who copying his example.

'Better not watch the game,' he said. 'We aren't playing, and we shall only take it out of ourselves if we grow anxious. Look at the ground and pretend it's fly-time.'

They did their best, but it was hard advice to follow. The hoofs were drumming and the sticks were rattling all up and down the ground, and yells of applause from the English troops told that the Archangels were pressing the Skidars hard. The native soldiers behind the ponies groaned and grunted, and said things in undertones, and presently they heard a long-drawn shout and a clatter of hurrahs!

'One to the Archangels,' said Shikast, without raising his head. 'Time's nearly up. Oh, my sire and – dam!'

'Faiz Ullah,' said the Maltese Cat, 'if you don't play to the last nail in your shoes this time, I'll kick you on the ground before all the other ponies.'

'I'll do my best when my time comes,' said the little Arab sturdily.

The *saises* looked at each other gravely as they rubbed their ponies' legs. This was the first time when long purses began to tell, and everybody knew it. Kittiwynk and the others came back with the sweat dripping over their hoofs and their tails telling sad stories.

'They're better than we are,' said Shiraz. 'I knew how it would be.'

'Shut your big head,' said the Maltese Cat; 'we've one goal to the good yet.'

'Yes, but it's two Arabs and two countrybreds to play now,' said Corks. 'Faiz Ullah, remember!' He spoke in a biting voice.

As Lutyens mounted Gray Dawn he looked at his men, and they did not look pretty. They were covered with dust and sweat in streaks. Their yellow boots were almost black, their wrists were red and lumpy, and their eyes seemed two inches deep in their heads, but the expression in the eyes was satisfactory.

'Did you take anything at tiffin?' said Lutyens, and the team shook their heads. They were too dry to talk.

'All right. The Archangels did. They are worse pumped than we are.'

'They've got the better ponies,' said Powell. 'I shan't be sorry when this business is over.'

That fifth quarter was a sad one in every way. Faiz Ullah played like a little red demon; and the Rabbit seemed to be everywhere at once, and Benami rode straight at anything and everything that came in his way, while the umpires on their ponies wheeled like gulls outside the shifting game. But the Archangels had the better mounts – they had kept their racers till late in the game – and never allowed the Skidars to play football. They hit the ball up and down the width of the ground till Benami and the rest were outpaced. Then they went forward, and time and again Lutyens and Gray Dawn were just, and only just, able to send the ball away with a long splitting back-hander. Gray Dawn forgot that he was an Arab; and turned from gray to blue as he galloped. Indeed, he forgot too well, for he did not keep his eyes on the ground as an Arab should, but stuck out his nose and scuttled for the dear honour of the game. They had watered the ground once or twice between the quarters, and a careless waterman had emptied the last of his skinful all in one place near the Skidar's goal. It was close to the end of play, and for the tenth time Gray Dawn was bolting after a ball when his near hind foot slipped on the greasy mud and he rolled over and over, pitching Lutyens just clear of the goal-post; and the triumphant Archangels made their goal. Then time was called – two goals all; but Lutyens had to be helped up, and Gray Dawn rose with his near hind leg strained somewhere.

'What's the damage?' said Powell, his arm round Lutyens.

'Collar-bone, of course,' said Lutyens between his teeth. It was the third time he had broken it in two years, and it hurt him.

Powell and the others whistled. 'Game's up,' said Hughes.

'Hold on. We've five good minutes yet, and it isn't my right hand,' said Lutyens. 'We'll stick it out.'

'I say,' said the captain of the Archangels, trotting up. 'Are you hurt, Lutyens? We'll wait if you care to put in a substitute. I wish – I mean – the fact is, you fellows deserve this game if any team does. Wish we could give you a man or some of our ponies – or something.'

'You're awfully good, but we'll play it to a finish, I think.'

The captain of the Archangels stared for a little. 'That's not half bad,' he said, and went back to his own side, while Lutyens borrowed a scarf from one of his native officers and made a sling of it. Then an Archangel galloped up with a big bath-sponge and advised Lutyens to put it under his armpit to ease his shoulder, and between them they tied up his left arm scientifically, and one of the native officers leaped forward with four long glasses that fizzed and bubbled.

The team looked at Lutyens piteously, and he nodded. It was the last quarter, and nothing would matter after that. They drank out the dark golden drink, and wiped their moustaches, and things looked more hopeful.

The Maltese Cat had put his nose into the front of Lutyens' shirt, and was trying to say how sorry he was.

'He knows,' said Lutyens proudly. 'The beggar knows. I've played him without a bridle before now – for fun.'

'It's no fun now,' said Powell. 'But we haven't a decent substitute.'

'No,' said Lutyens. 'It's the last quarter, and we've got to make our goal and win. I'll trust the Cat.'

'If you fall this time you'll suffer a little,' said Macnamara.

'I'll trust the Cat,' said Lutyens.

'You hear that?' said the Maltese Cat proudly to the others. 'It's worth while playing polo for ten years to have that said of you. Now then, my sons, come along. We'll kick up a little bit, just to show the Archangels *this* team haven't suffered.'

And, sure enough, as they went on to the ground the Maltese Cat, after satisfying himself that Lutyens was home in the saddle, kicked out three or four times, and Lutyens laughed. The reins were caught up anyhow in the tips of his strapped fingers, and he never pretended to rely on them. He knew the Cat would answer to the least pressure of the leg, and by way of showing off – for his shoulder hurt him very much – he bent the little fellow in a close figure-of-eight in and out between the goal-posts. There was a roar from the native officers and men, who dearly loved a piece of *dugabashi* (horse-trick work), as they called it, and the pipes very quietly and scornfully droned out the first bars of a common bazaar-tune called 'Freshly Fresh and Newly New,' just as a warning to the other regiments that the Skidars were fit. All the natives laughed.

'And now,' said the Cat, as they took their place, 'remember that this is the last quarter, and follow the ball!'

'Don't need to be told,' said Who's Who.

'Let me go on. All those people on all four sides will begin to crowd in – just as they did at Malta. You'll hear people calling out, and moving forward and being pushed back, and that is going to make the Archangel ponies very unhappy. But if a ball is struck to the boundary, you go after it, and let the people get out of your way. I went over the pole of a four-in-hand once, and picked a game out of the dust by it. Back me up when I run, and follow the ball.'

There was a sort of an all-round sound of sympathy and wonder as the last quarter opened, and then there began exactly what the Maltese Cat had foreseen. People crowded in close to the boundaries, and the Archangels' ponies kept looking sideways at the narrowing space. If you know how a man feels to be cramped at tennis – not because he wants to run out of the court, but because he likes to know that he can at a pinch – you will guess how ponies must feel when they are playing in a box of human beings.

'I'll bend some of those men if I can get away,' said Who's Who, as he rocketed behind the ball; and Bamboo nodded without speaking. They were playing the last ounce in them, and the Maltese Cat had left the goal undefended to join them. Lutyens gave him every order that he could to bring him back, but this was the first time in his career that the little wise gray had ever played polo on his own responsibility, and he was going to make the most of it.

'What are you doing here?' said Hughes, as the Cat crossed in front of him and rode off an Archangel.

'The Cat's in charge – mind the goal!' shouted Lutyens, and bowing forward hit the ball full, and followed on, forcing the Archangels towards their own goal.

'No football,' said the Cat. 'Keep the ball by the boundaries and cramp 'em. Play open order and drive 'em to the boundaries.'

Across and across the ground in big diagonals flew the ball, and whenever it came to a flying rush and a stroke close to the boundaries the Archangel ponies moved stiffly. They did not care to go headlong at a wall of men and carriages, though if the ground had been open they could have turned on a sixpence.

'Wriggle her up the sides,' said the Cat. 'Keep her close to the crowd. They hate the carriages. Shikast, keep her up this side.'

Shikast with Powell lay left and right behind the uneasy scuffle of an open scrimmage, and every time the ball was hit away Shikast galloped on it at such an angle that Powell was forced to hit it towards the boundary; and when the crowd had been driven away from that side, Lutyens would send the ball over to the other, and Shikast would slide desperately after it till his friends

'The Cat's in charge – mind the goal!'

came down to help. It was billiards, and not football, this time – billiards in a corner pocket; and the cues were not well chalked.

'If they get us out in the middle of the ground they'll walk away from us. Dribble her along the sides,' cried the Cat.

So they dribbled all along the boundary, where a pony could not come on their right-hand side; and the Archangels were furious, and the umpires had to neglect the game to shout at the people to get back, and several blundering mounted policemen tried to restore order, all close to the scrimmage, and the nerves of the Archangels' ponies stretched and broke like cobwebs.

Five or six times an Archangel hit the ball up into the middle of the ground, and each time the watchful Shikast gave Powell his chance to send it back, and after each return, when the dust had settled, men could see that the Skidars had gained a few yards.

Every now and again there were shouts of ''Side! Off side!' from the spectators; but the teams were too busy to care, and the umpires had all they could do to keep their maddened ponies clear of the scuffle.

At last Lutyens missed a short easy stroke, and the Skidars had to fly back helter-skelter to protect their own goal, Shikast leading. Powell stopped the ball with a back-hander when it was not fifty yards from the goal-posts, and Shikast spun round with a wrench that nearly hoisted Powell out of his saddle.

'Now's our last chance,' said the Cat, wheeling like a cockchafer on a pin. 'We've got to ride it out. Come along.'

Lutyens felt the little chap take a deep breath, and, as it were, crouch under his rider. The ball was hopping towards the right-hand boundary, an Archangel riding for it with both spurs and a whip; but neither spur nor whip would make his pony stretch himself as he neared the crowd. The Maltese Cat glided under his very nose, picking up his hind legs sharp, for there was not a foot to spare between his quarters and the other pony's bit. It was as neat an exhibition as fancy figure-skating. Lutyens hit with all the strength he had left, but the stick slipped a little in his hand, and the ball flew off to the left instead of keeping close to the boundary. Who's Who was far across the ground, thinking hard as he galloped. He repeated, stride for stride, the Cat's manoeuvres, with another Archangel pony, nipping the ball away from under his bridle, and clearing his opponent by half a fraction of an inch, for Who's Who was clumsy behind. Then he drove away towards the right as the Maltese Cat came up from the left; and Bamboo held a middle course exactly between them. The three were making a sort of Government-broad-arrow-shaped attack; and there was only the Archangels' back to guard the goal; but immediately behind them were three Archangels racing all they knew, and mixed up with them was Powell, sending Shikast along on what he felt was their last hope. It takes a very good man to stand up to the rush of seven crazy ponies in the last quarter of a Cup game, when men are riding with their necks for sale, and the ponies are delirious. The Archangels' back missed his stroke, and pulled aside just in time to let the rush go by. Bamboo and Who's Who shortened stride to give the Maltese Cat room, and Lutyens got the goal with a clean, smooth, smacking stroke that was heard all over the field. But there was no stopping the ponies. They poured through the goal-posts in one mixed mob, winners and losers together, for the pace had been terrific. The Maltese Cat knew by experience what would happen, and, to save Lutyens, turned to the right with one last effort that strained a back-sinew beyond hope of repair. As he did so he heard the right-hand goal-post crack as a pony cannoned into it – crack, splinter, and fall like a mast. It had been sawed three parts through in case of accidents, but it upset the pony nevertheless, and he blundered into another, who blundered into the left-hand post, and then there was confusion and dust and wood. Bamboo was lying on the ground, seeing stars; an Archangel pony rolled beside him, breathless and angry; Shikast had sat down dog-fashion to avoid falling over the others, and was sliding along on his little bobtail in a cloud of dust; and Powell was sitting on the ground, hammering with his stick and trying to cheer. All the others were shouting at the top of what was left of their voices, and the men who had been spilt were shouting too. As soon as the people saw no one was hurt, ten thousand native and English shouted and clapped and yelled, and before any one could stop them the pipers of the Skidars broke on to the ground, with all the native officers and men behind them, and marched up and down, playing a wild Northern tune called 'Zakhme Bagān,' and through the insolent blaring of the pipes and the high-pitched native yells you could hear the Archangels' band hammering, 'For they are all jolly good fellows,' and then reproachfully to the losing team, 'Ooh, Kafoozalum! Kafoozalum! Kafoozalum!'

Besides all these things and many more, there was a Commander-in-Chief, and an Inspector-General of Cavalry, and the principal veterinary officer in all India, standing on top of a regimental coach, yelling like schoolboys; and Brigadiers and Colonels and Commissioners, and hundreds of pretty ladies joined the chorus. But the Maltese Cat stood with his head down, wondering how many legs were left to him; and Lutyens watched the men and ponies pick themselves out of the wreck of the two goal-posts, and he patted the Cat very tenderly.

'I say,' said the captain of the Archangels, spitting a pebble out of his mouth, 'will you take three thousand for that pony – as he stands?'

'No, thank you. I've an idea he's saved my life,' said Lutyens, getting off and lying down at full length. Both teams were on the ground too, waving their boots in the air, and coughing and drawing deep breaths, as the *saises* ran up to take away the ponies, and an officious water-carrier sprinkled the players with dirty water till they sat up.

'My Aunt!' said Powell, rubbing his back and looking at the stumps of the goal-posts, 'that was a game!'

They played it over again, every stroke of it, that night at the big dinner, when the Free-for-All Cup was filled and passed down the table, and emptied and filled again, and everybody made most eloquent speeches. About two in the morning, when there might have been some singing, a wise little, plain little, gray little head looked in through the open door.

'Hurrah! Bring him in,' said the Archangels; and his *sais*, who was very happy indeed, patted the Maltese Cat on the flank, and he limped in to the blaze of light and the glittering uniforms, looking for Lutyens. He was used to messes, and men's bedrooms, and places where ponies are not usually encouraged, and in his youth had jumped on and off a mess-table for a bet. So he behaved himself very politely, and ate bread dipped in salt, and was petted all round the table, moving gingerly; and they drank his health, because he had done more to win the Cup than any man or horse on the ground.

That was glory and honour enough for the rest of his days, and the Maltese Cat did not complain much when the veterinary surgeon said that he would be no good for polo any more. When Lutyens married, his wife did not allow him to play, so he was forced to be an umpire; and his pony on these occasions was a flea-bitten gray with a neat polo-tail, lame all round, but desperately quick on his feet, and, as everybody knew, Past Pluperfect Prestissimo Player of the Game.

Mrs Pumphrey's Pekingese

JAMES HERRIOT

As a new young vet among the dales of Yorkshire, James Herriot encounters many peculiar characters, human and animal, not least among them that irrepressible canine glutton, Tricki Woo ...

As Autumn wore into Winter and the high tops were streaked with the first snows, the discomforts of practice in the Dales began to make themselves felt.

Driving for hours with frozen feet, climbing to the high barns in biting winds which seared and flattened the wiry hill grass. The interminable stripping off in draughty buildings and the washing of hands and chest in buckets of cold water, using scrubbing soap and often a piece of sacking for a towel.

I really found out the meaning of chapped hands. When there was a rush of work, my hands were never quite dry and the little red fissures crept up almost to my elbows.

This was when some small animal work came as a blessed relief. To step out of the rough, hard routine for a while; to walk into a warm drawing-room instead of a cow house and tackle something

94

less formidable than a horse or a bull. And among all those comfortable drawing-rooms there was none so beguiling as Mrs Pumphrey's.

Mrs Pumphrey was an elderly widow. Her late husband, a beer baron whose breweries and pubs were scattered widely over the broad bosom of Yorkshire, had left her a vast fortune and a beautiful house on the outskirts of Darrowby. Here she lived with a large staff of servants, a gardener, a chauffeur and Tricki Woo. Tricki Woo was a Pekingese and the apple of his mistress' eye.

Standing now in the magnificent doorway, I furtively rubbed the toes of my shoes on the backs of my trousers and blew on my cold hands. I could almost see the deep armchair drawn close to the leaping flames, the tray of cocktail biscuits, the bottle of excellent sherry. Because of the sherry, I was always careful to time my visits for half an hour before lunch.

A maid answered my ring, beaming on me as an honoured guest and led me to the room, crammed with expensive furniture and littered with glossy magazines and the latest novels. Mrs Pumphrey, in the high backed chair by the fire, put down her book with a cry of delight. 'Trick! Tricki! Here is your uncle Herriot.' I had been made an uncle very early and, sensing the advantages of the relationship, had made no objection.

Tricki, as always, bounded from his cushion, leaped on to the back of a sofa and put his paws on my shoulders. He then licked my face thoroughly before retiring, exhausted. He was soon exhausted because he was given roughly twice the amount of food needed for a dog of his size. And it was the wrong kind of food.

'Oh, Mr Herriot,' Mrs Pumphrey said, looking at her pet anxiously. 'I'm so glad you've come. Tricki has gone flop-bott again.'

This ailment, not to be found in any text book, was her way of describing the symptoms of Tricki's impacted anal glands. When the glands filled up, he showed discomfort by sitting down suddenly in mid walk and his mistress would rush to the phone in great agitation.

'Mr Herriot! Please come, he's going flop-bott again!'

I hoisted the little dog on to a table and, by pressure on the anus with a pad of cotton wool, I evacuated the glands.

It baffled me that the Peke was always so pleased to see me. Any dog who could still like a man who grabbed him and squeezed his bottom hard every time they met had to have an incredibly forgiving nature. But Tricki never showed any resentment; in fact he was an outstandingly equable little animal, bursting with intelligence, and I was genuinely attached to him. It was a pleasure to be his personal physician.

The squeezing over, I lifted my patient from the table, noticing the increased weight, the padding of extra flesh over the ribs. 'You know, Mrs Pumphrey, you're overfeeding him again. Didn't I tell you to cut out all those pieces of cake and give him more protein?'

'Oh yes, Mr Herriot,' Mrs Pumphrey wailed. 'But what can I do? He's so tired of chicken.'

I shrugged; it was hopeless. I allowed the maid to lead me to the palatial bathroom where I always performed a ritual handwashing after the operation. It was a huge room with a fully stocked dressing table, massive green ware and rows of glass shelves laden with toilet preparations. My private guest towel was laid out next to the slab of expensive soap.

Then I returned to the drawing-room, my sherry glass was filled and I settled down by the fire to listen to Mrs Pumphrey. It couldn't be called a conversation because she did all the talking, but I always found it rewarding.

Mrs Pumphrey was likeable, gave widely to charities and would help anybody in trouble. She was intelligent and amusing and had a lot of waffling charm; but most people have a blind spot and her's was Tricki Woo. The tales she told about her darling ranged far into the realms of fantasy and I waited eagerly for the next instalment.

'Oh Mr Herriot, I have the most exciting news. Tricki has a pen pal! Yes, he wrote a letter to the editor of *Doggy World* enclosing a donation, and told him that even though he was descended from a long line of Chinese emperors, he had decided to come down and mingle freely with the common dogs. He asked the editor to seek out a pen pal for him among the dogs he knew so that they could correspond to their mutual benefit. And for this purpose, Tricki said he would adopt the name of Mr Utterbunkum. And, do you know, he received the most beautiful letter from the editor' (I could imagine the sensible man leaping upon this potential gold mine) 'who said he would like to introduce Bonzo Fotheringham, a lonely Dalmatian who would be delighted to exchange letters with a new friend in Yorkshire.'

I sipped the sherry. Tricki snored on my lap. Mrs Pumphrey went on.

'But I'm so disappointed about the new Summerhouse – you know I got it specially for Tricki so we could sit out together on warm afternoons. It's such a nice little rustic shelter, but he's taken a passionate dislike to it. Simply loathes it – absolutely refuses to go inside. You should see the dreadful expression on his face when he looks at it. And do you know what he called it yesterday? Oh, I hardly dare tell you.' She looked around the room before leaning over and whispering: 'He called it "the bloody hut"!'

The maid struck fresh life into the fire and refilled my glass. The wind hurled a handful of sleet against the window. This, I thought was the life. I listened for more.

'And did I tell you, Mr Herriot, Tricki had another good win yesterday? You know, I'm sure he must study the racing columns, he's such a tremendous judge of form. Well, he told me to back Canny Lad in the three o'clock at Redcar yesterday and, as usual, it won. He put a shilling each way and got back nine shillings.'

These bets were always placed in the name of Tricki Woo and I thought with compassion of the reactions of the local bookies. The Darrowby turf accountants were a harassed and fugitive body of men. A board would appear at the end of some alley urging the population to invest with Joe Downs and enjoy perfect security. Joe would live for a few months on a knife edge while he pitted his wits against the knowledgeable citizens, but the end was always the same; a few favourites would win in a row and Joe would be gone in the night, taking his board with him. Once I had asked a local inhabitant about the sudden departure of one of these luck-less nomads. He replied unemotionally: 'Oh, we brok 'im.'

Losing a regular flow of shillings to a dog must have been a heavy cross for these unfortunate men to bear.

'I had such a frightening experience last week,' Mrs Pumphrey continued. 'I was sure I would have to call you out. Poor little Tricki – he went completely crackerdog!'

I mentally lined this up with flop-bott among the new canine diseases and asked for more information.

'It was awful. I was terrified. The gardener was throwing rings for Tricki – you know he does this for half an hour every day.' I had witnessed this spectacle several times. Hodgkin, a dour, bent old Yorkshireman who looked as though he hated all dogs and Tricki in particular, had to go out on the lawn every day and throw little rubber rings over and over again. Tricki bounded after them and brought them back, barking madly till the process was repeated. The bitter lines on the old man's face deepened as the game progressed. His lips moved continually, but it was impos-sible to hear what he was saying.

Mrs Pumphrey went on: 'Well, he was playing his game, and he does adore it so, when suddenly, without warning, he went crackerdog. He forgot all about his rings and began to run around in circles, barking and yelping in such a strange way. Then he fell over on his side and lay like a little dead thing. Do you know, Mr Herriot, I really thought he was dead, he lay so perfectly still. And what hurt me most was that Hodgkin began to laugh. He has been with me for twenty-four years and I have never even seen him smile, and yet, when he looked down at that still form, he broke into a queer, high-pitched cackle. It was horrid. I was just going to rush to the telephone when Tricki got up and walked away – he seemed perfectly normal.'

Hysteria, I thought, brought on by wrong feeding and over-excitement. I put down my glass and fixed Mrs Pumphrey with a severe glare. 'Now look, this is just what I was talking about. If you persist in feeding all that fancy rubbish to Tricki you are going to ruin his health. You really must get him on to a sensible dog diet of one or, at the most, two small meals a day of meat and brown bread or a little biscuit. And nothing in between.'

Mrs Pumphrey shrank into her chair, a picture of abject guilt. 'Oh, please don't speak to me like that. I do try to give him the right things, but it is so difficult. When he begs for his little titbits, I can't refuse him.' She dabbed her eyes with a handkerchief.

But I was unrelenting. 'All right, Mrs Pumphrey, it's up to you, but I warn you that if you go on as you are doing, Tricki will go crackerdog more and more often.'

I left the cosy haven with reluctance, pausing on the gravelled drive to look back at Mrs Pumphrey waving and Tricki, as always, standing against the window, his wide-mouthed face apparently in the middle of a hearty laugh.

Driving home, I mused on the many advantages of being Tricki's uncle. When he went to the seaside he sent me boxes of oak-smoked kippers; and when the tomatoes ripened in his greenhouse, he sent a pound or two every week. Tins of tobacco arrived regularly, sometimes with a photograph carrying a loving inscription.

But it was when the Christmas hamper arrived from Fortnum and Mason's that I decided that I was on a really good thing which should be helped along a bit. Hitherto, I had merely rung up and thanked Mrs Pumphrey for the gifts, and she had been rather cool, pointing out that it was Tricki who had sent the things and he was the one who should be thanked.

With the arrival of the hamper it came to me, blindingly, that I had been guilty of a grave error of tactics. I set myself to compose a letter to Tricki. Avoiding Siegfried's sardonic eye, I thanked my doggy nephew for his Christmas gifts and for all his generosity in the past. I expressed my sincere hopes that the festive fare had not upset his delicate digestion and suggested that if he did experience any discomfort he should have recourse to the black powder his uncle always prescribed. A vague feeling of professional shame was easily swamped by floating visions of kippers, tomatoes and hampers. I addressed the envelope to Master Tricki Pumphrey,

Barlby Grange and slipped it into the post box with only a slight feeling of guilt.

On my next visit, Mrs Pumphrey drew me to one side. 'Mr Herriot,' she whispered, 'Tricki adored your charming letter and he will keep it always, but he was very put out about one thing – you addressed it to Master Tricki and he does insist upon Mister. He was dreadfully affronted at first, quite beside himself, but when he saw it was from you he soon recovered his good temper. I can't think why he should have these little prejudices. Perhaps it is because he is an only dog – I do think an only dog develops more prejudices than one from a large family.'

Entering Skeldale House was like returning to a colder world. Siegfried bumped into me in the passage. 'Ah, who have we here? Why I do believe it's dear Uncle Herriot. And what have you been doing, Uncle? Slaving away at Barlby Grange, I expect. Poor fellow, you must be tired out. Do you really think it's worth it, working your fingers to the bone for another hamper?'

The Springfield Fox

ERNEST THOMPSON SETON

The hens had been mysteriously disappearing for over a month;
and when I came home to Springfield for the summer holidays it
was my duty to find the cause. This was soon done. The fowls were
carried away bodily one at a time, before going to roost or else after
leaving, which put tramps and neighbors out of court; they were
not taken from the high perches, which cleared all coons and owls;
or left partly eaten, so that weasels, skunks, or minks were not the
guilty ones, and the blame, therefore, was surely left at Reynard's
door.

The great pine wood of Erindale was on the other bank of the
river, and on looking carefully about the lower ford I saw a few
fox-tracks and a barred feather from one of our Plymouth Rock
chickens. On climbing the farther bank in search of more clews,
I heard a great outcry of crows behind me, and turning, saw a
number of these birds darting down at something in the ford. A
better view showed that it was the old story, thief catch thief, for
there in the middle of the ford was a fox with something in his jaws
– he was returning from our barnyard with another hen. The
crows, though shameless robbers themselves, are ever first to cry
'Stop thief,' and yet more than ready to take 'hush-money' in the
form of a share in the plunder.

And this was their game now. The fox to get back home must cross the river, where he was exposed to the full brunt of the crow mob. He made a dash for it, and would doubtless have gotten across with his booty had I not joined in the attack, whereupon he dropped the hen, scarce dead, and disappeared in the woods.

This large and regular levy of provisions wholly carried off could mean but one thing, a family of little foxes at home; and to find them I now was bound.

That evening I went with Ranger, my hound, across the river into the Erindale woods. As soon as the hound began to circle, we heard the short, sharp bark of a fox from a thickly wooded ravine close by. Ranger dashed in at once, struck a hot scent and went off on a lively straight-away till his voice was lost in the distance away over the upland.

After nearly an hour he came back, panting and warm, for it was baking August weather, and lay down at my feet.

But almost immediately the same foxy '*Yap yurrr*' was heard close at hand and off dashed the dog on another chase.

Away he went in the darkness, baying like a foghorn, straight away to the north. And the loud '*Boo, boo,*' became a low '*oo, oo,*' and that a feeble 'o-o' and then was lost. They must have gone some miles away, for even with ear to the ground I heard nothing of them though a mile was easy distance for Ranger's brazen voice.

As I waited in the black woods I heard a sweet sound of dripping water: '*Tink tank tenk tink, Ta tink tank tenk tonk.*'

I did not know of any spring so near, and in the hot night it was a glad find. But the sound led me to the bough of an oak-tree, where I found its source. Such a soft sweet song; full of delightful suggestion on such a night:

> *Tonk tank tenk tink*
> *Ta tink a tonk a tank a tink a*
> *Ta ta tink tank ta ta tonk tink*
> *Drink a tank a drink a drunk.*

It was the 'water-dripping' song of the saw-whet owl.

But suddenly a deep raucous breathing and a rustle of leaves showed that Ranger was back. He was completely fagged out. His tongue hung almost to the ground and was dripping with foam, his flanks were heaving and spume-flecks dribbled from his breast and sides. He stopped panting a moment to give my hand a dutiful lick, then flung himself flop on the leaves to drown all other sounds with his noisy panting.

But again that tantalizing '*Yap yurr*' was heard a few feet away, and the meaning of it all dawned on me.

We were close to the den where the little foxes were, and the old ones were taking turns in trying to lead us away.

It was late night now, so we went home feeling sure that the problem was nearly solved.

It was well known that there was an old fox with his family living in the neighborhood, but no one supposed them so near.

This fox had been called 'Scarface,' because of a scar reaching from his eye through and back of his ear; this was supposed to have been given him by a barbed-wire fence during a rabbit hunt, and as the hair came in white after it healed, it was always a strong mark.

The winter before I had met with him and had had a sample of his craftiness. I was out shooting, after a fall of snow, and had crossed the open fields to the edge of the brushy hollow back of the old mill. As my head rose to a view of the hollow I caught sight of a fox trotting at long range down the other side, in line to cross my course. Instantly I held motionless, and did not even lower or turn my head lest I should catch his eye by moving, until he went on out of sight in the thick cover at the bottom. As soon as he was hidden I bobbed down and ran to head him off where he should leave the cover on the other side, and was there in good time awaiting, but no fox came forth. A careful look showed the fresh track of a fox that had bounded from the cover, and following it with my eye I saw old Scarface himself far out of range behind me, sitting on his haunches and grinning as though much amused.

A study of the trail made all clear. He had seen me at the moment I saw him, but he, also like a true hunter, had concealed the fact, putting on an air of unconcern till out of sight, when he had run for his life around behind me and amused himself by watching my stillborn trick.

In the springtime I had yet another instance of Scarface's cunning. I was walking with a friend along the road over the high pasture. We passed within thirty feet of a ridge on which were several gray and brown boulders. When at the nearest point my friend said:

'Stone number three looks to me very much like a fox curled up.'

But I could not see it, and we passed. We had not gone many yards farther when the wind blew on this bowlder as on fur.

My friend said, 'I am sure that is a fox, lying asleep.'

'We'll soon settle that,' I replied, and turned back, but as soon as I had taken one step from the road, up jumped Scarface, for it was he, and ran. A fire had swept the middle of the pasture, leaving a broad belt of black; over this he skurried till he came to the unburnt yellow grass again, where he squatted down and was lost to view. He had been watching us all the time, and would not have moved had we kept to the road. The wonderful part of this is, not that he resembled the round stones and dry grass, but that he *knew he did*, and was ready to profit by it.

We soon found that it was Scarface and his wife Vixen that had made our woods their home and our barnyard their base of supplies.

Next morning a search in the pines showed a great bank of earth that had been scratched up within a few months. It must have come from a hole, and yet there was none to be seen. It is well known that a really cute fox, on digging a new den, brings all the earth out at the first hole made, but carries on a tunnel into some distant thicket. Then closing up for good the first made and too well-marked door, uses only the entrance hidden in the thicket.

So after a little search at the other side of a knoll, I found the real entry and good proof that there was a nest of little foxes inside.

The Springfield Fox

Rising above the brush on the hillside was a great hollow basswood. It leaned a good deal and had a large hole at the bottom, and a smaller one at top.

We boys had often used this tree in playing Swiss Family Robinson, and by cutting steps in its soft punky walls had made it easy to go up and down in the hollow. Now it came in handy, for next day when the sun was warm I went there to watch, and from this perch on the roof, I soon saw the interesting family that lived in the cellar near by. There were four little foxes; they looked curiously like little lambs, with their woolly coats, their long thick legs and innocent expressions, and yet a second glance at their broad, sharp-nosed, sharp-eyed visages showed that each of these innocents was the makings of a crafty old fox.

They played about, basking in the sun, or wrestling with each other till a slight sound made them skurry under ground. But their alarm was needless, for the cause of it was their mother; she stepped from the bushes bringing another hen – number seventeen as I remember. A low call from her and the little fellows came tumbling out. Then began a scene that I thought charming, but which my uncle would not have enjoyed at all.

They rushed on the hen, and tussled and fought with it, and each other, while the mother, keeping a sharp eye for enemies, looked on with fond delight. The expression on her face was remarkable. It was first a grinning of delight, but her usual look of wildness and cunning was there, nor were cruelty and nervousness lacking, but over all was the unmistakable look of the mother's pride and love.

The base of my tree was hidden in the bushes and much lower than the knoll where the den was. So I could come and go at will without scaring the foxes.

For many days I went there and saw much of the training of the young ones. They early learned to turn to statuettes at any strange sound, and then on hearing it again or finding other cause for fear, to run for shelter.

Some animals have so much mother-love that it overflows and benefits outsiders. Not so old Vixen it would seem. Her pleasure in the cubs led to most refined cruelty. For she often brought home to them mice and birds alive, and with diabolic gentleness would avoid doing them serious hurt so that the cubs might have larger scope to torment them.

There was a woodchuck that lived over in the hill orchard. He was neither handsome nor interesting, but he knew how to take care of himself. He had digged a den between the roots of an old pine stump, so that the foxes could not follow him by digging. But hard work was not their way of life; wits they believed worth more than elbow-grease. This woodchuck usually sunned himself on the stump each morning. If he saw a fox near he went down in the door of his den, or if the enemy was very near he went inside and stayed long enough for the danger to pass.

One morning Vixen and her mate seemed to decide that it was time the children knew something about the broad subject of Woodchucks, and further that this orchard woodchuck would serve nicely for an object-lesson. So they went together to the orchard-fence unseen by old Chuckie on his stump. Scarface then showed himself in the orchard and quietly walked in a line so as to pass by the stump at a distance, but never once turned his head or allowed the ever-watchful woodchuck to think himself seen. When the fox entered the field the woodchuck quietly dropped down to the mouth of his den; here he waited as the fox passed, but concluding that after all wisdom is the better part, went into his hole.

This was what the foxes wanted. Vixen had kept out of sight, but now ran swiftly to the stump and hid behind it. Scarface had kept straight on, going very slowly. The woodchuck had not been frightened, so before long his head popped up between the roots and he looked around. There was that fox still going on, farther and farther away. The woodchuck grew bold as the fox went, and came out farther, and then seeing the coast clear, he scrambled onto the stump, and with one spring Vixen had him and shook him till he lay senseless. Scarface had watched out of the corner of his eye and now came running back. But Vixen took the chuck in her jaws and made for the den, so he saw he wasn't needed.

The Springfield Fox

Back to the den came Vix, and carried the chuck so carefully that he was able to struggle a little when she got there. A low '*woof*' at the den brought the little fellows out like schoolboys to play. She threw the wounded animal to them and they set on him like four little furies, uttering little growls and biting little bites with all the strength of their baby jaws, but the woodchuck fought for his life and beating them off slowly hobbled to the shelter of a thicket. The little ones pursued like a pack of hounds and dragged at his tail and flanks, but could not hold him back. So Vix overtook him with a couple of bounds and dragged him again into the open for the children to worry. Again and again this rough sport went on till one of the little ones was badly bitten, and his squeal of pain roused Vix to end the woodchuck's misery and serve him up at once.

Not far from the den was a hollow overgrown with coarse grass, the playground of a colony of field-mice. The earliest lesson in woodcraft that the little ones took, away from the den, was in this hollow. Here they had their first course of mice, the easiest of all game. In teaching, the main thing was example, aided by a deep-set instinct. The old fox, also, had one or two signs meaning 'lie still and watch,' 'come, do as I do,' and so on, that were much used.

So the merry lot went to this hollow one calm evening and Mother Fox made them lie still in the grass. Presently a faint squeak showed that the game was astir. Vix rose up and went on tip-toe into the grass – not crouching but as high as she could stand, sometimes on her hind legs so as to get a better view. The runs that the mice follow are hidden under the grass tangle, and the only way to know the whereabouts of a mouse is by seeing the slight shaking of the grass, which is the reason why mice are hunted only on calm days.

And the trick is to locate the mouse and seize him first and see him afterward. Vix soon made a spring, and in the middle of the bunch of dead grass that she grabbed was a field-mouse squeaking his last squeak.

He was soon gobbled, and the four awkward little foxes tried to do the same as their mother, and when at length the eldest for the first time in his life caught game, he quivered with excitement and ground his pearly little milk-teeth into the mouse with a rush of inborn savageness that must have surprised even himself.

Another home lesson was on the red-squirrel. One of these noisy, vulgar creatures, lived close by and used to waste part of each day scolding the foxes, from some safe perch. The cubs made many vain attempts to catch him as he ran across their glade from one tree to another, or spluttered and scolded at them a foot or so out of reach. But old Vixen was up in natural history – she knew squirrel nature and took the case in hand when the proper time came. She hid the children and lay down flat in the middle of the open glade. The saucy low-minded squirrel came and scolded as usual. But she moved no hair. He came nearer and at last right overhead to chatter:

'You brute you, you brute you.'

But Vix lay as dead. This was very perplexing, so the squirrel came down the trunk and peeping about made a nervous dash across the grass, to another tree, again to scold from a safe perch.

'You brute you, you useless brute, scarrr-scarrrrr.'

But flat and lifeless on the grass lay Vix. This was most tantalizing to the squirrel. He was naturally curious and disposed to be venturesome, so again he came to the ground and skurried across the glade nearer than before.

Still as death lay Vix, 'surely she was dead.' And the little foxes began to wonder if their mother wasn't asleep.

But the squirrel was working himself into a little craze of foolhardy curiosity. He had dropped a piece of bark on Vix's head, he had used up his list of bad words and he had done it all over again, without getting a sign of life. So after a couple more dashes across the glade he ventured within a few feet of the really watchful Vix, who sprang to her feet and pinned him in a twinkling.

'And the little ones picked the bones e-oh.'

Thus the rudiments of their education were laid, and afterward as they grew stronger they were taken farther afield to begin the higher branches of trailing and scenting.

The Springfield Fox

For each kind of prey they were taught a way to hunt, for every animal has some great strength or it could not live, and some great weakness or the others could not live. The squirrel's weakness was foolish curiosity; the fox's that he can't climb a tree. And the training of the little foxes was all shaped to take advantage of the weakness of the other creatures and to make up for their own by defter play where they are strong.

From their parents they learned the chief axioms of the fox world. How, is not easy to say. But that they learned this in company with their parents was clear. Here are some that foxes taught me, without saying a word:-

Never sleep on your straight track.

Your nose is before your eyes, then trust it first.

A fool runs down the wind.

Running rills cure many ills.

Never take the open if you can keep the cover.

Never leave a straight trail if a crooked one will do.

If it's strange, it's hostile.

Dust and water burn the scent.

Never hunt mice in a rabbit-woods, or rabbits in a henyard.

Keep off the grass.

Inklings of the meanings of these were already entering the little ones' minds – thus, 'Never follow what you can't smell,' was wise, they could see, because if you can't smell it, then the wind is so that it must smell you.

One by one they learned the birds and beasts of their home woods, and then as they were able to go abroad with their parents they learned new animals. They were beginning to think they knew the scent of everything that moved. But one night the mother took them to a field where was a strange black flat thing on the ground. She brought them on purpose to smell it, but at the first whiff their every hair stood on end, they trembled, they knew not why – it seemed to tingle through their blood and fill them with instinctive hate and fear. And when she saw its full effect she told them –

'*That is man-scent.*'

They played about, basking in the sun

Meanwhile the hens continued to disappear. I had not betrayed the den of cubs. Indeed, I thought a good deal more of the little rascals than I did of the hens; but uncle was dreadfully wrought up and made most disparaging remarks about my woodcraft. To please him I one day took the hound across the woods and seating myself on a stump on the open hillside, I bade the dog go on. Within three minutes he sang out in the tongue all hunters know so well, 'Fox! fox! fox! straight away down the valley.'

After awhile I heard them coming back. There I saw the fox – Scarface – loping lightly across the river-bottom to the stream. In he went and trotted along in the shallow water near the margin for two hundred yards, then came out straight toward me. Though in full view, he saw me not but came up the hill watching over his shoulder for the hound. Within ten feet of me he turned and sat with his back to me while he craned his neck and showed an eager interest in the doings of the hound. Ranger came bawling along the trail till he came to the running water, the killer of scent, and here he was puzzled; but there was only one thing to do; that was by going up and down both banks find where the fox had left the river.

The fox before me shifted his position a little to get a better view and watched with a most human interest all the circling of the hound. He was so close that I saw the hair of his shoulder bristle a little when the dog came in sight. I could see the jumping of his heart on his ribs, and the gleam of his yellow eye. When the dog was wholly baulked by the water trick, it was comical to see: – he could not sit still, but rocked up and down in glee, and reared on his hind feet to get a better view of the slow-plodding hound. With mouth opened nearly to his ears, though not at all winded, he panted noisily for a moment, or rather he laughed gleefully, just as a dog laughs by grinning and panting.

Old Scarface wriggled in huge enjoyment as the hound puzzled over the trail so long that when he did find it, it was so stale he could barely follow it, and did not feel justified in tonguing on it at all.

As soon as the hound was working up the hill, the fox quietly went into the woods. I had been sitting in plain view only ten feet away, but I had the wind and kept still and the fox never knew that his life had for twenty minutes been in the power of the foe he most feared. Ranger also would have passed me as near as the fox, but I spoke to him, and with a little nervous start he quit the trail and looking sheepish lay down by my feet.

This little comedy was played with variations for several days, but it was all in plain view from the house across the river. My uncle, impatient at the daily loss of hens, went out himself, sat on the open knoll, and when old Scarface trotted to his lookout to watch the dull hound on the river flat below, my uncle remorselessly shot him in the back, at the very moment when he was grinning over a new triumph.

But still the hens were disappearing. My uncle was wrathy. He determined to conduct the war himself, and sowed the woods with poison baits, trusting to luck that our own dogs would not get them. He indulged in contemptuous remarks on my by-gone woodcraft, and went out evenings with a gun and the two dogs, to see what he could destroy.

Vix knew right well what a poisoned bait was; she passed them by or else treated them with active contempt, but one she dropped down the hole of an old enemy, a skunk, who was never afterward seen. Formerly old Scarface was always ready to take charge of the dogs, and keep them out of mischief. But now that Vix had the whole burden of the brood, she could no longer spend time in breaking every track to the den, and was not always at hand to meet and mislead the foes that might be coming too near.

The end is easily foreseen. Ranger followed a hot trail to the den, and Spot, the fox-terrier, announced that the family was at home, and then did his best to go in after them.

The whole secret was now out, and the whole family doomed. The hired man came around with pick and shovel to dig them out, while we and the dogs stood by. Old Vix soon showed herself in the near woods, and led the dogs away off down the river, where she shook them off when she thought proper, by the simple device of springing on a sheep's back. The frightened animal ran for several hundred yards, then Vix got off, knowing that there was now a hopeless gap in the scent, and returned to the den. But the dogs, baffled by the break in the trail, soon did the same, to find Vix hanging about in despair, vainly trying to decoy us away from her treasures.

Meanwhile Paddy plied both pick and shovel with vigor and effect. The yellow, gravelly sand was heaping on both sides, and the shoulders of the sturdy digger were sinking below the level. After an hour's digging, enlivened by frantic rushes of the dogs after the old fox, who hovered near in the woods, Pat called:

'Here they are, sor!'

It was the den at the end of the burrow, and cowering as far back as they could, were the four little woolly cubs.

Before I could interfere, a murderous blow from the shovel, and a sudden rush for the fierce little terrier, ended the lives of three. The fourth and smallest was barely saved by holding him by his tail high out of reach of the excited dogs.

He gave one short squeal, and his poor mother came at the cry, and circled so near that she would have been shot but for the accidental protection of the dogs, who somehow always seemed to get between, and whom she once more led away on a fruitless chase.

The little one saved alive was dropped into a bag, where he lay quite still. His unfortunate brothers were thrown back into their nursery bed, and buried under a few shovelfuls of earth.

We guilty ones then went back into the house, and the little fox was soon chained in the yard. No one knew just why he was kept alive, but in all a change of feeling had set in, and the idea of killing him was without a supporter.

He was a pretty little fellow, like a cross between a fox and a lamb. His woolly visage and form were strangely lamb-like and innocent, but one could find in his yellow eyes a gleam of cunning and savageness as unlamb-like as it possibly could be.

As long as anyone was near he crouched sullen and cowed in his shelter-box, and it was a full hour after being left alone before he ventured to look out.

My window now took the place of the hollow basswood. A number of hens of the breed he knew so well were about the cub in the yard. Late that afternoon as they strayed near the captive there was a sudden rattle of the chain, and the youngster dashed at the nearest one and would have caught him but for the chain which brought him up with a jerk. He got on his feet and slunk back to his box, and though he afterward made several rushes he so gauged his leap as to win or fail within the length of the chain and never again was brought up by its cruel jerk.

As night came down the little fellow became very uneasy, sneaking out of his box, but going back at each slight alarm, tugging at his chain, or at times biting it in fury while he held it down with his fore paws. Suddenly he paused as though listening, then raising his little black nose he poured out a short quavering cry.

Once or twice this was repeated, the time between being occupied in worrying the chain and running about. Then an answer came. The far-away *Yap-yurrr* of the old fox. A few minutes later a shadowy form appeared on the wood-pile. The little one slunk into his box, but at once returned and ran to meet his mother with all the gladness that a fox could show. Quick as a flash she seized him and turned to bear him away by the road she came. But the moment the end of the chain was reached the cub was rudely jerked from the old one's mouth, and she, scared by the opening of a window, fled over the wood-pile.

An hour afterward the cub had ceased to run about or cry. I peeped out, and by the light of the moon saw the form of the mother at full length on the ground by the little one, gnawing at something – the clank of iron told what, it was that cruel chain. And Tip, the little one, meanwhile was helping himself to a warm drink.

On my going out she fled into the dark woods, but there by the shelter-box were two little mice, bloody and still warm, food for the cub brought by the devoted mother. And in the morning I found the chain was very bright for a foot or two next the little one's collar.

On walking across the woods to the ruined den, I again found signs of Vixen. The poor heart-broken mother had come and dug out the bedraggled bodies of her little ones.

There lay the three little baby foxes all licked smooth now, and by them were two of our hens fresh killed. The newly heaved earth was printed all over with tell-tale signs – signs that told me that here by the side of her dead she had watched like Rizpah. Here she had brought their usual meal, the spoil of her nightly hunt. Here she had stretched herself beside them and vainly offered them their natural drink and yearned to feed and warm them as of old; but only stiff little bodies under their soft wool she found, and little cold noses still and unresponsive.

A deep impress of elbows, breast, and hocks showed where she had laid in silent grief and watched them for long and mourned as a wild mother can mourn for its young. But from that time she came no more to the ruined den, for now she surely knew that her little ones were dead.

Tip the captive, the weakling of the brood, was now the heir to all her love. The dogs were loosed to guard the hens. The hired man had orders to shoot the old fox on sight – so had I, but was resolved never to see her. Chicken-heads, that a fox loves and a dog will not touch, had been poisoned and scattered through the woods; and the only way to the yard where Tip was tied, was by climbing the wood-pile after braving all other dangers. And yet each night old Vix was there to nurse her baby and bring it fresh-killed hens and game. Again and again I saw her, although she came now without awaiting the querulous cry of the captive.

The second night of the captivity I heard the rattle of the chain, and then made out that the old fox was there, hard at work digging a hole by the little one's kennel. When it was deep enough to half bury her, she gathered into it all the slack of the chain, and filled it again with earth. Then in triumph thinking she had gotten rid of the chain, she seized little Tip by the neck and turned to dash off up the wood-pile, but alas! only to have him jerked roughly from her grasp.

Poor little fellow, he whimpered sadly as he crawled into his box. After half an hour there was a great outcry among the dogs, and by their straight-away tonguing through the far woods I knew they were chasing Vix. Away up north they went in the direction of the railway and their noise faded from hearing. Next morning the hound had not come back. We soon knew why. Foxes long ago learned what a railroad is; they soon devised several ways of turning it to account. One way is when hunted to walk the rails for a long distance just before a train comes. The scent, always poor on iron, is destroyed by the train and there is always a chance of hounds being killed by the engine. But another way more sure, but harder to play, is to lead the hounds straight to a high trestle just ahead of the train, so that the engine overtakes them on it and they are surely dashed to destruction.

This trick was skilfully played, and down below we found the mangled remains of old Ranger and learned that Vix was already wreaking her revenge.

That same night she returned to the yard before Spot's weary limbs could bring him back and killed another hen and brought it to Tip, and stretched her panting length beside him that he might quench his thirst. For she seemed to think he had no food but what she brought.

It was that hen that betrayed to my uncle the nightly visits.

My own sympathies were all turning to Vix, and I would have no hand in planning further murders. Next night my uncle himself watched, gun in hand, for an hour. Then when it became cold and the moon clouded over he remembered other important business elsewhere, and left Paddy in his place.

But Paddy was 'onaisy' as the stillness and anxiety of watching worked on his nerves. And the loud bang! bang! an hour later left us sure only that powder had been burned.

In the morning we found Vix had not failed her young one. Again next night found my uncle on guard, for another hen had been taken. Soon after dark a single shot was heard, but Vix dropped the game she was bringing and escaped. Another attempt made that night called forth another gun-shot. Yet next day it was seen by the brightness of the chain that she had come again and vainly tried for hours to cut that hateful bond.

Such courage and stanch fidelity were bound to win respect, if not toleration. At any rate, there was no gunner in wait next night, when all was still. Could it be of any use? Driven off thrice with gun-shots, would she make another try to feed or free her captive young one?

Would she? Hers was a mother's love. There was but one to watch them this time, the fourth night, when the quavering whine of the little one was followed by that shadowy form above the wood-pile.

But carrying no fowl or food that could be seen. Had the keen huntress failed at last? Had she no head of game for this her only charge, or had she learned to trust his captors for his food?

No, far from all this. The wild-wood mother's heart and hate were true. Her only thought had been to set him free. All means she knew she tried, and every danger braved to tend him well and help him to be free. But all had failed.

Like a shadow she came and in a moment was gone, and Tip seized on something dropped, and crunched and chewed with relish what she brought. But even as he ate, a knife-like pang shot through and a scream of pain escaped him. Then there was a momentary struggle and the little fox was dead.

The mother's love was strong in Vix, but a higher thought was stronger. She knew right well the poison's power; she knew the poison bait, and would have taught him had he lived to know and shun it too. But now at last when she must choose for him a wretched prisoner's life or sudden death, she quenched the mother in her breast and freed him by the one remaining door.

·   ·   ·   ·   ·

It is when the snow is on the ground that we take the census of the woods, and when the winter came it told me that Vix no longer roamed the woods of Erindale. Where she went it never told, but only this, that she was gone.

Gone, perhaps, to some other far-off haunt to leave behind the sad remembrance of her murdered little ones and mate. Or gone, may be, deliberately, from the scene of a sorrowful life, as many a wild-wood mother has gone, by the means that she herself had used to free her young one, the last of all her brood.

A Spot of Decorating

MICHAEL BOND

Paddington is no ordinary bear. After his arrival from darkest Peru, he is adopted by the long-suffering Brown family, who soon become used to his enthusiastic, but usually disastrous attempts to help about the house ...

Paddington gave a deep sigh and pulled his hat down over his ears in an effort to keep out the noise. There was such a hullabaloo going on it was difficult to write up the notes in his scrapbook.

The excitement had all started when Mr and Mrs Brown and Mrs Bird received an unexpected invitation to a wedding. Luckily both Jonathan and Judy were out for the day or things might have been far worse. Paddington hadn't been included in the invitation, but he didn't really mind. He didn't like weddings very much – apart from the free cake – and he'd been promised a piece of that whether he went or not.

All the same he was beginning to wish everyone would hurry up and go. He had a special reason for wanting to be alone that day.

He sighed again, wiped the pen carefully on the back of his paw, and then mopped up some ink blots which somehow or other had found their way on to the table. He was only just in time, for at that moment the door burst open and Mrs Brown rushed in.

'Ah, there you are, Paddington!' She stopped short in the middle of the room and stared at him. 'Why on earth are you wearing your hat indoors?' she asked. 'And why is your tongue all blue?'

Paddington stuck out his tongue as far as he could. 'It *is* a funny colour,' he admitted, squinting down at it with interest. 'Perhaps I'm sickening for something!'

'You'll be sickening for something all right if you don't clear up this mess,' grumbled Mrs Bird as she entered. 'Just look at it. Bottles of ink. Glue. Bits of paper. My best sewing scissors. Marmalade all over the table runner, and goodness knows what else.'

Paddington looked around. It *was* in a bit of a state.

'I've almost finished,' he announced. 'I've just got to rule a few more lines and things. I've been writing my memories.'

Paddington took his scrapbook very seriously and spent many long hours carefully pasting in pictures and writing up his adventures. Since he'd been at the Browns' so much had happened it was now more than half full.

'Well, make sure you *do* clear everything up.' said Mrs Brown, 'or we shan't bring you back any cake. Now do take care of yourself. And don't forget – when the baker comes we want two loaves.' With that she waved good-bye and followed Mrs Bird out of the room.

'You know,' said Mrs Bird, as she stepped into the car, 'I have a feeling that bear has something up his paw. He seemed most anxious for us to leave.'

'Oh, I don't know,' said Mrs Brown. 'I don't see what he *can* do. We shan't be away all that long.'

'Ah!' replied Mrs Bird darkly. 'That's as may be. But he's been hanging about on the landing upstairs half the morning. I'm sure he's up to something.'

Mr Brown, who didn't like weddings much either, and was secretly wishing he could stay at home with Paddington, looked over his shoulder as he let in the clutch. 'Perhaps I ought to stay as well,' he said. 'Then I could get on with decorating his new room.'

'Now, Henry,' said Mrs Brown firmly. 'You're coming to the wedding and that's that. Paddington will be quite all right by himself. He's a very capable bear. And as for you wanting to get on with decorating his new room ... you haven't done a thing towards it for over a fortnight, so I'm sure it can wait another day.'

Paddington's new room had become a sore point in the Brown household. It was over two weeks since Mr Brown had first thought of doing it. So far he had stripped all the old wallpaper from the walls, removed the picture rails, the wood round the doors, the door handle, and everything else that was loose, or that he had made loose, and bought a lot of bright new wallpaper, some whitewash, and some paint. There matters had rested.

In the back of the car Mrs Bird pretended she hadn't heard a thing. An idea had suddenly come into her mind and she was hoping it hadn't entered Paddington's as well; but Mrs Bird knew the workings of Paddington's mind better than most and she feared the worst. Had she but known, her fears were being realized at that very moment. Paddington was busy scratching out the words 'AT A LEWSE END' in his scrapbook and was adding, in large capital letters, the ominous ones: 'DECKERATING MY NEW ROOM!'

It was while he'd been writing 'AT A LEWSE END' in his scrapbook earlier in the day that the idea had come to him. Paddington had noticed in the past that he often got his best ideas when he was 'at a loose end'.

For a long while all his belongings had been packed away ready for the big move to his new room, and he was beginning to get impatient. Every time he wanted anything special he had to undo yards of string and brown paper.

Having underlined the words in red, Paddington cleared everything up, locked his scrapbook carefully in his suitcase, and hurried upstairs. He had several times offered to lend a paw with the decorating, but for some reason or other Mr Brown had put his foot down on the idea and hadn't even allowed him in the room while work was in progress. Paddington couldn't quite understand why. He was sure he would be very good at it.

The room in question was an old box-room which had been out of use for a number of years, and when he entered it, Paddington found it was even more interesting than he had expected.

He closed the door carefully behind him and sniffed. There was an exciting smell of paint and whitewash in the air. Not only that, but there were some steps, a trestle table, several brushes, a number of rolls of wallpaper, and a big pail of whitewash.

The room had a lovely echo as well, and he spent a long time sitting in the middle of the floor while he was stirring the paint, just listening to his new voice.

There were so many different and interesting things around that it was a job to know what to do first. Eventually Paddington decided on the painting. Choosing one of Mr Brown's best brushes, he dipped it into the pot of paint and then looked round the room for something to dab it on.

It wasn't until he had been working on the window-frame for several minutes that he began to wish he had started something else. The brush made his arm ache, and when he tried dipping his paw in the paint pot instead and rubbing it on, more paint seemed to go on to the glass than the wooden part, so that the room became quite dark.

'Perhaps,' said Paddington, waving the brush in the air and addressing the room in general, 'perhaps if I do the ceiling first with the whitewash I can cover all the drips on the wall with the wallpaper.'

But when Paddington started work on the whitewashing he found it was almost as hard as painting. Even by standing on tip-toe at the very top of the steps, he had a job to reach the ceiling. The bucket of whitewash was much too heavy for him to lift, so that he had to come down the steps every time in order to dip the brush in. And when he carried the brush up again, the whitewash ran down his paw and made his fur all matted.

Looking around him, Paddington began to wish he was still 'at a loose end'. Things were beginning to get in rather a mess again.

A Spot of Decorating

He felt sure Mrs Bird would have something to say when she saw it.

It was then that he had a brainwave. Paddington was a resourceful bear and he didn't like being beaten by things. Recently he had become interested in a house which was being built nearby. He had first seen it from the window of his bedroom and since then he'd spent many hours talking to the men and watching while they hoisted their tools and cement up to the top floor by means of a rope and pulley. Once, Mr Briggs, the foreman, had even taken him up in the bucket too, and had let him lay several bricks.

Now the Browns' house was an old one and in the middle of the ceiling there was a large hook where a big lamp had once hung. Not only that, but in one corner of the room there was a thin coil of rope as well. . . .

Paddington set to work quickly. First he tied one end of the rope to the handle of the bucket. Then he climbed up the steps and passed the other end through the hook in the ceiling. But even so, when he had climbed down again, it still took him a long time to pull the bucket anywhere near the top of the steps. It was full to the brim with whitewash and very heavy, so that he had to stop every few seconds and tie the other end of the rope to the steps for safety.

It was when he undid the rope for the last time that things started to go wrong. As Paddington closed his eyes and leaned back for the final pull he suddenly felt to his surprise as if he was floating on air. It was a most strange feeling. He reached out one foot and waved it around. There was definitely nothing there. He opened one eye and then nearly let go of the rope in astonishment as he saw the bucket of whitewash going past him on its way down.

Suddenly everything seemed to happen at once. Before he could even reach out a paw or shout for help, his head hit the ceiling and there was a clang as the bucket hit the floor.

For a few seconds Paddington clung there, kicking the air and not knowing what to do. Then there was a gurgling sound from below. Looking down, he saw to his horror that all the whitewash was running out of the bucket. He felt the rope begin to move again as the bucket got lighter, and then it shot past him again as he descended, to land with a bump in the middle of a sea of whitewash.

Even then his troubles weren't over. As he tried to regain his balance on the slippery floor, he let go of the rope, and with a rushing noise the bucket shot downwards again and landed on top of his head, completely covering him.

Paddington lay on his back in the whitewash for several minutes, trying to get his breath back and wondering what had hit him. When he did sit up and take the bucket off his head he quickly put it back on again.

There was whitewash all over the floor, the paint pots had been upset into little rivers of brown and green, and Mr Brown's decorating cap was floating in one corner of the room. When Paddington saw it he felt very glad he'd left *his* hat downstairs.

One thing was certain – he was going to have a lot of explaining to do. And that was going to be even more difficult than usual, because he couldn't even explain to himself quite what had gone wrong.

It was some while later, when he was sitting on the upturned bucket thinking about things, that the idea of doing the wallpapering came to him. Paddington had a hopeful nature and he believed in looking on the bright side. If he did the wallpapering really well, the others might not even notice the mess he'd made.

Paddington was fairly confident about the wallpapering. Unknown to Mr Brown, he had often watched him in the past through a crack in the door, and it looked quite simple. All you had to do was to brush some sticky stuff on the back of the paper and then put it on the wall. The high parts weren't too difficult, even for a bear, because you could fold the paper in two and put a broom in the middle where the fold was. Then you simply pushed the broom up and down the wall in case there were any nasty wrinkles.

Paddington felt much more cheerful now he'd thought of the wallpapering. He found some paste already mixed in another bucket, which he put on top of the trestle while he unrolled the paper. It was a little difficult at first because every time he tried to unroll the paper he had to crawl along the trestle pushing it with his paws and the other end rolled up again and followed behind him. But eventually he managed to get one piece completely covered in paste.

He climbed down off the trestle, carefully avoiding the worst of the whitewash, which by now was beginning to dry in large lumps, and lifted the sheet of wallpaper on to a broom. It was a long sheet of paper, much longer than it had seemed when he was putting the paste on, and somehow or other, as Paddington waved the broom about over his head, it began to wrap itself around him. After a struggle he managed to push his way out and headed in the general direction of a piece of wall. He stood back and surveyed the result. The paper was torn in several places, and there seemed to be a lot of paste on the outside, but Paddington felt quite pleased with himself. He decided to try another piece, then another, running backwards and forwards between the trestle and the walls as fast as his legs could carry him, in an effort to get it all finished before the Browns returned.

Some of the pieces didn't quite join, others overlapped, and on most of them were some very odd-looking patches of paste and whitewash. None of the pieces were as straight as he would have liked, but when he put his head on one side and squinted, Paddington felt the overall effect was quite nice, and he felt very pleased with himself.

It was as he was taking a final look round the room at his handiwork that he noticed something very strange. There was a window, and there was also a fireplace. But there was no longer any sign of a door. Paddington stopped squinting and his eyes grew rounder and rounder. He distinctly remembered there *had* been a door because he had come through it. He blinked at all four walls. It was difficult to see properly because the paint on the window-glass had started to dry and there was hardly any light coming through – but there most definitely wasn't a door!

'I can't understand it,' said Mr Brown as he entered the dining-room. 'I've looked everywhere and there's no sign of Paddington. I told you I should have stayed at home with him.'

Mrs Brown looked worried. 'Oh dear, I hope nothing's happened to him. It's so unlike him to go out without leaving a note.'

'He's not in his room,' said Judy.

'Mr Gruber hasn't seen him either,' added Jonathan. 'I've just been down to the market and he says he hasn't seen him since they had cocoa together this morning.'

'Have *you* seen Paddington anywhere?' asked Mrs Brown as Mrs Bird entered, carrying a tray of supper things.

'I don't know about Paddington,' Mrs Bird. 'I've been having enough trouble over the water pipes without missing bears. I think they've got an air lock or something. They've been banging away ever since we came in.'

Mr Brown listened for a moment. 'It *does* sound like water pipes,' he said. 'And yet . . . it isn't regular enough, somehow.' He went outside into the hall. 'It's a sort of thumping noise. . . .'

'Crikey!' shouted Jonathan. 'Listen . . . it's someone sending an S.O.S.'

Everyone exchanged glances and then, in one voice, cried: 'Paddington!'

'Mercy me,' said Mrs Bird as they burst through the papered-up-door. 'There must have been an earthquake or something. And either that's Paddington or it's his ghost!' She pointed towards a small, white figure as it rose from an upturned bucket to greet them.

'I couldn't find the door,' Paddington, plaintively. 'I think I must have papered it over when I did the decorating. It was there when I came in. I remember seeing it. So I banged on the floor with a broom handle.'

'Gosh!' said Jonathan, admiringly. 'What a mess!'

'You . . . papered . . . it over . . . when . . . you . . . did . . . the . . . decorating,' repeated Mr Brown. He was a bit slow to grasp things sometimes.

'That's right,' said Paddington. 'I did it as a surprise.' He waved a paw round the room. 'I'm afraid it's in a bit of a mess, but it isn't dry yet.'

While the idea was slowly sinking into Mr Brown's mind, Mrs Bird came to Paddington's rescue. 'Now it's not a bit of good holding an inquest,' she said. 'What's done is done. And if you ask me it's a good thing too. Now perhaps we shall get some proper decorators in to do the job.' With that she took hold of Paddington's paw and led him out of the room.

'As for you, young bear – you're going straight into a hot bath before all that plaster and stuff gets hard!'

Mr Brown looked after the retreating figures of Mrs Bird and Paddington and then at the long trail of white footprints and pawmarks. 'Bears!' he said, bitterly.

Paddington hung about in his room for a long time after his bath and waited until the last possible minute before going down stairs to supper. He had a nasty feeling he was in disgrace. But surprisingly the word 'decorating' wasn't mentioned at all that evening.

Even more surprisingly, while he was sitting up in bed drinking his cocoa, several people came to see him and each of them gave him sixpence. It was all very mysterious, but Paddington didn't like to ask why in case they changed their minds.

It was Judy who solved the problem for him when she came in to say good night.

'I expect Mummy and Mrs Bird gave you sixpence because they don't want Daddy to do any more decorating,' she explained. 'He always starts things and never finishes them. And I expect Daddy gave you one because he didn't want to finish it anyway. Now they're getting a proper decorator in, so everyone's happy!'

Paddington sipped his cocoa thoughtfully. 'Perhaps if I did another room I'd get another one and sixpence,' he said.

'Oh no, you don't, said Judy sternly. 'You've done quite enough for one day. If I were you I shouldn't mention the word "decorating" for a long time to come.'

'Perhaps you're right,' said Paddington sleepily, as he stretched out his paws. 'But I *was* at a loose end.'

Eggbert

GERALD DURRELL

**Gerald Durrell and his young wife, Jacquie, are on a
collecting trip in Argentina, based on a run-down
estancia called Los Ingleses ...**

The great screamers were one of the commonest birds round Los
Ingleses; within a radius of a mile or so one could see ten or twelve
pairs of these stately creatures, pacing side by side through the
grass, or wheeling through the sky on wide wings, making the air
ring with their melodious trumpet-calls. How to catch the eight I
wanted was a problem, for, as well as being the commonest of the
pampa birds, they were also the most wary. Their goose-like habit
of grazing in huge flocks, completely devastating enormous fields
of alfalfa in the winter, has earned the wrath of the Argentine
farmers, and they are hunted and killed whenever possible. So,
while you could approach fairly close to most of the bird-life on the
pampa, you were extremely lucky if you got within a hundred and
fifty yards of a pair of screamers. We knew they were nesting all
about us, but the nests were well concealed; and though we
realized that several times we had been close to finding one, by the
way the parents flew low over us with loud cries, we had never
been successful.

Eggbert

One evening we were out at a small lake, thickly fringed with reed, setting up flight-nets to try to obtain some ducks. Having fixed my side of the net, I hauled myself out of the brackish water and wandered through the reedbeds. I stopped to examine a small nest, rather like a reed-warbler's, which was cunningly suspended between two leaves, and which proved to be empty, when my attention was attracted to a pile of grey clay which winked at me. Just as I was becoming convinced that there must be something wrong with me, the pile of clay winked again. Then, as the patch of ground at which I had been staring came into focus, I saw that I was not looking at a patch of clay, but at an almost fully grown baby screamer, crouched among the reeds, still as a stone, with only the lids flicking over its dark eyes to give it away. I went forward slowly and squatted down near it. Still it did not move. I reached forward and touched its head, but it lay quite quietly, ignoring me. I picked it up and put it under my arm like a domestic fowl, carrying it back to the car. It made no effort to struggle and displayed no symptoms of panic. Just as I reached the car, however, a pair of adult screamers flew over quite low, and, on seeing us, gave a series of wild cries. Immediately the bird in my arms turned from a placid and well-behaved creature into a flapping, panic-stricken beast that took me all my time to subdue and place in a box.

When we returned to the *estancia*, Dormouse's brother John came out to see how we had fared. With considerable pride I showed him my screamer.

'One of those damn things,' he said in disgust. 'I didn't know you wanted *them*.'

'Of course I do,' I said indignantly; 'they're a most attractive show in any zoo.'

'How many do you want?' asked John.

'Well, I need eight, really, though judging by the difficulty we had in getting this one I doubt whether I'll get that many,' I said gloomily.

'Oh, don't worry about that; I'll get eight for you,' said John airily. 'When d'you want them? . . . Tomorrow?'

'I don't want to be greedy,' I said sarcastically, 'so suppose you just bring me four tomorrow, and four the next day?'

'O.K.,' said John laconically, and wandered off.

Beyond reflecting that John had a peculiar sense of humour if he could joke about such a sacred subject as screamer-catching, I thought no more about it until the following morning I saw him mounting his horse. A peon, already mounted, waited nearby.

'Oh, Gerry,' he called, as his horse waltzed round and round impatiently, 'did you say eight or a dozen?'

'Eight or a dozen what?'

'*Chajás*, of course,' he said in mild surprise.

I glared at him.

'I want eight,' I said, 'and then you can get me a dozen or so tomorrow.'

'O.K.,' said John, and, turning his horse, cantered off through the eucalyptus trees.

At lunch-time I was in the small hut in which we housed the animals, attempting to make a cage. Three pieces of wood had split, and I had hit myself twice on the hand with the hammer, and nearly taken the top off my thumb with the saw. Altogether I was not in the most jovial of moods, and Jacquie and Ian had long since left me to my own devices. I was making another frenzied assault on the cage, when there was the clop of hooves, and John's voice hailed me cheerfully from outside.

'Hola, Gerry,' he called. 'Here are your *chajás*.'

This was the last straw. Clutching a hammer murderously, I strode out to explain to John, in no uncertain terms, that I was in no mood for practical jokes. He was leaning against the sweating flanks of his horse, a smile on his face. But what brought me up short and made my irritation evaporate was the sight of two large sacks lying at his feet, sacks that bulged, sacks that heaved and quivered. The peon was getting off another horse and also lowering a couple of sacks to the ground, sacks that seemed heavy, and that gave forth a rustling sound.

'Are you serious?' I asked faintly. 'Are those sacks really full of screamers?'

'But of course,' said John surprised. 'What did you think?'

'I thought you were joking,' I said meekly. 'How many have you got?'

'Eight, like you asked for,' said John.

'Eight?' I squawked hoarsely.

'Yes, only eight. I'm sorry I couldn't get a dozen, but I'll try and get you eight more tomorrow.'

'No, no, don't . . . Let me get these established first.'

'But you said . . .' began John, bewildered.

'Never mind what I said,' I interjected hastily; 'just don't get me any more until I tell you.'

'Right,' he said cheerfully; 'you know best. By the way, there's a very young one in one of the sacks. I had to put him in there. I hope he's all right. You'd better have a look.'

Feeling that the age of miracles was not past, I staggered into the hut with the heavy, heaving sacks, and then went in search of Jacquie and Ian to tell them the good news and get them to help me unpack the birds. Most of the screamers that we hauled out, tousled and indignant, from inside the sacks, were about the same size as the one I had caught the day before. But right at the very bottom of the last sack we emptied we discovered the young one that John had mentioned. He was quite the most pathetic, the most ridiculous-looking and the most charming baby bird I had ever seen.

He could not have been much more than a week old. His body was about the size of a coconut, and completely circular. At the end of a long neck was a high, domed head, with a tiny beak and a pair of friendly brown eyes. His legs and feet, which were greyish-pink, appeared to be four times too big for him, and not completely under control. On his back were two small, flaccid bits of skin, like a couple of cast-off glove fingers which had become attached there by accident, which did duty as wings. He was clad entirely in what appeared to be a badly knitted bright yellow suit of cotton wool. He rolled out of the sack, fell on his back, struggled manfully on to his enormous flat feet, and stood there, his ridiculous wings slightly raised, surveying us with interest.

Then he opened his beak and shyly said 'Wheep'. As we were too
enchanted to respond to this greeting, he very slowly and carefully
picked up one huge foot, swayed forward, put it down and then
brought the other one up alongside it. He stood and beamed at us
with evident delight at having accomplished such a complicated
manoeuvre. He had a short rest, said 'wheep' again, and then
proceeded to take another step, in order to show us that the first
one had been no fluke, but a solid achievement. Unfortunately,
when he had taken the first step, he had not watched what he was
doing, and so his left foot was resting on the toes of his right foot.
The results were disastrous. He struggled wildly to extricate his
right foot from underneath his left, swaying dangerously. Then,
with a mighty heave, he succeeded in lifting both feet from the
ground, and promptly fell flat on his face. At our burst of laughter,
he looked up into our faces from his recumbent posture, and gave
another deprecating 'wheep'.

At first, owing to his shape and the colouring of his suit, we
called this baby, Egg. But later, as he grew older, it was changed
to a more sedate Eggbert. Now, I have met a lot of amusing birds
at one time and another, but they generally appeared funny
because their appearance was ridiculous, and so even the most
commonplace action took on some element of humour. But I have
never met a bird like Eggbert, who not only *looked* funny without
doing anything, but also acted in a riotously comical manner
whenever he moved. I have never met a bird, before or since, that
could make me literally laugh until I cried. Very few human
comedians can do that to me. Yet Eggbert had only to stand there
on his outsize feet, cock his head on one side and say 'wheep!' in
a slyly interrogative way, and I would feel unconquerable laughter
bubbling up inside me. Every afternoon we would take Eggbert
out of his cage and allow him an hour's constitutional on the lawn.
We looked forward to these walks as eagerly as he did, but an hour
was enough. At the end of that time we would be forced to return
him to his cage, in sheer self-defence.

Eggbert's feet were the bane of his life. There was so much of
them, and they would get tangled together when he walked. Then

there was the danger that he would tread on his own toes and fall down and make an exhibition of himself, as he had done on the first day. So he kept a very close watch on his feet for any signs of insubordination. He would sometimes stand for as long as ten minutes with bent head, gravely staring at his toes as they wiggled gently in the grass, spread out like the arms of a starfish. Eggbert's whole desire, obviously, was to be dissociated from these outsize feet. He felt irritated by them. Without them, he was sure, he could gambol about the lawn with the airy grace of a dried thistle-head. Occasionally, having watched his feet for some time, he would decide that he had lulled them into a sense of false security. Then, when they least suspected it, he would launch his body forward in an effort to speed across the lawn and leave these hateful extremities behind. But although he tried this trick many times, it never succeeded. The feet were always too quick for him, and as soon as he moved they would deliberately and maliciously twist themselves into a knot, and Eggbert would fall head first into the daisies.

His feet were continually letting him down, in more ways than one. Eggbert had a deep ambition to capture a butterfly. Why this was we could not find out, for Eggbert could not tell us. All we knew was that screamers were supposed to be entirely vegetarian, but whenever a butterfly hovered within six feet of Eggbert his whole being seemed to be filled with bloodlust, his eyes would take on a fanatical and most unvegetarian-like gleam, and he would endeavour to stalk it. However, in order to stalk a butterfly with any hope of success one has to keep one's eyes firmly fixed on it. This Eggbert knew, but the trouble was that as soon as he watched the butterfly with quivering concentration, his feet, left to their own devices, would start to play up, treading on each other's toes, crossing over each other, and sometimes even trying to walk in the wrong direction. As soon as Eggbert dragged his eyes away from the quarry, his feet would start to behave, but by the time he looked back again the butterfly would have disappeared. Then came the never-to-be-forgotten day when Eggbert was standing in the sun, feet turned out, dreaming to himself, and

He . . . examined the plants minutely and suspiciously

a large, ill-mannered and obviously working-class butterfly of the worst type flew rapidly across the lawn, flapped down and settled on Eggbert's beak, made what can only be described as a rude gesture with its antennae, and soared up into the air again. Eggbert, quivering with justifiable rage, pecked at it as it swooped over his domed forehead. Unfortunately, he leaned too far back, and for one awful moment he swayed and then he crashed on to his back, his feet waving helplessly in the air. As he lay there, demoralized and helpless, the cowardly butterfly took the opportunity to land on his protruberant, fluff-covered tummy, and have a quick wash-and-brush-up before flying off again. This painful episode naturally only made Eggbert feel even more belligerently inclined towards the lepidoptera, but in spite of all his efforts he never caught one.

At first, Eggbert gave us some concern over his food. He rejected with disdain such commonplace vegetation as cabbage, lettuce, clover and alfalfa. We tried him on biscuit with hard-boiled egg, and he regarded us with horror for trying to force him into cannibalism. Fruit, bran, maize and a variety of other things were inspected briefly and then ignored. In desperation I suggested that the only thing to do was to let him out in the kitchen garden in the faint hope that he would, young as he was, give us some indication of the sort of menu he desired. By this time Eggbert's food problem was worrying practically the whole *estancia*, so there was quite a crowd of anxious people assembled in the kitchen garden when we carried Eggbert out for the experiment. He greeted the assembled company with a friendly 'wheep', stood on his own foot and fell down, regained his equilibrium with an effort, and started off on his tour, while we followed in a hushed and expectant group. He passed through the rows of cabbages without a glance, and seemed mainly concerned with gaining control over his feet. At the tomatoes he started to look about him with interest but just as it seemed he was coming to some sort of decision, his attention was distracted by a large locust. Among the potatoes he was overcome with fatigue, so he had a short nap while we stood patiently and waited. He awoke, apparently much refreshed, greeted us with surprise, yawned, and then ambled drunkenly on his journey. The carrots were passed with scorn. Among the peas he obviously felt that a little relaxation would be in order, and he tried to inveigle us into playing hide-and-seek among the plants. He reluctantly gave up this idea and moved on to the beans when he discovered that we refused to be sidetracked from the matter in hand. The bean-flowers seemed to fascinate him, but the interest was apparently aesthetic rather than gastronomic. Among the parsley and mint he was seized with a tickling sensation in the sole of his left foot, and his attempts to stand on one leg to search for the cause of the irritation made him fall back heavily into a pool of rainwater. When he had been picked up, dried and comforted, he staggered off and entered the neat rows of spinach. Here he came to a sudden halt and examined the plants minutely and suspiciously. Then he edged forward and glared at them from close range with his head on one side. The suspense was terrific. Just as he leant forward to peck at a leaf, he tripped and fell head first into a large spinach plant. He extricated himself with difficulty and tried again. This time he managed to seize the tip of a leaf in his beak. He tugged at it, but the leaf was a tough one and would not give way. He leant back, legs wide apart, and tugged frantically. The end of the leaf broke, and Eggbert was once more on his back, but this time looking distinctly triumphant with a tiny fragment of spinach in his beak. Amid much applause, he was carried back to his cage, and a large plate of chopped spinach was prepared for him. But then a new difficulty made its appearance. Even finely chopped spinach was too coarse for him, for having gulped it down he would straight away proceed to be sick.

'It's far too coarse, even when we chop it up finely,' I said; 'I'm afraid we'll have to prepare it in much the same way as his mother used to.'

'How's that?' asked Jacquie with interest.

'Well, they regurgitate a mass of semi-digested leaf for the young, so that it's soft and pulp-like.'

'Are you suggesting that we should try *that*?' inquired Jacquie suspiciously.

'No, no. Only I think that the nearest we can get to it is to offer him *chewed* spinach.'

'Oh, well, rather you than me,' said my wife gaily.

'But that's just the trouble,' I explained; 'I smoke, and I don't think he'd care to have a mixture of spinach and nicotine.'

'In other words, as I don't smoke, I suppose you want me to chew it?'

'That's the general idea.'

'If anyone had told me,' said Jacquie plaintively, 'that when I married you I should have to spend my spare time chewing spinach for birds, I would never have believed them.'

'It's for the good of the cause,' I pointed out.

'In fact,' she continued darkly, ignoring my remark, 'if anyone *had* told me that, and I'd *believed* them, I don't think I would have married you.'

She picked up a large plate of spinach, gave me a cold look, and took it off to a quiet corner to chew. During the time we had Eggbert he got through a lot of spinach, all of which Jacquie chewed for him with the monotonous persistence of one of the larger ungulates. At the end she calculated she had masticated something in the region of a hundredweight or so of leaves. Even today, spinach is not among her favourite vegetables.

Kym

JOYCE STRANGER

Kym is a pedigree Siamese cat with a winning way and a very strong will, as Joyce Stranger and her family soon find out . . .

Most animals learn by experience, but to a cat in a human world there are so many different experiences that often one lesson doesn't stand him in good stead, as a slightly different situation may have the same results.

To Kym, tins contained food, and food was meant for him. He could jump anywhere, on to any shelf or table, and could find a way of getting food from any container. Arthur the TV cat didn't invent the use of a paw for food.

Kym knew about it long before Arthur was born.

A paw, dipped into the milk jug, brought him a rewarding drink. I had to learn always to remove milk jugs and cream jugs from the table. A large ham once provided him with material for an assault course. I heard a shout and found my husband busy separating Kym from the big piece of ham I had cooked to cut and come again.

We cut off the ham where the kitten had anchored himself. Before we had even finished, he was back again at the other end.

Kym

Meat, if he got at it, was dragged to the floor. Fish was definitely his prerogative, not ours. When we had fish and chips after a weekend away, to save me from extra cooking when I was tired, we always had to set aside a small portion from each of us for Kym or the resulting row was unendurable, and we were kept busy fielding him from our plates.

Shut him outside the door, and the noise was deafening. Put him in the garden, and he promptly came and sat on the windowsill, bellowing. All we could do was to make sure he had his share.

At times, when I was alone in the house, I sat reading with my plate of food on my lap, not being addicted to the extra work involved in laying a table just for one, and not needing all the etceteras. Kym would be on the floor, watching for his moment. When I was distracted by my book, a lean paw snaked out, a long claw grabbed a piece of meat and he dived under the sideboard away from me.

I never learned!

Once, after I had endured an operation, the family gave me my dinner in bed as I was just out of hospital. My husband, who is rather a splendid cook and puts me to shame, had made roast pork, with all the trimmings. Kym decided to come and help me convalesce. It was no use banning him from the room as the noise he made when shut out was enough to send any invalid back to hospital.

He sat on my bed while I ate. I wasn't reading; I was busy balancing the tray and trying not to drop food on the bedclothes. The long paw kept angling towards my meat. He watched every movement, and finally, annoyed because I wasn't getting much into me as I was too busy fielding my plate, I gave him a hard tap across the paws.

He turned his back, stalked with total dignity to the bottom of the bed, and sat there, tail twitching angrily, while I finished my meal. It was very hard not to laugh, but that would only have added to his annoyance and wasn't really fair. He didn't forgive me until supper time.

He used his paw, often, to test the temperature of his own food. He liked it tepid, but not ice cold from the refrigerator. He was very particular about the heat of the food he ate. He touched it gingerly, feeling it to see if he could actually stand the food in his mouth. If it were too hot, he eased a small piece off the plate, on his claw, like eating winkles with a pin, and kept it there for a few seconds before finally eating it, apparently having found by trial and error that the food gradually cooled.

He loved eating cornflakes in this way, not because they were hot, but apparently because he found it enormously satisfying to spear each flake and lift it to his mouth gently, savouring the taste. Then he drank the milk, having finished all the solids.

He preferred coley to meat, and there was only one brand of proprietary catfood that he would eat. He would rather die than touch all the other carefully prepared and tested foods. They just weren't edible as far as he was concerned. He loved mince and brown bread; and the giblets from the chickens; and a little liver, not too much, as too much was constipating if cooked and had the reverse effect if raw.

If I were reduced to giving him tinned food, he preferred to starve. Nothing would make him eat something if he didn't like it. I could put it down for meal after meal. All he did was to go foraging in the neighbourhood and steal. Once he slipped in next door and stole Dusty's dinner; once he went across the road and stole from their ginger cat. Once he went down the road and stole from another friend of mine.

So I gave up all tinned foods except the one and even that he would only eat on rare occasions. Fresh food or else, every time. Not a delicate feeder, but a very fussy one. And no way for me to win. Ever.

For all that, tins remained a source of fascination to Kym. When we had cream out of a tin or out of a plastic container, he was allowed to lick the remains. This was bliss, so that he crouched, reminding me of Harold Monro's poem, *Milk for the Cat*. Monro wrote;

Kym

A long dim ecstasy holds her life;
Her world is an infinite shapeless white.

Kym, licking cream, was exactly like that. Eyes half closed, intent
on savouring the utmost from the wonderful, far too rare taste, he
was obviously translated into a world beyond our understanding.
He was all sensation, delighting in each second, prolonging it for
endless minutes, until the carton was so clean it might have been
scrubbed.

Only then did he return to the present, and lick my hand, and
purr deeply and satisfyingly, a noisy continuing rumble that
showed how much he had enjoyed his treat. On birthdays, which
were on 2 March, he always had a spoonful of cream to himself.
Yet milk was usually ignored, unless it was stolen from the jug or
mixed with cornflakes.

Tins were to steal from as well, no matter what the contents.
Baked beans, sardines, pilchards, corned beef; if he found an
empty tin in went his prospecting paw, to be tasted when he had
managed to get some of the contents smeared on to it.

Which must have been how he came to have one of the most
idiotic adventures of his life, and one of the most aggravating.

It was one of those days.

Nothing had gone right from the time I got up. I had been
greeted by fretful calls from the twins' bedroom and found them
both covered in spots.

Our elder son was just back at school after some spotty children's infection so it wasn't surprising, but it was annoying, as I had
had a busy day planned. I cancelled my plans, waited for the
doctor, and went into the kitchen where I found the fire out and
water in the hearth.

The boiler had developed a leak.

So it was also cold and I was waiting for the plumber.

And that day every hawker in the district and the Avon lady
decided to call, so that I trogged upstairs with drinks and jigsaw
puzzles and crayons and books to crayon and books to read, and
more drinks, and downstairs to answer the doorbell sure it was the

doctor or the plumber and increasingly annoyed because it was neither.

Finally the twins went to sleep and I collapsed into a chair, still doctorless and plumberless, and decided to write to my sister.

I had also managed to burn the lunch, through a loud yell from upstairs of 'Mummy, I've spilt my drink.'

By the time the sheets were changed and the floor mopped up, the lunch was only a memory of what it might have been and we had scrambled eggs on toast instead.

Kym had vanished early that morning, as it was a moderately bright day in spite of the cold. But he ought to have been home long ago and I added a mild worry about him to all the other irritations of the day.

'One thing, nothing else *can* go wrong,' I had just written, being unwise, when Kym came down the front path, crying frantically.

He was walking in the oddest way, every leg stiff, and I couldn't imagine what on earth was wrong.

I picked him up.

He was glistening from top to tail, mouth, front legs, chest, hind legs, and tail, all solid and shining, gummed together. He was smothered, thick, in VARNISH that had set like a rock on him.

I rang the vet.

There was a small silence and a deep sigh.

'Only Kym could do a thing like that,' the voice at the other end of the line said. 'All we can do is shave him under anaesthetic. You'd better get him in quick and I'll sedate him and we'll do it in the morning.'

The wails were only outdone by the noise the twins were making, demanding to know what was going on. Inevitably my husband had the car, as he had had a meeting which might go on late. He very rarely took it in. Only on those days did I ever seem to need it. It was on one of those days that our twin son managed to break his nose.

I told his secretary what had happened. She was a genius at getting messages wrong, and being totally unable to understand what had really happened although I did try to make it as plain as possible, she told my husband I wanted the car as I had varnished the cat.

Not very surprisingly he decided I had gone out of my mind and was playing a very untimely practical joke on him, which he most certainly didn't appreciate while he was at work. He ignored the message.

I had needed both him and the car as someone had to be there for the doctor and the plumber.

Not to mention the twins who weren't old enough to leave on their own.

Time passed and everyone came, but no car. I met it at the usual time at the door, showed my very startled husband the cat, asked him to keep an eye on both supper and twins, leaped into the car and set off.

We made excellent time for the whole ten yards from our house to the main road. I had forgotten about rush hours. Kym was as unhappy as any cat could be. He yelled at the top of his voice, non-stop, as he was driven at a pitiful crawl all of the five miles to the vet, right along one of the busiest roads in the area. There is a fifty mile an hour limit, but whoever thought that up was joking. We were never out of second gear.

The vet was speechless when he saw the cat.

I left Kym, wondering which of our neighbours had found a tin of varnish spilled all over the place. It must have travelled too, as Kym had obviously walked about for some time, dripping varnish. He had the stuff all over all four paws.

He had also tried to lick it off and his mouth was gummed solid.

And you can't dip cats in solvent.

I rang next morning and was told I could have my cat back at two. I asked the neighbour who had lost her fish to Kym if she would come with me and hold him. He couldn't stand the cat basket, and the journey to the vet had been tricky, apart from the rush hour.

That particular vet is on a very busy main road, opposite the cemetery. Visits to him were always trying, as there is difficulty in parking, difficulty in crossing the road and inevitably surgeries were during rush hours. We now have a local vet, which is much more convenient. I was sorry to change – but we only have a five-minute trip now in an emergency.

I parked outside the cemetery, managed at last to cross the road, and went in to get my cat. He was still hazy from the anaesthetic, swearing like a particularly vicious trooper, slashing at the girl who tried to give him to me.

She refused to handle him. He was a horrible animal.

I spoke to him softly.

'Kym.'

He was out of the cage in an instant, into my arms, trying to get under my clothing, purring, talking excitedly, pushing his paw down the neck of the dress I was wearing. I put on his collar and lead and held him and soothed him.

He was almost totally bald.

There was a patch of fur between his ears and a tiny saddle round his back. There was no fur on any of his legs. His tail was stripped except for a poodle clump of fluff at the end. There was a little fur underneath him. His whiskers had gone and his mouth looked sore.

But there was no doubt whatever that he was overjoyed to see me. He had endured all kinds of horrible things since I left him behind, and he felt very peculiar indeed, still woozy from the anaesthetic.

I stood waiting to cross the road.

Two cars approached, slowed down and the drivers stared. A lorry, hurtling towards us, changed gear with a screech that upset Kym, and an astounded face looked at me and my cat. The driver rolled his eyes heavenward with a 'There's one born every minute' look on his face, and drove on, obviously sure this idiot woman had had her Siamese clipped like a poodle for fashion's sake.

We got across the road at last and Kym spent the journey telling my friend just how terrible it had all been. He tried to stand, but his legs still didn't belong to him, and when he got home he weaved up and down for hours, trying to get some strength back into himself.

Needless to say, he was starving. Nothing made any difference to his appetite except serious illness.

He looked extremely odd for months. Luckily it was summer, and he did not have to endure the cold.

By the time the fur had grown again he had matured.

This proved to be a pity, as he promptly developed an Emperor complex. He was by then a very large cat for his breed, with a magnificent coat which darkened at every moult, so that the cream was turning to a tawny brown on his hind quarters. The seal points were richly black, and his crossed vivid blue eyes in his all-black mask gave him a saturnine expression, which he accentuated often by flattening his ears.

He had been mercilessly chased by other cats when he was small, and he determined to get his own back now. The only cat he tolerated was coal black Tigger, a farm cat that had been imported by the family who lived two doors away from us and who was the same age as Kym.

Kym and Tigger became the best of friends, playing together, sleeping together under the bushes, hunting together. Kym would shout from our garden and a few minutes later Tigger came running in, though he would never allow me to touch him.

Their friendship continued all summer.

They were charming together, playing hide and seek through the shrubs in the garden, racing one another up the trees, indulging in endless games of touch and run, chasing one another's tails, or lying close against one another under the catmint, which they both loved to such an extent that it died off, unable to stand their attentions.

Then, one night, Kym failed to come home. This was totally unusual. He was always there, starving, yelling at me for being so slow, nipping me impatiently if he didn't have his food put down *this instant*. He had a voracious appetite which happily encompassed theft, his own food, Tigger's food and mice.

There was no sign of him.

At that time everyone knew everyone in the road, so that when I asked my neighbours if they had seen Kym there was a general alert, by word of mouth, over the garden fences, and everyone hunted their gardens.

No sign of him anywhere.

Then Tigger's owners turned up to ask if Kym and Tigger were in our house, as Tigger had vanished too.

We hunted together. We went into the fields, calling, but the fields then were a large area, with crops growing, with cattle, and with all kinds of wild life, including a fox or two. Had they fallen victim to a fox? We didn't know. I suspected Kym would have fought valiantly and might have been hurt but not killed by a fox. He was a great battler, now chasing every cat but Tigger off his territory.

There was no sign of the cats.

We parted despondently, wondering if they had been stolen. My mother had recently lost a beautiful tawny cat in a Croydon suburb and the police had been sure that he had been picked up by thieves as he was one of a large number that vanished in that area. Illegal vivisection laboratories pay well for cats. And their fur makes gloves.

The thought was not conducive to sleep and by five in the morning, as soon as it was light, I was out again, calling through the fields, and searching the gutters where a dead cat might be put, having been hit by a car.

I met Tigger's owner, out on the same quest. We looked together, but no cats appeared.

I got breakfast and saw everyone off, feeling defeated. I hate an animal to die, but I hate even more not knowing what has happened to it. I was just getting ready to go shopping when a small whirlwind stormed in, yelling at me, coming so fast he banged into me, and so hungry he bit me several times on my way to the refrigerator to get his food, which he bolted as if he had never been fed in his life.

He then sat on the windowsill and declaimed.

A few minutes later the doorbell rang. It was my neighbour asking if Kym had come home yet. She knew where the cats had been. Her son had opened up the garage that morning to get his bicycle to go to school. They had no car, and he left later than our children.

There was a small explosion from a packing case at the back of the garage. The two cats had gone in there and gone to sleep. No one had heard them, a fact I found hard to believe until the same thing happened again years later, and I found Kym in a neighbour's garden shed. She hadn't heard him, but I, who was listening, had. Neighbours of hers on the other side had thought he was in the garden, calling, and had ignored the noise.

After that whenever the cats went missing we searched the sheds, the garages and the greenhouses thoroughly as sometimes they would be curled up warmly and be deaf to all calls.

Kym's friendship with Tigger lasted until early the next year when my neighbours, who were going on holiday, suggested that I should look after Tigger while they were away and they would do the same for Kym later.

Tigger could sleep in his own house and I was to have the key. I thought I could feed the two cats together in my kitchen. This seemed even more probable when as soon as the taxi had taken the family away, Tigger landed on my doorstep suggesting I might feed him. By the end of the three weeks he came for me when he was hungry, or wanted to go indoors, or it was wet, and led me to his home, waiting for me to put him inside.

He never was fed in my kitchen for the simple reason that as soon as I put food down for him, Kym attacked him, as far as I could see out of jealousy. Tigger was lonely, and had jumped to my lap.

That was unforgivable. No one else was entitled to my lap. Kym sprang, spitting, and Tigger fled. Thereafter he received the same treatment as all the other cats that dared encroach on Kym's territory.

Tigger remained very lonely, but I could never fuss him anywhere near our house. I had to take him into his own home and cuddle him there. He would only eat sitting on my lap. If I put the food down and left it, it was untouched when I returned, but so long as I held him and comforted him, he would relax and feed.

Feeding Tigger often took half an hour, as he demanded affection. He was used to it from his owners and missed it horribly. They found when they came to do the same for Kym, that he insisted on attention too. Cats are only aloof if no one bothers about them.

I fed Tigger often after that, but I always had to take care that Kym was nowhere near when I fussed the other cat. And Tigger, who had never come to me, continued to come to me only when his family were away. In between whiles I could go jump the moon. But as soon as the taxi had gone, he was on my doorstep, demanding my attention, knowing that I would feed him and see that he didn't get wet.

Kym's fights remained a major problem all his life. Most cats tried to defend themselves, so that he was constantly bitten. Many of the bites abscessed. Injections became part of our lives, and those trips to the vet.

On one occasion I tried to stop a fight. I was about to go to London for a long publicity tour for *The Running Foxes* and I knew that if Kym were bitten and it abscessed, the family would not spot the injury until the abscess had really taken hold. I was by now so used to them that I knew the early symptoms, and could get one injection instead of three to clear it up, as it hadn't developed by then.

Kym was fighting the enormous tabby tom from the farm. The yells and screams alerted me. I raced across the road and grabbed Kym just as he was chasing the other cat. He must have thought Tabby had returned and jumped him. He lashed round, sank his teeth into my hand, and raked his claws down my arm.

It was entirely my own fault as I hadn't spoken. I had just grabbed. No animal will stand for that.

As soon as I spoke he realised what he had done and leaped into my arms, pushing his face against mine, patting me anxiously with his paw, as if to say he hadn't known and he hadn't meant to. He rolled against me, purring.

He had been bitten, quite badly.

We both had injections that time. I was amused to read a few days later that the Prime Minister's wife, Mary Wilson, had suffered the same treatment from her Siamese cat – and probably for the same reason. Our son got caught the same way a year or two after.

Some years later the same tabby came into our road. By then he was a very slow old cat, in rather bad condition. He ambled into the sunshine, and Kym began to stalk him, tail swishing, shouting his challenge.

Tabby gave Kym one look, and dropped, full length, in the middle of the road, lying absolutely still, stretched out, nothing moving but his eyes.

Kym stared at him and circled him, not knowing what to make of a cat that didn't try to fight back.

Tabby didn't move.

Kym circled him again, this time silently. Nothing happened at all.

Puzzled, Kym sat down and washed his shoulder, hard, still watching the older cat, and then, as again nothing happened, he put up a hind leg to wash that.

Tabby's indolence was forgotten.

He streaked away, faster than I had believed possible, while Kym was still trying to make out what to do. Tabby vanished into next door's garden and, as I had been standing near our gate watching them, I called Kym in and fed him, feeling the old boy deserved to get away without trouble, as he had obviously shown that he had no intention of fighting, and most probably wasn't capable of it.

I never did find out which cat was the cause of Kym's worst injury as I had a horrible suspicion that the other cat might be dead, and I did not dare ask questions. Kym came limping home one bright sunny day with his ear bitten through, his paw very badly bitten, and an enormous chewed hole on his head, right between the ears.

He had several injections but the head wound abscessed and nothing we could do would get it clear.

Finally the vet operated, removing all the flesh down to the bone, and I had to bathe that every few hours to try and keep it from healing over until all the poison had gone. He couldn't go out either as we could not risk further injury. That might have been fatal.

After that I developed an early warning system and as soon as I heard Kym's battle-cry, I raced out to fetch him in, and tried to ensure that we had no further fights of that magnitude. He might have tangled with our stray, an immense black and white tom that all cat owners worried about, as he was in a dreadful state, with discharging eyes and nose and cankered ears, but he was so fast that none of us could get him; not even the R.S.P.C.A. inspector managed to catch him.

We finally caught him when he was very old and obviously dying. I asked the vet to come and give him his final shot, after bringing him into our garage and warming him and feeding him for what must have been the first time for years. He was seething with fleas and lice, and had an appalling injury that must have come from a car, on one side. He had been crying round the houses like a dispossessed demon for weeks before I managed to entice him in with catfood. He was too weak to run.

Kym himself had gone by then. He and the old cat must have been about the same age.

I felt sorry for the stray, wandering for all those years, with no home and no food given to him, and no one to care about him. He was neither truly wild nor tame, but one of the outcasts caused by man, as his owners had moved away and left him behind to roam like a wild beast for the rest of his life. He was around, uncaught, for more than eight years, and as wary as any wild beast in the woods.

The Mrs Mopp I had then, who was a darling who cleaned up for us for more than ten years, once commented that her idea of hell was to be like the old cat, unwanted, and her idea of heaven was to be a cat like Kym, in a house where he was treasured.

'I think I'll be a Siamese next time round,' she said one day, watching him bask by the fire while we both put our coats on to brave the snow.

Cub Life

JOY ADAMSON

For many years my home has been in the Northern Frontier Province of Kenya, that vast stretch of semi-arid thornbush, covering some hundred and twenty thousand square miles, which extends from Mount Kenya to the Abyssinian border.

Civilisation has made little impact on this part of Africa; there are no settlers; the local tribes live very much as their forefathers did, and the place abounds in wild life of every description.

My husband, George, is Senior Game Warden of this huge territory and our home is on the southern border of the Province, near Isiolo, a small township of about thirty Whites, all of whom are government officials engaged in the task of administering the territory.

George has many duties, such as enforcing the Game Laws, preventing poaching and dealing with dangerous animals that have molested the tribesmen. His work causes him to travel over tremendous distances; these journeys we call safaris. Whenever it is possible I accompany my husband on such trips and in this way I have had unique opportunities of coming to grips with this wild, unchanged land, where life is tough and nature asserts her own laws.

This story has its beginning on one of these safaris. A Boran tribesman had been killed by a man-eating lion. It was reported to George that this animal, accompanied by two lionesses, was living in some nearby hills and so it became his duty to track them down. This was why we were camping far to the north of Isiolo among the Boran tribesmen.

Early on the morning of the 1st of February, 1956, I found myself in camp alone with Pati, a rock hyrax who had been living with us as a pet for six and a half years. She looked like a marmot or a guinea-pig; though zoologists will have it that on account of the bone structure of its feet and teeth, the hyrax is most nearly related to rhinos and elephants.

Pati snuggled her soft fur against my neck and from this safe position watched all that went on. The country around us was dry with outcrops of granite and only sparse vegetation; all the same there were animals to be seen, for there were plenty of gerenuk and other gazelles, creatures that have adapted themselves to these dry conditions and rarely, if ever, drink.

Suddenly I heard the vibrations of a car; this could only mean that George was returning much earlier than expected. Soon our Landrover broke through the thornbush and stopped near our tents, and I heard George shout: 'Joy, where are you? Quick, I have something for you . . .'

I rushed out with Pati on my shoulder and saw the skin of a lion. But before I could ask about the hunt, George pointed to the back of the car. There were three lion cubs, tiny balls of spotted fur, each trying to hide its face from everything that went on. They were only a few days old and their eyes were still covered with a bluish film. They could hardly crawl, nevertheless they tried to creep away. I took them on my lap to comfort them, while George, who was most distressed, told me what had happened. Towards dawn, he and another game warden, Ken, had been guided near to the place where the man-eater was said to lie up. When first light broke they were charged by a lioness who rushed out from behind some rocks. Though they had no wish to kill her, she was very close and the way back was hazardous; so George signalled to Ken to shoot; he hit and wounded her. The lioness disappeared, and when they went forward they found a heavy trail of blood leading upwards. Cautiously, step by step, they went over the crest of the hill till they came to a huge flat rock. George climbed on to it to get a better view, while Ken skirted around below. Then he saw Ken peer under the rock, pause, raise his rifle and fire both barrels. There was a growl; the lioness appeared and came straight at Ken. George could not shoot for Ken was in his line of fire; fortunately a Game Scout who was in a more favourable position fired his rifle and caused the animal to swerve; then George was able to kill her. She was a big lioness in the prime of life, her teats swollen with milk. It was only when he saw this that George realised why she had been so angry and faced them so courageously. Then he blamed himself for not having recognised earlier that her behaviour showed that she was defending her litter.

Now he ordered a search to be made for the cubs; presently he and Ken heard slight sounds coming out of a crack in the rock face. They put their arms down the crevice as far as they could reach; loud infantile growls and snarls greeted this unsuccessful manœuvre. Next they cut a long hooked stick and after a lot of probing managed to drag the cubs out; they could not have been more than two or three weeks old. They were carried to the car where the two biggest growled and spat during the whole of the journey back to camp. The third and smallest, however, offered no resistance and seemed quite unconcerned. Now the three cubs lay in my lap, and how could I resist making a fuss of them?

To my amazement Pati, who was usually very jealous of any rival, soon came to nestle among them, and obviously accepted them as desirable companions. From that day onwards, the four became inseparable. During these early days Pati was the biggest of the company and also, being six years old, was very dignified compared with the clumsy little velvet bags who couldn't walk without losing their balance.

It was two days before the cubs accepted their first milk. Until then, whatever trick I tried to make them swallow diluted unsweetened milk only resulted in their pulling up their tiny noses and protesting: 'ng-ng, ng-ng'; very much as we did as children, before we had learned better manners and been taught to say, 'No, thank you.'

Once they had accepted the milk, they could not get enough of it, and every two hours I had to warm it and clean the flexible rubber tube, which we had taken from the wireless set to serve as a teat until we were able to get a proper baby's bottle. We had sent at once to the nearest African market, which was about fifty miles away, not only for the teat but also for cod-liver oil, glucose and cases of unsweetened milk, and had at the same time sent an S O S to the District Commissioner at Isiolo, about 150 miles away, announcing the arrival there within a fortnight of Three Royal Babies, asking him to be good enough to have a comfortable wooden home made in time for our return.

Within a few days the cubs had settled down and were everybody's pets. Pati, their most conscientious self-appointed Nanny, remained in charge; she was devoted to them, and never minded being pulled and trodden on by the three fast-growing little bullies. All the cubs were females. Even at this age each had a definite character; the 'Big One' had a benevolent superiority and was generous towards the others; the second was a clown; always laughing and spanking her milk bottle with both her front paws as she drank, her eyes closed in bliss. I named her Lustica, which means the 'Jolly One.'

The third cub was the weakling in size, but the pluckiest in spirit. She pioneered all round, and was always sent by the others to reconnoitre when something looked suspicious to them. I called her Elsa, because she reminded me of someone of that name.

In the natural course of events Elsa would probably have been the throw-out of the pride.* The average number of cubs in a litter is four, of which one usually dies soon after birth and another is

---

*A 'pride' is a loose term used to describe the association of more than two lions. It may consist of one or more families living together with some adults, or of a number of adults living together for the purpose of hunting in combination, in contradistinction to a pair of lions or a solitary lion.

often too weak to be reared. It is for this reason that one usually sees only two cubs with a lioness. Their mother looks after them till they are two years old. For the first year she provides their food; she regurgitates it, thus making it acceptable to them. During the second year the cubs are allowed to take part in the hunting, but they get severely disciplined if they lose their self-control. Since at this time they are unable to kill on their own, they have to rely for their food on what may be left over from a kill by the full-grown lions of the pride. Often very little remains for them, so they are usually in a bad, scruffy condition at this age. Sometimes they can't bear the hunger; then either they break through the line of gorging adults and are likely to be killed, or they leave the pride, in small groups, and, because they do not yet know how to kill properly, often run into trouble. Nature's law is harsh and lions have to learn the hard way from the beginning.

The quartet – Pati and the three cubs – spent most of the day in the tent under my camp bed; this evidently seemed to them a safe place and the nearest thing they could find to their natural nursery. They were by nature house-trained and always took great care to reach the sand outside. There were a few accidents during the first few days, but afterwards, on the rare occasions when a little pool disgraced their home, they miaowed and made comical grimaces of disgust. In every way they were wonderfully clean and had no smell except for a very pleasant one like honey – or was it cod-liver oil? Their tongues were already as rough as sandpaper; as they grew older we could feel them, even through our khaki clothes, when they licked us.

When, after two weeks, we returned to Isiolo, our Royal Babies had a palace awaiting them, everyone came to see them and they received a royal welcome. They loved Europeans and especially small children, but had a marked dislike of Africans; the only exception was a young Somali, called Nuru. He was our garden boy; now we appointed him guardian and lion-keeper in chief. The post pleased him for it raised his social status; it also meant that when the cubs got tired of romping all over the house and its surroundings and preferred to sleep under some shady bush, he was able to sit near them for long hours, watching to see that no snakes or baboons molested them.

For twelve weeks we kept them on a diet of unsweetened milk mixed with cod-liver oil, glucose, bone-meal and a little salt. Soon they showed us that they only required three-hourly feeds, and then gradually the intervals became longer.

By now their eyes were fully opened, but they could not yet judge distances and often missed their target. To help them over this difficulty, we gave them rubber balls and old inner tubes to play with – the latter were perfect for tug-of-war games. Indeed, anything made of rubber, or that was soft and flexible, fascinated them. They would try to take the inner tube from each other, the attacker rolling sideways on to the possessor, pressing her weight between the end of the tube and its owner. If no success was achieved by this method, the rivals would simply pull with all their might. Then, when the battle had been won, the victor would parade with the trophy in front of the others and provoke an attack. If this invitation was ignored, the rubber would be placed in front of their noses, while the owner pretended to be unaware that it might be stolen from her.

Surprise was the most important element in all their games. They stalked each other – and us – from the earliest age and knew by instinct how to do it properly.

They always attacked from the rear; keeping under cover, they crouched, then crept slowly towards the unsuspecting victim until the final rush was made at flying speed and resulted in the attacker landing with all her weight on the back of her quarry, throwing it to the ground. When we were the object of such an attack we always pretended to be unaware and looked the other way until the final onslaught took place. This delighted the cubs.

Pati always wanted to be in the game, though, as the cubs were soon three times her size, she took good care to keep out of the way of heavy spankings and to avoid being squashed by her charges. In all other circumstances she retained her authority by sheer character; if the cubs became too aggressive she put them in their

The cubs . . . reappeared with a variety of trophies

places by just turning round and facing them. I admired her spirit, for, small as she was, it needed a lot of courage to convince them of her fearlessness; the more so that her only defences were her sharp teeth, quick reactions, intelligence and pluck.

She had come to us when she was newly-born, and had entirely adapted her life to ours. Unlike her cousin the tree hyrax, she was not a nocturnal animal, and at night she would sleep round my neck like a fur. She was a vegetarian but had a craving for alcohol and for the strongest spirits at that; whenever the opportunity arose she would pull the bottle over, extract the cork and swig the liquor. As this was very bad for Pati's health, not to mention her morale, we took every precaution to prevent any indulgence in whisky or gin.

Her excretory habits were peculiar; rock hyraxes always use the same place, for preference the edge of a rock; at home Pati invariably perched herself on the rim of the lavatory seat, and thus situated presented a comical sight. On safari where no such refinements were provided for her she was completely bewildered, so we had eventually to rig up a small lavatory for her.

I never found a flea or a tick on her, so at first I was puzzled by her habit of constantly scratching herself. She had round toe-nails, like those of a miniature rhino, on her well-padded feet; four toes in front and three behind. On the inner toe of her hind legs there was a claw known as the grooming claw. With this she used to keep her fur sleek and her care for her coat explained her constant scratchings.

Pati had no visible tail; she had a gland along the middle of her spine, which was visible as a white patch in her otherwise brindled-grey fur. This gland discharged a secretion and the hair around it used to rise when she became excited by pleasure or alarm. As the cubs grew larger her hair stood up all too frequently owing to the fear which their playful but rough antics caused her. Indeed, had she not always been quick to seek refuge on a window-sill, a ladder or some other high object, she would often have been in danger of being mistaken by them for a rubber ball. Until the cubs came Pati had always been number one among our pets. So

I was very touched that she should continue to love the little rascals even though they diverted our visitors' attention from herself.

As the lions became increasingly aware of their strength, they tested it on everything they could find. For instance, a ground sheet, however large, *had* to be dragged about, and they would set to work in proper feline fashion, placing it under the bodies and pulling it between their front legs, as in later life they would drag a kill. Another favourite game was 'king of the castle.' A cub would jump on to a potato sack and keep her attacker at bay until she was suddenly dethroned by the other sister coming up from behind. The victor was usually Elsa who, seeing the other two locked in combat, made the most of her opportunity.

Our few banana trees were also regarded as delightful toys, and very soon their luxuriant leaves hung in tattered fringes. Tree climbing was another favourite game. The little lions were born acrobats, but often they ventured so high that they could not turn to come down, and we were obliged to rescue them.

When at dawn Nuru let them out, they shot out of doors with a whole night's pent-up energy, and this moment could be compared to the start of a greyhound race. On one such occasion they spotted a tent in which two men who had come to visit us were staying. Within five minutes it was a wreck and we were wakened by the cries of our guests who were vainly trying to rescue their belongings, while the cubs, wild with excitement, dived into the wreckage and reappeared with a variety of trophies – slippers, pyjamas, shreds of mosquito netting. We had to enforce discipline that time with a small stick.

Putting them to bed was also no mean task. Imagine three very naughty little girls, who like all children hated bedtime, but who could run twice as fast as those who were in charge of them and had the added advantage of being able to see in the dark.

We were often obliged to resort to subterfuge. One very successful trick was to tie an old bag to a length of rope and drag it steadily towards and then into the pen; usually they could not resist chasing it.

Outdoor games were all very well but the cubs also developed a fancy for books and cushions. So, to save our library and other possessions, we were eventually obliged to ban them from the house; to effect this we made a shoulder-high door of strong wire on a wooden frame and placed it across the entrance to the veranda. The cubs resented it very much, so to compensate for their lost playground we hung a tyre from a tree, and this proved to be grand for chewing and also as a swing. Another toy we gave them was an empty wooden honey barrel which made a resounding boom when it was pushed. But best of all was a hessian bag. We filled it with old inner tubes and tied it to a branch, from which it dangled invitingly. It had another rope attached to it, and when the cubs hung on to the bag we pulled and swung them high up into the air; the more we laughed the better they enjoyed the game.

Yet none of these toys caused them to forget that there was at all times a barrier in front of the veranda and they often came and rubbed their soft noses against the wire.

Late one afternoon some friends had arrived for a sun-downer; intrigued by the sounds of merriment inside, the cubs soon turned up, but that evening they behaved in a disciplined fashion; there was no nose-rubbing against the wire; all three kept a foot away from it. This exemplary conduct aroused my suspicion, so I got up to investigate its cause. To my horror, I saw a large red spitting cobra between the cubs and the door. In spite of the presence of three lions on one side and of ourselves on the other, it wriggled determinedly across the veranda steps, and by the time we had fetched a shotgun it had disappeared.

No barricades, cobras or prohibitions made Lustica give up her intention of entering the house; repeatedly she tried all the doors. Pressing a handle proved easy enough; even turning a knob could be done; only when we quickly fitted bolts all round was she defeated, and even so I once caught her trying to push the bolt aside with her teeth. Thwarted in her purpose, she had her revenge upon us for about this time she tore the laundry off the clothes line and galloped off into the bush with it.

When the cubs were three months old they had teeth big enough to make it possible for them to eat meat. So now I gave them raw minced meat, which was the best we could do to imitate their mother's regurgitated food. For several days they refused to touch it and pulled grimaces of disgust. Then Lustica made the experiment, and found it to her taste. The others took courage from her and soon there was a fight at every meal. This meant that poor Elsa, who was still weaker than the others, had little chance of getting her fair share, so I kept the titbits for her and used to take her on to my lap for her meals. She loved this; rolling her head from side to side and closing her eyes, she showed how happy she was. At these times she would suck my thumbs and massage my thighs with her front paws as though she were kneading her mother's belly in order to get more milk. It was during these hours that the bond between us developed. We combined playing with feeding, and my days were happily spent with these charming creatures.

They were lazy by nature and it needed a lot of persuasion to get them to move from a comfortable position. Even the most desirable marrow bone was not worth the effort of getting up, and they would roll into position to get at it by the easiest way. But best of all they liked me to hold their bone for them while they lay on their backs, paws in the air, and sucked at it.

When the cubs went into the bush they often had adventures. One morning I was following them, for I had given them a worming powder and wished to see the result. I saw them a little way off asleep. Suddenly I noticed a stream of black soldier ants approaching them. Indeed some were already climbing up their bodies. Knowing how fiercely these ants will attack anything that lies in their path and how powerful their mandibles are, I was just about to wake up the cubs when the ants changed their direction.

Soon afterwards five donkeys approached and the cubs woke up. This was the first time they had seen such big animals, and they certainly showed the proverbial courage of a lion, for they all charged simultaneously. This put them into such good heart that when, a few days later, our forty pack donkeys and mules came near the house, the three little lions fearlessly put the whole caval-cade to flight.

At five months they were in splendid condition and getting stronger every day. They were quite free except at night, when they slept in an enclosure of rock and sand which led off from their wooden shelter. This was a necessary precaution, for wild lions, hyenas, jackals and elephants frequently roam round our house and any of these might have killed them.

The more we grew to know the cubs the more we loved them, so it was hard to accept the fact that we could not keep for ever three fast-growing lions. Regretfully we decided that two must go and that it would be better that the two big ones, who were always together and less dependent on us than Elsa, should be the ones to leave. Our African servants agreed with our choice; when asked their opinion they unanimously chose the smallest. Perhaps they were influenced by visions of the future and thought: 'If there must be a lion in the household, then let it be as small as possible.'

As to Elsa we felt that if she had only ourselves as friends she would be easy to train, not only for life at Isiolo but also as a travelling companion on our safaris.

As the home for Lustica and the Big One, we chose the Rotterdam-Blydorp Zoo and made arrangements for them to make the journey by air.

Since they would have to leave from the Nairobi airfield, which was one hundred and eighty miles away, we decided to get them accustomed to motoring, and took them for short daily trips in my one-and-a-half-ton truck, which had a wired box body. We also began to feed them in it, so that they might get used to it and consider it as one of their play pens.

On the last day we padded the car with soft sand-bags.

When we drove off, Elsa ran a short way down the drive and then stood with the most mournful expression in her eyes watching the car in which her two sisters were disappearing. I travelled in the back with the cubs and had armed myself with a small first-aid kit, fully expecting to be scratched during the long journey. However, my medical precautions were put to shame, for, after an hour of restlessness, the cubs lay on the bags beside me, embracing me with their paws. We travelled like this for eleven hours, delayed by two blow-outs. The lions could not have been more trusting. When we reached Nairobi they looked at me with their large eyes, puzzled to know what to make of all the strange noises and smells. Then the plane carried them off for ever from their native land.

After a few days we received a cable announcing the safe arrival of our cubs in Holland. When I visited them, about three years later, they accepted me as a friendly person and allowed me to stroke them, but they did not recognise me. They lived in splendid conditions and, on the whole, I was glad to know that almost certainly they had no recollections of a freer life.

His First Flight

LIAM O'FLAHERTY

The young seagull was alone on his ledge. His two brothers and his sister had already flown away the day before. He had been afraid to fly with them. Somehow when he had taken a little run forward to the brink of the ledge and attempted to flap his wings he became afraid. The great expanse of sea stretched down beneath, and it was such a long way down – miles down. He felt certain that his wings would never support him, so he bent his head and ran away back to the little hole under the ledge where he slept at night.

Even when each of his brothers and his little sister, whose wings were far shorter than his own, ran to the brink, flapped their wings, and flew away he failed to muster up courage to take that plunge which appeared to him so desperate. His father and mother had come around calling to him shrilly, upbraiding him, threatening to let him starve on his ledge unless he flew away. But for the life of him he could not move.

That was twenty-four hours ago. Since then nobody had come near him. The day before, all day long he had watched his parents flying about with his brothers and sister, perfecting them in the art of flight, teaching them how to skim the waves and how to dive for fish. He had, in fact, seen his older brother catch his first herring and devour it, standing on a rock, while his parents circled around raising a proud cackle. And all the morning the whole family had walked about on the big plateau midway down the opposite cliff, taunting him with his cowardice.

The sun was now ascending the sky, blazing warmly on his ledge that faced south. He felt the heat because he had not eaten since the previous nightfall. Then he had found a dried piece of mackerel's tail at the far end of his ledge. Now there was not a single scrap of food left. He had searched every inch, rooting among the rough, dirt-caked straw nest where he and his brothers and sister had been hatched. He even gnawed at the dried pieces of spotted eggshell. It was like eating part of himself.

He had then trotted back and forth from one end of the ledge to the other, his grey body the colour of the cliff, his long grey legs stepping daintily, trying to find some means of reaching his parents without having to fly. But on each side of him the ledge ended in a sheer fall of precipice, with the sea beneath. And between him and his parents there was a deep, wide chasm.

Surely he could reach them without flying if he could only move northwards along the cliff face? But then on what could he walk? There was no ledge, and he was not a fly. And above him he could see nothing. The precipice was sheer, and the top of it was perhaps farther away than the sea beneath him.

He stepped slowly out to the brink of the ledge, and, standing on one leg with the other leg hidden under his wing, he closed one eye, then the other, and pretended to be falling asleep. Still they took no notice of him. He saw his two brothers and sister lying on the plateau dozing, with their heads sunk into their necks. His father was preening the feathers on his white back. Only his mother was looking at him.

She was standing on a little high hump on the plateau, her white breast thrust forward. Now and again she tore at a piece of fish that lay at her feet, and then scraped each side of her beak on the rock. The sight of the food maddened him. How he loved to tear food that way, scraping his beak now and again to whet it! He uttered a low cackle. His mother cackled too, and looked over at him.

Ga, ga, ga, he cried, begging her to bring him over some food. *Gawl-ool-ah*, she screamed back derisively. But he kept calling plaintively, and after a minute or so he uttered a joyful scream. His mother had picked up a piece of the fish and was flying across to him with it. He leaned out eagerly, tapping the rock with his feet, trying to get nearer to her as she flew across. But when she was just opposite him, abreast of the ledge, she halted, her legs hanging limp, her wings motionless, the piece of fish in her beak almost within reach of his beak.

He waited a moment in surprise, wondering why she did not come nearer, and then maddened by hunger, he dived at the fish. With a loud scream he fell outwards and downwards into space. His mother had swooped upwards. As he passed beneath her he heard the swish of her wings.

Then a monstrous terror seized him and his heart stood still. He could hear nothing. But it only lasted a moment. The next moment he felt his wings spread outwards. The wind rushed against his breast feathers, then under his stomach and against his wings. He could feel the tips of his wings cutting through the air. He was not falling headlong now. He was soaring gradually downwards and outwards. He was no longer afraid. He just felt a bit dizzy. Then he flapped his wings once and he soared upwards.

He uttered a joyous scream and flapped them again. He soared higher. He raised his breast and banked against the wind. *Ga, ga, ga. Ga, ga, ga. Gawl-ool-ah.* His mother swooped past him, her wings making a loud noise. He answered her with another scream. Then his father flew over him screaming. Then he saw his two brothers and sister flying around him, curvetting and banking and soaring and diving.

Then he completely forgot that he had not always been able to fly, and commenced himself to dive and soar and curvet, shrieking shrilly.

He was near the sea now, flying straight over it, facing out over the ocean. He saw a vast green sea beneath him, with little ridges moving over it, and he turned his beak sideways and crowed amusedly. His parents and his brothers and sister had landed on this green floor in front of him. They were beckoning to him, calling shrilly. He dropped his legs to stand on the green sea. His legs sank into it. He screamed with fright and attempted to rise again, flapping his wings. But he was tired and weak with hunger and he could not rise, exhausted by the strange exercise. His feet sank into the green sea, and then his belly touched it and he sank no farther.

He was floating on it. And around him his family was screaming, praising him, and their beaks were offering him scraps of dogfish.

He had made his first flight.

Mr Toad

KENNETH GRAHAME

Mole, Rat and Badger decide to take their friend, Mr Toad, to task for his reckless and ramshackle way of life . . .

It was a bright morning in the early part of summer; the river had resumed its wonted banks and its accustomed pace, and a hot sun seemed to be pulling everything green and bushy and spiky up out of the earth towards him, as if by strings. The Mole and the Water Rat had been up since dawn very busy on matters connected with boats and the opening of the boating season; painting and varnishing, mending paddles, repairing cushions, hunting for missing boat-hooks, and so on; and were finishing breakfast in their little parlour and eagerly discussing their plans for the day, when a heavy knock sounded at the door.

'Bother!' said the Rat, all over egg. 'See who it is, Mole, like a good chap, since you've finished.'

The Mole went to attend his summons, and the Rat heard him utter a cry of surprise. Then he flung the parlour door open, and announced with much importance, 'Mr Badger!'

This was a wonderful thing, indeed, that the Badger should pay a formal call on them, or indeed on anybody. He generally had to

be caught, if you wanted him badly, as he slipped quietly along a
hedgerow of an early morning or a late evening, or else hunted up
in his own house in the middle of the wood, which was a serious
undertaking.

The Badger strode heavily into the room, and stood looking at
the two animals with an expression full of seriousness. The Rat let
his egg-spoon fall on the table-cloth, and sat open-mouthed.

'The hour has come!' said the Badger at last with great solemnity.

'What hour?' asked the Rat uneasily, glancing at the clock on
the mantelpiece.

'*Whose* hour, you should rather say,' replied the Badger. 'Why,
Toad's hour! The hour of Toad! I said I would take him in hand
as soon as the winter was well over, and I'm going to take him in
hand to-day!'

'Toad's hour, of course!' cried the Mole delightedly. 'Hooray!
I remember now! *We'll* teach him to be a sensible Toad!'

'This very morning,' continued the Badger, taking an armchair, 'as I learnt last night from a trustworthy source, another
new and exceptionally powerful motor-car will arrive at Toad Hall
on approval or return. At this very moment, perhaps, Toad is busy
arraying himself in those singularly hideous habiliments so dear
to him, which transform him from a (comparatively) good-looking
Toad into an Object which throws any decent-minded animal that
comes across it into a violent fit. We must be up and doing, ere it
is too late. You two animals will accompany me instantly to Toad
Hall, and the work of rescue shall be accomplished.'

'Right you are!' cried the Rat, starting up. 'We'll rescue the
poor unhappy animal! We'll convert him! He'll be the most converted Toad that ever was before we've done with him!'

They set off up the road on their mission of mercy, Badger
leading the way. Animals when in company walk in a proper and
sensible manner, in single file, instead of sprawling all across the
road and being of no use or support to each other in case of sudden
trouble or danger.

They reached the carriage-drive of Toad Hall to find, as the

Badger had anticipated, a shiny new motor-car, of great size, painted a bright red (Toad's favourite colour), standing in front of the house. As they neared the door it was flung open, and Mr Toad, arrayed in goggles, cap, gaiters, and enormous overcoat, came swaggering down the steps, drawing on his gauntleted gloves.

'Hullo! come on, you fellows!' he cried cheerfully on catching sight of them. 'You're just in time to come with me for a jolly – to come for a jolly – for a – er – jolly –'

His hearty accents faltered and fell away as he noticed the stern unbending look on the countenances of his silent friends, and his invitation remained unfinished.

The Badger strode up the steps. 'Take him inside,' he said sternly to his companions. Then, as Toad was hustled through the door, struggling and protesting, he turned to the chauffeur in charge of the new motor-car.

'I'm afraid you won't be wanted to-day,' he said. 'Mr Toad has changed his mind. He will not require the car. Please understand that this is final. You needn't wait.' Then he followed the others inside and shut the door.

'Now, then!' he said to the Toad, when the four of them stood together in the hall, 'first of all, take those ridiculous things off!'

'Shan't!' replied Toad, with great spirit. 'What is the meaning of this gross outrage? I demand an instant explanation.'

'Take them off him, then, you two,' ordered the Badger briefly.

They had to lay Toad out on the floor, kicking and calling all sorts of names, before they could get to work properly. Then the Rat sat on him, and the Mole got his motor-clothes off him bit by bit, and they stood him up on his legs again. A good deal of his blustering spirit seemed to have evaporated with the removal of his fine panoply. Now that he was merely Toad, and no longer the Terror of the Highway, he giggled feebly and looked from one to the other appealingly, seeming quite to understand the situation.

'You knew it must come to this, sooner or later, Toad,' the Badger explained severely. 'You've disregarded all the warnings we've given you, you've gone on squandering the money your father left you, and you're getting us animals a bad name in the district by your furious driving and your smashes and your rows with the police. Independence is all very well, but we animals never allow our friends to make fools of themselves beyond a certain limit; and that limit you've reached. Now, you're a good fellow in many respects, and I don't want to be too hard on you. I'll make one more effort to bring you to reason. You will come with me into the smoking-room, and there you will hear some facts about yourself; and we'll see whether you come out of that room the same Toad as you went in.'

He took Toad firmly by the arm, led him into the smoking-room, and closed the door behind them.

'*That's* no good!' said the Rat contemptuously. '*Talking* to Toad'll never cure him. He'll *say* anything.'

They made themselves comfortable in armchairs and waited patiently. Through the closed door they could just hear the long continuous drone of the Badger's voice, rising and falling in waves of oratory; and presently they noticed that the sermon began to be punctuated at intervals by long-drawn sobs, evidently proceeding from the bosom of Toad, who was a soft-hearted and affectionate fellow, very easily converted – for the time being – to any point of view.

After some three-quarters of an hour the door opened, and the Badger reappeared, solemnly leading by the paw a very limp and dejected Toad. His skin hung baggily about him, his legs wobbled, and his cheeks were furrowed by the tears so plentifully called forth by the Badger's moving discourse.

'Sit down there, Toad,' said the Badger kindly, pointing to a chair. 'My friends,' he went on, 'I am pleased to inform you that Toad has at last seen the error of his ways. He is truly sorry for his misguided conduct in the past, and he has undertaken to give up motor-cars entirely and for ever. I have his solemn promise to that effect.'

'That is very good news,' said the Mole gravely.

'Very good news indeed,' observed the Rat dubiously, 'if only – *if* only –'

He was looking very hard at Toad as he said this, and could not help thinking he perceived something vaguely resembling a twinkle in that animal's still sorrowful eye.

'There's only one thing more to be done,' continued the gratified Badger. 'Toad, I want you solemnly to repeat, before your friends here, what you fully admitted to me in the smoking-room just now. First, you are sorry for what you've done, and you see the folly of it all?'

There was a long, long pause. Toad looked desperately this way and that, while the other animals waited in grave silence. At last he spoke.

'No!' he said a little sullenly, but stoutly; 'I'm *not* sorry. And it wasn't folly at all! It was simply glorious!'

'What?' cried the Badger, greatly scandalized. 'You backsliding animal, didn't you tell me just now, in there –'

'O, yes, yes, in *there*,' said Toad impatiently. 'I'd have said anything in *there*. You're so eloquent, dear Badger, and so moving, and so convincing, and put all your points so frightfully well – you can do what you like with me in *there*, and you know it. But I've been searching my mind since, and going over things in it, and I find that I'm not a bit sorry or repentant really, so it's no earthly good saying I am; now, is it?'

'Then you don't promise,' said the Badger, 'never to touch a motor-car again?'

'Certainly not!' replied Toad emphatically. 'On the contrary, I faithfully promise that the very first motor-car I see, poop-poop! off I go in it!'

'Told you so, didn't I?' observed the Rat to the Mole.

'Very well, then,' said the Badger firmly, rising to his feet. 'Since you won't yield to persuasion, we'll try what force can do. I feared it would come to this all along. You've often asked us three to come and stay with you, Toad, in this handsome house of yours; well, now we're going to. When we've converted you to a proper point of view we may quit, but not before. Take him upstairs, you two, and lock him up in his bedroom, while we arrange matters between ourselves.'

'It's for your own good, Toady, you know,' said the Rat kindly, as Toad, kicking and struggling, was hauled up the stairs by his two faithful friends. 'Think what fun we shall all have together, just as we used to, when you've quite got over this – this painful attack of yours!'

'We'll take great care of everything for you till you're well, Toad,' said the Mole; 'and we'll see your money isn't wasted, as it has been.'

'No more of those regrettable incidents with the police, Toad,' said the Rat, as they thrust him into his bedroom.

'And no more weeks in hospital, being ordered about by female nurses, Toad,' added the Mole, turning the key on him.

They descended the stair, Toad shouting abuse at them through the keyhole; and the three friends then met in conference on the situation.

'It's going to be a tedious business,' said the Badger sighing. 'I've never seen Toad so determined. However, we will see it out. He must never be left an instant unguarded. We shall have to take it in turns to be with him, till the poison has worked itself out of his system.'

They arranged watches accordingly. Each animal took it in turns to sleep in Toad's room at night, and they divided the day up between them. At first Toad was undoubtedly very trying to his careful guardians. When his violent paroxysms possessed him he would arrange bedroom chairs in rude resemblance of a motor-car and would crouch on the foremost of them, bent forward and staring fixedly ahead, making uncouth and ghastly noises, till the climax was reached, when, turning a complete somersault, he would lie prostrate amidst the ruins of the chairs, apparently completely satisfied for the moment. As time passed, however, these painful seizures grew gradually less frequent, and his friends strove to divert his mind into fresh channels. But his interest in other matters did not seem to revive, and he grew apparently languid and depressed.

One fine morning the Rat, whose turn it was to go on duty, went upstairs to relieve Badger, whom he found fidgeting to be off and stretch his legs in a long ramble round his wood and down his earths and burrows. 'Toad's still in bed,' he told the Rat, outside the door. 'Can't get much out of him, except, "O, leave him alone, he wants nothing, perhaps he'll be better presently, it may pass off in time, don't be unduly anxious," and so on. Now, you look out, Rat! When Toad's quiet and submissive, and playing at being the hero of a Sunday-school prize, then he's at his artfullest. There's sure to be something up. I know him. Well, now I must be off.'

'How are you to-day, old chap?' inquired the Rat cheerfully, as he approached Toad's bedside.

He had to wait some minutes for an answer. At last a feeble voice replied, 'Thank you so much, dear Ratty! So good of you to inquire! But first tell me how you are yourself, and the excellent Mole?'

'O, *we're* all right,' replied the Rat. 'Mole,' he added incautiously, 'is going out for a run round with Badger. They'll be out till luncheon-time, so you and I will spend a pleasant morning together, and I'll do my best to amuse you. Now jump up, there's a good fellow, and don't lie moping there on a fine morning like this!'

'Dear, kind Rat,' murmured Toad, 'how little you realize my condition, and how very far I am from "jumping up" now – if ever! But do not trouble about me. I hate being a burden to my friends, and I do not expect to be one much longer. Indeed, I almost hope not.'

'Well, I hope not, too,' said the Rat heartily. 'You've been a fine bother to us all this time, and I'm glad to hear it's going to stop. And in weather like this, and the boating season just beginning! It's too bad of you, Toad! It isn't the trouble we mind, but you're making us miss such an awful lot.'

'I'm afraid it *is* the trouble you mind, though,' replied the Toad languidly. 'I can quite understand it. It's natural enough. You're tired of bothering about me. I mustn't ask you to do anything further. I'm a nuisance, I know.'

'You are, indeed,' said the Rat. 'But I tell you, I'd take any trouble on earth for you, if only you'd be a sensible animal.'

'If I thought that, Ratty,' murmured Toad, more feebly than ever, 'then I would beg you – for the last time, probably – to step round to the village as quickly as possible – even now it may be too late – and fetch the doctor. But don't you bother. It's only a trouble, and perhaps we may as well let things take their course.'

'Why, what do you want a doctor for?' inquired the Rat, coming closer and examining him. He certainly lay very still and flat, and his voice was weaker and his manner much changed.

'Surely you have noticed of late –' murmured Toad. 'But no – why should you? Noticing things is only a trouble. To-morrow, indeed, you may be saying to yourself, "O, if only I had noticed sooner! If only I had done something!" But no; it's a trouble. Never mind – forget that I asked.'

'Look here, old man,' said the Rat, beginning to get rather alarmed, 'of course I'll fetch a doctor to you, if you really think you want him. But you can hardly be bad enough for that yet. Let's talk about something else.'

'I fear, dear friend,' said Toad, with a sad smile, 'that "talk" can do little in a case like this – or doctors either, for that matter; still, one must grasp at the slightest straw. And, by the way – while you are about it – I *hate* to give you additional trouble, but I happen to remember that you will pass the door – would you mind at the same time asking the lawyer to step up? It would be a convenience to me, and there are moments – perhaps I should say there is *a* moment – when one must face disagreeable tasks, at whatever cost to exhausted nature!'

'A lawyer! O, he must be really bad!' the affrighted Rat said to himself, as he hurried from the room, not forgetting, however, to lock the door carefully behind him.

Outside, he stopped to consider. The other two were far away, and he had no one to consult.

'It's best to be on the safe side,' he said, on reflection. 'I've known Toad fancy himself frightfully bad before, without the slightest reason; but I've never heard him ask for a lawyer! If there's nothing really the matter, the doctor will tell him he's an old ass, and cheer him up; and that will be something gained. I'd better humour him and go; it won't take very long.' So he ran off to the village on his errand of mercy.

The Toad, who had hopped lightly out of bed as soon as he heard the key turned in the lock, watched him eagerly from the window till he disappeared down the carriage-drive. Then, laughing heartily, he dressed as quickly as possible in the smartest suit he could lay hands on at the moment, filled his pockets with cash which he took from a small drawer in the dressing-table, and next, knotting the sheets from his bed together and tying one end of the improvised rope round the central mullion of the handsome Tudor window which formed such a feature of his bedroom, he scrambled out, slid lightly to the ground, and, taking the opposite direction to the Rat, marched off light-heartedly, whistling a merry tune.

It was a gloomy luncheon for Rat when the Badger and the Mole at length returned, and he had to face them at table with his pitiful and unconvincing story. The Badger's caustic, not to say brutal, remarks may be imagined, and therefore passed over; but it was painful to the Rat that even the Mole, though he took his friend's side as far as possible, could not help saying, 'You've been a bit of a duffer this time, Ratty! Toad, too, of all animals!'

'He did it awfully well,' said the crestfallen Rat.

'He did *you* awfully well!' rejoined the Badger hotly. 'However, talking won't mend matters. He's got clear away for the time, that's certain; and the worst of it is, he'll be so conceited with what he'll think is his cleverness that he may commit any folly. One comfort is, we're free now, and needn't waste any more of our precious time doing sentry-go. But we'd better continue to sleep at Toad Hall for a while longer. Toad may be brought back at any moment – on a stretcher, or between two policemen.'

So spoke the Badger, not knowing what the future held in store, or how much water, and of how turbid a character, was to run under bridges before Toad should sit at ease again in his ancestral Hall.

Watership Down

RICHARD ADAMS

**To escape the persecution of a malicious warren
government, Hazel leads a group of rabbits on a journey into the unknown – fraught with danger, but free . . .**

Fu Inlé means 'After moonrise'. Rabbits, of course, have no idea
of precise time or of punctuality. In this respect they are much the
same as primitive people, who often take several days over
assembling for some purpose and then several more to get started.
Before such people can act together, a kind of telepathic feeling
has to flow through them and ripen to the point when they all
know that they are ready to begin. Anyone who has seen the
martins and swallows in September, assembling on the telephone
wires, twittering, making short flights singly and in groups over
the open, stubbly fields, returning to form longer and even longer
lines above the yellowing verges of the lanes – the hundreds of
individual birds merging and blending, in a mounting excitement,
into swarms, and these swarms coming loosely and untidily
together to create a great, unorganized flock, thick at the centre
and ragged at the edges, which breaks and re-forms continually
like clouds or waves – until that moment when the greater part
(but not all) of them know that the time has come: they are off, and

have begun once more that great southward flight which many will not survive; anyone seeing this has seen at work the current that flows (among creatures who think of themselves primarily as part of a group and only secondarily, if at all, as individuals) to fuse them together and impel them into action without conscious thought or will: has seen at work the angel which drove the First Crusade into Antioch and drives the lemmings into the sea.

It was actually about an hour after moonrise and a good while before midnight when Hazel and Fiver once more came out of their burrow behind the brambles and slipped quietly along the bottom of the ditch. With them was a third rabbit, *Hlao* – Pipkin – a friend of Fiver. (Hlao means any small concavity in the grass where moisture may collect, e.g. the dimple formed by a dandelion or thistle-cup.) He too was small, and inclined to be timid, and Hazel and Fiver had spent the greater part of their last evening in the warren in persuading him to join them. Pipkin had agreed rather hesitantly. He still felt extremely nervous about what might happen once they left the warren and had decided that the best way to avoid trouble would be to keep close to Hazel and do exactly what he said.

The three were still in the ditch when Hazel heard a movement above. He looked up quickly.

'Who's there?' he said, 'Dandelion?'

'No, I'm Hawkbit,' said the rabbit who was peering over the edge. He jumped down among them, landing rather heavily. 'Do you remember me, Hazel? We were in the same burrow during the snow last winter. Dandelion told me you were going to leave the warren tonight. If you are, I'll come with you.'

Hazel could recall Hawkbit – a rather slow, stupid rabbit, whose company for five snow-bound days underground had been distinctly tedious. Still, he thought, this was no time to pick and choose. Although Bigwig might succeed in talking over one or two, most of the rabbits they could expect to join them would not come from the Owsla. They would be outskirters who were getting a thin time and wondering what to do about it. He was running over some of these in his mind when Dandelion appeared.

'The sooner we're off the better, I reckon,' said Dandelion. 'I don't much like the look of things. After I'd persuaded Hawkbit here to join us, I was just starting to talk to a few more, when I found that Toadflax fellow had followed me down the run. "I want to know what you're up to," he said, and I don't think he believed me when I told him I was only trying to find out whether there were any rabbits who wanted to leave the warren. He asked me if I was sure I wasn't working up some kind of plot against the Threarah and he got awfully angry and suspicious. It put the wind up me, to tell you the truth, so I've just brought Hawkbit along and left it at that.'

'I don't blame you,' said Hazel. 'Knowing Toadflax, I'm surprised he didn't knock you over first and ask questions afterwards. All the same, let's wait a little longer. Blackberry ought to be here soon.'

Time passed. They crouched in silence while the moon shadows moved northward in the grass. At last, just as Hazel was about to run down the slope to Blackberry's burrow, he saw him come out of his hole, followed by no less than three rabbits. One of these, Buckthorn, Hazel knew well. He was glad to see him, for he knew him for a tough, sturdy fellow, who was considered certain to get into the Owsla as soon as he reached full weight.

'But I dare say he's impatient,' thought Hazel, 'or he may have come off worst in some scuffle over a doe and taken it hard. Well, with him and Bigwig, at least we shan't be too badly off if we run into any fighting.'

He did not recognize the other two rabbits and when Blackberry told him their names – Speedwell and Acorn – he was none the wiser. But this was not surprising, for they were typical outskirters – thin-looking six-monthers, with the strained, wary look of those who are only too well used to the thin end of the stick. They looked curiously at Fiver. From what Blackberry had told them, they had been almost expecting to find Fiver foretelling doom in a poetic torrent. Instead, he seemed more calm and normal than the rest. The certainty of going had lifted a weight from Fiver.

More time went slowly by. Blackberry scrambled up into the

fern and then returned to the top of the bank, fidgeting nervously and half-inclined to bolt at nothing. Hazel and Fiver remained in the ditch, nibbling half-heartedly at the dark grass. At last Hazel heard what he was listening for; a rabbit – or was it two? – approaching from the wood.

A few moments later Bigwig was in the ditch. Behind him came a hefty, brisk-looking rabbit, something over twelve months old. He was well-known by sight to all the warren, for his fur was entirely grey, with patches of near-white that now caught the moonlight as he sat scratching himself without speaking. This was Silver, a nephew of the Threarah, who was serving his first month in the Owsla.

Hazel could not help feeling relieved that Bigwig had brought only Silver – a quiet, straightforward fellow, who had not yet really found his feet among the veterans. When Bigwig had spoken earlier of sounding out the Owsla, Hazel had been in two minds. It was only too likely that they would encounter dangers beyond the warren and that they would stand in need of some good fighters. Again, if Fiver was right and the whole warren was in imminent peril, then of course they ought to welcome any rabbit who was ready to join them. On the other hand, there seemed no point in taking particular pains to get hold of rabbits who were going to behave like Toadflax.

'Wherever we settle down in the end,' thought Hazel, 'I'm determined to see that Pipkin and Fiver aren't sat on and cuffed around until they're ready to run any risk just to get away. But is Bigwig going to see it like that?'

'You know Silver, don't you?' asked Bigwig, breaking in on his thoughts. 'Apparently some of the younger fellows in the Owsla have been giving him a thin time – teasing him about his fur, you know, and saying he only got his place because of the Threarah. I thought I was going to get some more, but I suppose nearly all the Owsla feel they're very well off as they are.'

He looked about him. 'I say, there aren't many here, are there? Do you think it's really worth going on with this idea?'

Silver seemed about to speak when suddenly there was a pattering in the undergrowth above and three more rabbits came over the bank from the wood. Their movement was direct and purposeful, quite unlike the earlier, haphazard approach of those who were now gathered in the ditch. The largest of the three newcomers was in front and the other two followed him, as though under orders. Hazel, sensing at once that they had nothing in common with himself and his companions, started and sat up tensely. Fiver muttered in his ear, 'Oh, Hazel, they've come to –' but broke off short. Bigwig turned towards them and stared, his nose working rapidly. The three came straight up to him.

'Thlayli?' said the leader.

'You know me perfectly well,' replied Bigwig, 'and I know you, Holly. What do you want?'

'You're under arrest.'

'Under arrest? What do you mean? What for?'

'Spreading dissension and inciting to mutiny. Silver, you're under arrest too, for failing to report to Toadflax this evening and causing your duty to devolve on a comrade. You're both to come with me.'

Immediately Bigwig fell upon him, scratching and kicking. Holly fought back. His followers closed in, looking for an opening to join the fight and pin Bigwig down. Suddenly, from the top of the bank, Buckthorn flung himself headlong into the scuffle, knocked one of the guards flying with a kick from his back legs and then closed with the other. He was followed a moment later by Dandelion, who landed full on the rabbit whom Buckthorn had kicked. Both guards broke clear, looked round for a moment and then leapt up the bank into the wood. Holly struggled free of Bigwig and crouched on his haunches, scuffling his front paws and growling, as rabbits will when angry. He was about to speak when Hazel faced him.

'Go,' said Hazel, firmly and quietly, 'or we'll kill you.'

'Do you know what this means?' replied Holly. 'I am Captain of Owsla. You know that, don't you?'

'Go,' repeated Hazel, 'or you will be killed.'

Buckthorn flung himself headlong into the scuffle

'It is you who will be killed,' replied Holly. Without another word he too went back up the bank and vanished into the wood.

Dandelion was bleeding from the shoulder. He licked the wound for a few moments and then turned to Hazel.

'They won't be long coming back, you know, Hazel,' he said. 'They've gone to turn out the Owsla, and then we'll be for it right enough.'

'We ought to go at once,' said Fiver.

'Yes, the time's come now all right,' replied Hazel. 'Come on, down to the stream. Then we'll follow the bank – that'll help us to keep together.'

'If you'll take my advice –' began Bigwig.

'If we stay here any longer I shan't be able to,' answered Hazel.

With Fiver beside him, he led the way out of the ditch and down the slope. In less than a minute the little band of rabbits had disappeared into the dim, moonlit night.

It was getting on towards moonset when they left the fields and entered the wood. Straggling, catching up with one another, keeping more or less together, they had wandered over half a mile down the fields, always following the course of the brook. Although Hazel guessed that they must now have gone further from the warren than any rabbit he had ever talked to, he was not sure whether they were yet safely away: and it was while he was wondering – not for the first time – whether he could hear sounds of pursuit that he first noticed the dark masses of the trees and the brook disappearing among them.

Rabbits avoid close woodland, where the ground is shady, damp and grassless and they feel menaced by the undergrowth. Hazel did not care for the look of the trees. Still, he thought, Holly would no doubt think twice before following them into a place like that, and to keep beside the brook might well prove safer than wandering about the fields in one direction and another, with the risk of finding themselves, in the end, back at the warren. He decided to go straight into the wood without consulting Bigwig, and to trust that the rest would follow.

'If we don't run into any trouble and the brook takes us through the wood,' he thought, 'we really shall be clear of the warren and then we can look for somewhere to rest for a bit. Most of them still seem to be more or less all right, but Fiver and Pipkin will have had as much as they can stand before long.'

From the moment he entered it the wood seemed full of noises. There was a smell of damp leaves and moss, and everywhere the splash of water went whispering about. Just inside, the brook made a little fall into a pool and the sound, enclosed among the trees, echoed as though in a cave. Roosting birds rustled overhead; the night breeze stirred the leaves; here and there a dead twig fell. And there were more sinister, unidentified sounds, from further away; sounds of movement.

To rabbits, everything unknown is dangerous. The first reaction is to startle, the second to bolt. Again and again they startled, until they were close to exhaustion. But what did these sounds mean and where, in this wilderness, could they bolt to?

The rabbits crept closer together. Their progress grew slower. Before long they lost the course of the brook, slipping across the moonlit patches as fugitives and halting in the bushes with raised ears and staring eyes. The moon was low now and the light, wherever it slanted through the trees, seemed thicker, older and more yellow.

From a thick pile of dead leaves beneath a holly tree, Hazel looked down a narrow path, lined on either side with fern and sprouting fire-weed. The fern moved slightly in the breeze, but along the path there was nothing to be seen except a scatter of last year's fallen acorns under an oak. What was in the bracken? What lay round the further bend? And what would happen to a rabbit who left the shelter of the holly tree and ran down the path? He turned to Dandelion beside him.

'You'd better wait here,' he said. 'When I get to the bend I'll stamp. But if I run into trouble, get the others away.'

Without waiting for an answer he ran into the open and down the path. A few seconds brought him to the oak. He paused a moment, staring about him, and then ran on to the bend. Beyond, the path was the same – empty in the darkening moonlight and leading gently downhill into the deep shadow of a grove of ilex trees. Hazel stamped, and a few moments later Dandelion was beside him in the bracken. Even in the midst of his fear and strain it occurred to him that Dandelion must be very fast: he had covered the distance in a flash.

'Well done,' whispered Dandelion. 'Running our risks for us are you – like El-ahrairah?'*

Hazel gave him a quick, friendly glance. It was warm praise and cheered him. What Robin Hood is to the English and John Henry to the American Negroes, Elil-Hrair-Rah, or El-ahrairah – The Prince with a Thousand Enemies – is to rabbits. Uncle Remus might well have heard of him, for some of El-ahrairah's adventures are those of Brer Rabbit. For that matter, Odysseus himself might have borrowed a trick or two from the rabbit hero, for he is very old and was never at a loss for a trick to deceive his enemies. Once, so they say, he had to get home by swimming across a river in which there was a large and hungry pike. El-ahrairah combed himself until he had enough fur to cover a clay rabbit, which he pushed into the water. The pike rushed at it, bit it and left it in disgust. After a little, it drifted to the bank and El-ahrairah dragged it out and waited a while before pushing it in again. After an hour of this, the pike left it alone and when it had done so for the fifth time, El-ahrairah swam across himself and went home. Some rabbits say he controls the weather, because the wind, the damp and the dew are friends and instruments to rabbits against their enemies.

'Hazel, we'll have to stop here,' said Bigwig, coming up between the panting, crouching bodies of the others. 'I know it's not a good place, but Fiver and this other half-sized fellow you've got here – they're pretty well all in. They won't be able to go on if we don't rest.'

The truth was that every one of them was tired. Many rabbits spend all their lives in the same place and never run more than

*The stresses are the same as in the phrase 'Never say die'.

a hundred yards at a stretch. Even though they may live and sleep above ground for months at a time, they prefer not to be out of distance of some sort of refuge that will serve for a hole. They have two natural gaits – the gentle, lolloping, forward movement of the warren on a summer evening and the lightning dash for cover that every human has seen at some time or other. It is difficult to imagine a rabbit plodding steadily on: they are not built for it. It is true that young rabbits are great migrants and capable of journeying for miles, but they do not take to it readily.

Hazel and his companions had spent the night doing everything that came unnaturally to them, and this for the first time. They had been moving in a group, or trying to: actually, they had straggled widely at times. They had been trying to maintain a steady pace, between hopping and running, and it had come hard. Since entering the wood they had been in severe anxiety. Several were almost *tharn* – that is, in that state of staring, glazed paralysis that comes over terrified or exhausted rabbits, so that they sit and watch their enemies – weasels or humans – approach to take their lives. Pipkin sat trembling under a fern, his ears drooping on either side of his head. He held one paw forward in an awkward, unnatural way and kept licking it miserably. Fiver was little better off. He still looked cheerful, but very weary. Hazel realized that until they were rested they would all be safer where they were than stumbling along in the open, with no strength left to run from an enemy. But if they lay brooding, unable to feed or go underground, all their troubles would come crowding into their hearts, their fears would mount and they might very likely scatter, or even try to return to the warren. He had an idea.

'Yes, all right, we'll rest here,' he said. 'Let's go in among this fern. Come on, Dandelion, tell us a story. I know you're handy that way. Pipkin here can't wait to hear it.'

Dandelion looked at Pipkin and realized what it was that Hazel was asking him to do. Choking back his own fear of the desolate, grassless woodland, the before-dawn-returning owls that they could hear some way off and the extraordinary, rank animal smell that seemed to come from somewhere rather nearer, he began.

'Long ago, Frith made the world. He made all the stars too and the world is one of the stars. He made them by scattering his droppings over the sky and this is why the grass and the trees grow so thick on the world. Frith makes the brooks flow. They follow him as he goes through the sky and when he leaves the sky they look for him all night. Frith made all the animals and birds, but when he first made them they were all the same. The sparrow and the kestrel were friends and they both ate seeds and flies. And the fox and the rabbit were friends and they both ate grass. And there was plenty of grass and plenty of flies, because the world was new and Frith shone down bright and warm all day.

'Now El-ahrairah was among the animals in those days and he had many wives. He had so many wives that there was no counting them and the wives had so many young that even Frith could not count them and they ate the grass and the dandelions and the lettuces and the clover and El-ahrairah was the father of them all.' (Bigwig growled appreciatively.) 'And after a time,' went on Dandelion, 'after a time the grass began to grow thin and the rabbits wandered everywhere, multiplying and eating as they went.

'Then Frith said to El-ahrairah, "Prince Rabbit, if you cannot control your people, I shall find ways to control them. So mark what I say." But El-ahrairah would not listen and he said to Frith, "My people are the strongest in the world, for they breed faster and eat more than any of the other people. And this shows how much they love Lord Frith, for of all the animals they are the most responsive to his warmth and brightness. You must realize, my lord, how important they are and not hinder them in their beautiful lives."

'Frith could have killed El-ahrairah at once, but he had a mind to keep him in the world, because he needed him to sport and jest and play tricks. So he determined to get the better of him not by means of his own great power but by means of a trick. He gave out that he would hold a great meeting and that at that meeting he would give a present to every animal and bird, to make each one different from the rest. And all the creatures set out to go to the meeting-place. But they all arrived at different times, because Frith made sure that it would happen so. And when the blackbird came, he gave him his beautiful song, and when the cow came, he gave her sharp horns and the strength to be afraid of no other creature. And so in their turn came the fox and the stoat and the weasel. And to each of them Frith gave the cunning and the fierceness and the desire to hunt and slay and eat the children of El-ahrairah. And so they went away from Frith full of nothing but hunger to kill the rabbits.

'Now all this time, El-ahrairah was dancing and mating and boasting that he was going to Frith's meeting to receive a great gift. And at last he set out for the meeting-place. But as he was going there, he stopped to rest on a soft, sandy hillside. And while he was resting, over the hill came flying the dark Swift, screaming as he went, "News! News! News!" For you know, this is what he has said ever since that day. So El-ahrairah called up to him and said, "What news?" "Why," said the Swift, "I would not be you, El-ahrairah. For Frith has given the fox and the weasel cunning hearts and sharp teeth and to the cat he has given silent feet and eyes that can see in the dark and they are gone away from Frith's place to kill and devour all that belongs to El-ahrairah." And he dashed on over the hills. And at that moment El-ahrairah heard the voice of Frith calling, "Where is El-ahrairah? For all the others have taken their gifts and gone and I have come to look for him."

'Then El-ahrairah knew that Frith was too clever for him and he was frightened. He thought that the fox and the weasel were coming with Frith and he turned to the face of the hill and began to dig. He dug a hole, but he had dug only a little of it when Frith came over the hill alone. And he saw El-ahrairah's bottom sticking out of the hole and the sand flying out in showers as the digging went on. When he saw that, he called out, "My friend have you seen El-ahrairah, for I am looking for him to give him my gift?" "No," answered El-ahrairah, without coming out, "I have not seen him. He is far away. He could not come." So Frith said, "Then come out of that hole and I will bless you instead of him." "No, I cannot," said El-ahrairah, "I am busy. The fox and the weasel are coming. If you want to bless me you can bless my bottom, for it is sticking out of the hole." '

All the rabbits had heard the story before: on winter nights, when the cold draught moved down the warren passages and the icy wet lay in the pits of the runs below their burrows; and on summer evenings, in the grass under the red may and the sweet, carrion-scented elder bloom. Dandelion was telling it well and even Pipkin forgot his weariness and danger, and remembered instead the great indestructibility of the Rabbits. Each one of them saw himself as El-ahrairah, who could be impudent to Frith and get away with it.

'Then,' said Dandelion, 'Frith felt himself in friendship with El-ahrairah, because of his resourcefulness, and because he would not give up even when he thought the fox and the weasel were coming. And he said, "Very well, I will bless your bottom as it sticks out of the hole. Bottom, be strength and warning and speed for ever and save the life of your master. Be it so!" And as he spoke, El-ahrairah's tail grew shining white and flashed like a star: and his back legs grew long and powerful and he thumped the hillside until the very beetles fell off the grass-stems. He came out of the hole and tore across the hill faster than any creature in the world. And Frith called after him, "El-ahrairah, your people cannot rule the world, for I will not have it so. All the world will be your enemy, Prince with a Thousand Enemies, and whenever they catch you, they will kill you. But first they must catch you, digger, listener, runner, prince with the swift warning. Be cunning and full of tricks and your people shall never be destroyed." And every evening, when Frith has done his day's work and lies calm and easy in the red sky, El-ahrairah and his children and his children's children come out of their holes and feed and play in his sight, for they are his friends and he has promised them that they can never be destroyed.'

The Royal Kittens

BARBARA SLEIGH

Carbonel, the King of the Cats, returns to his friends, John and Rosemary, to enlist their help in a most important mission ... They arrange to meet in the Green Cave, a bower created by the unpruned branches of some currant bushes, to examine a mysterious potion they have been instructed to obtain ...

It was long past teatime when John and Rosemary reached home. Mrs Brown was not there. In her place was a plate with some crumbs on it, and a note propped against the sugar basin which said, COULDN'T WAIT. WON'T HANG. GET YOUR OWN.

Rosemary explained that this meant her mother had gone back to the sewing-room because the dress she was making would not fall in the folds she wanted, and that they were to see about tea for themselves.

'I'm terribly hungry,' said John. 'Let's take it with us to the Green Cave.'

They put a plate of buns and two pieces of cake on a tray. Rosemary added cups of tea, and a saucer of milk for Carbonel; then they carried it into the garden.

The black cat was waiting for them on the path by the currant bushes. As soon as he saw them, he disappeared among the leaves, and when John and Rosemary wriggled after him, with some difficulty because of the tea tray, they found him in the Green Cave sitting serenely on the rusty biscuit tin which had held the brandy snaps. Looking up at him from the kneeling position that was necessary in the cramped space between the bushes, they were a little awed by his quiet dignity. He was looking fixedly at the bottle which they had put on the tray.

'Come on! Let's see what the directions say,' said John, as he tore off the wrapping paper. 'It has an ordinary chemist's label. "The Mixture,"' he read. '"Half a teaspoon to be taken after meals as required." Well, I'm always requiring meals. I'm requiring my tea like billy-oh!'

'I don't think it means "meals as required",' said Rosemary, 'but "the mixture as required – after meals".'

'Oh,' said John. 'Well, let's hurry up and have our tea now. I'm starving!'

They each took a currant bun which they polished off with not much politeness but with great speed. Carbonel ignored the saucer of milk which Rosemary had poured for him. He sat staring expectantly at the children with wide, golden eyes.

'We'd better eat the cake, too, to make it a meal,' said John. 'One bun is just a snack.'

They finished the cake and drank the tea. What had not slopped in the saucers was cold and rather nasty, but Rosemary swallowed every drop of hers very slowly, because she found herself wanting to put off the moment of drinking the strange, red mixture. John was clearly feeling the same way.

'Look here,' he said. 'There can't be anything to be afraid of. The chemist's assistant could hear Carbonel talking, when he licked his thumb with the red liquid on it, so we know it does what we want it to do. Let's drink at exactly the same minute, then whatever it is will happen to us both at the same time.'

Rosemary nodded, Carbonel came down from the tin, and purring encouragement, rubbed his head against her shoulder. They took their teaspoons and half filled them with the liquid, which fell sluggishly from the bottle. It had a strange, heady smell, rather like crushed chrysanthemum leaves. They knelt together with spoons raised.

'I'll say "One, two, three, go!" ' said John.

Rosemary nodded again. She became aware that, except for John's voice, it was very still in the Green Cave. Even the canopy of leaves above them had ceased its restless stirring. The only moving things were two fat caterpillars with tufted backs, making their way slowly along a twig on a level with Rosemary's nose. She stared at them unheedingly while John said, 'One! Two! Three! Go!'

Rosemary took a deep breath, swallowed the spoonful quickly, and shut her eyes.

Behind the red darkness of her tightly closed lids, she felt the liquid fizzing slightly on her tongue. It tasted sharp, but not unpleasant, and glowed comfortingly as it slipped down her throat. There was a tickling in her nose and a tight, uncomfortable feeling in her ears. She felt an enormous sneeze welling up inside her, the father and mother of all sneezes. She tried to fight it down, but it was no good. Suddenly she shattered the silence with three violent sneezes, each one echoed closely by another from John. The two children looked at each other with startled eyes.

The silence was gone. They were surrounded by what at first sounded like a humming noise. Then the hum seemed to break up into innumerable little voices, some high and shrill, some soft and purring, some abrupt as the plucking of a violin string. Rosemary was startled to distinguish a small, singsong voice quite close to her ear saying over and over again, 'Up we go! Up we go!'

She looked around, and saw with astonishment that it was the second of the two caterpillars.

'Where are you going?' she asked.

The second caterpillar halted for a moment, waved its front half about uncertainly, and then hurried after its companion.

'Don't look round now,' it said breathlessly, 'but I think we're being spoken to – by a human! What a mercy the great blundering things can't hear us talking!'

'But I *can* hear you talking!' said Rosemary, a little nettled at being called 'blundering'.

Both the caterpillars turned around in astonishment, lost their balance and fell off the twig onto the grass below in two tightly rolled coils from which they refused to budge.

'Rosie!' said John. 'There's a super beetle here, all green and blue, and he says –'

'John and Rosemary, will you kindly pay attention!'

They turned to where Carbonel sat enthroned on the biscuit tin, the end of his tail twitching in irritation.

'That is, of course, unless you find the conversation of beetles and caterpillars more worth while than mine!'

'Carbonel! How glorious!' said Rosemary happily. 'We can hear you talking too!'

'Which is not much use unless you're prepared to listen. After all the trouble I've taken with you!'

'The trouble *you've* taken with *us*!' said John.

But Carbonel swept on. 'I thought I should never get you to understand what I wanted, and when at last you did realize you had to find Mrs Cantrip, and I tried to stop you from wasting your time by going off to the Copper Kettle, would you take any notice? Oh, dear me, no!'

'Don't let's waste time now by being cross!' said Rosemary. 'We did the best we could, and we never expected to be able to hear beetles and caterpillars talking as well as you. It is rather exciting, you know!'

She put out her hand, and laid it gently over the angry, twitching end of Carbonel's tail. For a moment she could feel it stirring beneath her palm. Then, gradually, the furry movement slowed down and ceased altogether.

'Oh, come off it, Carbonel!' said John affectionately.

The black cat took him at his word and stepped down from the box.

'Very well,' he said. 'I have no doubt you did do your best, and I am grateful. And I must say, you were very quick witted to bargain with *her* for the prescription. Now, pay attention, both of you, because I don't have much time. I have not gone to all this trouble for the pleasure of a mere chat, though I won't deny I am pleased to see you both again. Very pleased. I need your help.'

'Of course we'll help you! Won't we, John?' said Rosemary.

'Tomorrow I must go away,' Carbonel said.

'Go away!' said Rosemary in dismay. 'Where to?'

'And when we've just found out how to talk to you!' said John.

'There you go again! Listen, and I will explain. You know that I am a royal cat, and that my people have their own laws and customs. After dark, the wall tops are our highways and the roofs our mountains and our plains. The Town Hall has been the royal seat of my ancestors for two hundred years, and there I hope my descendants will rule after me. Now that is where I need your help. My royal children –'

'Kittens! Your kittens!' said Rosemary excitedly. 'Carbonel, how lovely! How many have you got? And why didn't you tell us? We should –'

'I am trying to tell you now!' said Carbonel severely.

'But –'

'Shut up, Rosie!' said John under his breath.

'You may not know,' went on Carbonel, 'that it is our custom for each cat to select a human family to look after.'

'Don't you mean the humans choose a cat?' said John.

'Certainly not!' said Carbonel coldly. 'The humans, of course, repay a little of their debt to us with a place by the fire, a saucer of milk, little offerings of fish and meat according to their humble means.'

'But besides catching mice, what –' began John. It was Rosemary's turn to give a warning nudge.

'Our great gift to the human race is our example.'

'Example?'

'That is what I said. You fuss and flurry and rush about all day, and for what? In the midst of it all, we sit calm and unruffled, meditating on the mystery of Life and Eternity.'

'But your kittens,' said Rosemary. 'Do tell us about them! How many are there? And are they like you? Oh, I must see them.'

'There are two of them, a boy and a girl,' said Carbonel. 'They are said to be remarkably handsome – but whether they are like me you must judge for yourselves,' he added modestly.

'Then we can see them?'

'Certainly. I have chosen you to look after them while I am away.'

'Of course we'll look after them for you! We'd love to, wouldn't we, John? I shall have to ask Mother, of course, but I'm sure she will say yes.'

'Guard them faithfully till I come back.'

'When will that be?' asked John.

'Three days? Three weeks? Three months? Who can tell?'

'But why must you go?' persisted John.

'Once every seven years I and my royal brothers are summoned to the presence of the Great Cat.'

'But who are your royal brothers?' asked Rosemary.

'You must not think that I am the only cat king,' explained Carbonel. 'Every city in the world where there are cats has a king to rule over them, just as I rule over the cats of Fallowhithe. When the Summons comes, we must all obey. There will be lean, blue-eyed cats from Siam, long-haired cats from Persia, great tawny jungle cats, and thin, big-boned cats from Egypt. Cats of every colour – black as coal, white as milk, grey as woodsmoke. Whatever the colour, whatever the kind, when the Summons comes we all must answer.'

'But who will look after your kingdom for you while you are away?' asked John.

'My beautiful Queen, my lovely Blandamour, will rule with the help of my cousin Merbeck. Blandamour is wise and good, but I cannot answer for all the queens of the neighbouring towns. Queen Grisana of Broomhurst is ambitious, and her husband is old. Do not let my kittens stray. They are a little –' There was a pause, as though Carbonel were searching for the right word. 'High spirited,' he concluded. 'Early tomorrow morning, before I go, I shall visit you again and bring my royal children with me.'

It was getting dark in the Green Cave, and the shadow that was

Carbonel slipped silently down from the cooky jar and rubbed against Rosemary, and his purring filled the little space under the currant bushes like an organ. A warm tongue licked her cheek.

'Dear Carbonel!' said Rosemary, putting her arms around him for a minute. 'Of course we'll do our best to take care of your kittens, but do you think –'

She broke off. The black cat had slipped from her and melted into the other shadows.

They did not ask that night if they might have the kittens after all. Rosemary felt that her mother was not in a 'yes-of-course-darling' mood. She was still having trouble with a dress she was making, and only looked in to tell them to take the sausages on the cracked plate for supper.

'Never mind,' said John. 'You can ask at breakfast tomorrow. Don't forget, Carbonel said he was coming early.'

But Carbonel's idea of early was rather different from theirs.

Rosemary was awakened next morning by a fly which buzzed persistently around her pillow. She brushed it away with a sleepy hand once or twice, and turned over; but the fly continued to buzz. Presently she became aware that it was not just buzzing. It was saying over and over again in a shrill, angry voice, 'For goodness' sake, wake up!'

Rosemary opened one eye sleepily, and saw the fly a few inches away on the curve of her pillow. It was jumping up and down angrily on all of its six legs.

'I am awake,' said Rosemary sleepily, and gave a cavernous yawn.

The fly made a noise that sounded like an outraged squeak, and braced itself.

'Don't do that,' it said in an agitated voice. 'I once knew a fly who was swallowed by a yawn!'

'How horrible!' said Rosemary, thinking more of the yawner than the fly. She was wide awake now and sitting up.

'Here am I, simply come to deliver a message to oblige, and my very life is threatened! First you go flapping like a windmill, and then –'

'I'm so sorry,' said Rosemary humbly.

'And you should be,' said the fly a little more calmly. 'Many people would just have flown off without delivering the message. But not me. I'm not that kind of fly. Luckily for you, I have a weakness for royalty.'

'Royalty?' interrupted Rosemary. 'Is it from Carbonel? The message, I mean.'

The fly nodded importantly.

'I was just to tell you, "We are here." Kings talk like that, you know,' it added condescendingly.

'But where is "here"?' asked Rosemary.

'The greenhouse at the bottom of the garden. Oh! There you go again!'

Without warning, Rosemary had flung back the bedclothes and jumped out of bed. Buzzing angrily, the fly circled round her as she dressed.

'I am sorry!' she said again, 'and of course, I'm very grateful to you, but I must go and tell John at once. I think I've got some sugar you can have somewhere.'

She felt in the pocket of her school blazer and brought out a rather dusty sugar lump, which she put on the dressing table. Then, in one movement, she pushed her toes into her slippers and her arms into her dressing gown.

John and Rosemary did not waste time dressing. They crept downstairs into the shining, early morning garden. It was so early that the shadows were still long and narrow, and the dew from the grass, which needed cutting, was cold on their bare ankles.

The birds and the small daylight creatures were all awake. The faint hum that Rosemary and John had noticed after drinking the red mixture was all around them, like the hum of a busy market place, but fainter and on a higher note. If they stood still, they could distinguish the little voices of which it was made. Only the birds sang loudly and excitedly of all the things they hoped to do on such a glorious day. Rosemary wanted to stop and listen, but John pulled her on.

The greenhouse was quite small. It had not been used for some time. The lock was broken, and several of the panes were cracked. The coloured tiles patterning the floor had come loose from their moorings and rocked beneath Rosemary's and John's feet when they walked on them. The greenhouse no longer held rows of pots, full of delicate flowers. There was only one remaining climbing plant which had run riot over the walls and roof. Mrs Brown called it plumbago. It was flowering now, and great trusses of pale blue blossoms hung among the dark green leaves. John and Rosemary ran down the path and opened the door.

On the shelf which had once housed pots of geraniums and primulas and lacy ferns, before a curtain of blue flowers, sat Carbonel. Beside him was a snow-white Persian, and between them were two kittens, one coal-black with white paws and the other tortoise-shell. All four sat quite still with their tails wrapped neatly around their front paws from left to right. The children hesitated by the open door. A blue flower fell silently between the kittens, and the black one raised a paw as if to pat it.

'Calidor!' said Carbonel sternly, and the kitten instantly wrapped his tail round his paws again, as if that would keep them out of mischief.

'Good morning, Rosemary. Good morning, John.'

'Good morning,' said the children together, and John, to his surprise, found himself adding, 'Sir.'

'My dear,' said Carbonel, turning to the white cat. 'I have great pleasure in presenting my two friends, John and Rosemary.'

The white cat gazed at them with wide, faraway blue eyes and bowed her head graciously. 'My husband has often spoken of you. His friends will always be mine.'

'Thank you,' said John rather lamely.

'Present the children, my love,' said Blandamour. Carbonel bent his head in acknowledgement.

'My son, Prince Calidor, and my daughter, Princess Pergamond. Make your bows, my children.'

The two kittens stood up, and with black legs splayed out and small tails erect, made rather wobbly bows. John bobbed his head, and Rosemary lifted the skirt of her nightdress and made a little curtsy.

'I give my children into your care,' said Carbonel. 'Protect their nine lives as if they were your own. And you, my children, repeat the royal rules each day and put them into practice.'

'Yes, Father,' said the kittens in shrill chorus.

'And obey John and Rosemary in all things.'

'Yes, Father.'

'Remember, they are in your charge and you are in theirs.'

'Yes, Father.'

'And when I come back, let me hear nothing to your discredit.'

The black kitten, whose eyes had wandered to the drifting blue flowers again, began to say 'Yes, Father,' and hastily changed it to 'No.'

Carbonel turned to Blandamour. 'My love, it is time for me to go. Come with me to the crossroads and see me on my way.'

The black cat jumped silently to the tiled floor and went out into the sunlit garden, and Blandamour followed. John and Rosemary, watching them leap to the top of the garden wall, ran to wave good-bye. Standing on the garden roller, their chins level with the top of the wall, they could see Carbonel and Blandamour growing smaller and smaller as they trotted along the wall. It skirted the end of the gardens of number one hundred, number ninety-nine and number ninety-eight. At number ninety-seven, the wall curved, and the two cats disappeared from view.

'Well, that's that!' said John, jumping down from the roller and wiping the moss from his hands on to his pyjamas.

'Come on. Let's get back to the kittens. Aren't they gorgeous!' said Rosemary.

They ran back to the greenhouse. To their surprise, only the tortoise-shell kitten was to be seen. She was standing on her hind paws on a flower pot, peering into an old watering can.

'Where's the other one? Where's Calidor?' asked Rosemary, looking round anxiously.

'He's in here,' said Pergamond in a muffled voice, because she was still peering into the can. 'It sounds as though he's paddling. Why don't you answer, Calidor?'

There was a splash and a faint mew. John rushed to the watering can and, putting in his hand, lifted out a bedraggled kitten, dripping with dirty water and mewing pitifully.

'You poor little thing!' said Rosemary, trying to wipe off the slime with her nightdress.

But the kitten only whimpered, 'Where's Woppit! Want Woppit!'

'What on earth is Woppit?' asked John.

'Here be old Woppit, my pretty dears!' said a voice behind them, and there in the doorway was a dusty, dishevelled, elderly tabby cat.

'Bother!' said Pergamond crossly.

'As if they could keep old Woppit away! "Too big for a nurse now," they said. But I knows better! Me that's looked after 'em since before their blessed blue eyes was open. They thought they'd hoodwinked old Woppit and whisked you away without her knowing. But I smells here, and I asks there, and sure enough, I've found my little furry sweetings! And where's my precious princeling puss?'

All the time she was talking, Woppit was purring loudly and comfortably. But when she caught sight of Calidor, bedraggled and miserable in Rosemary's lap, her untidy fur bristled with indignation.

'What have the horrid humans been doing to you then, my pet? I knew it all along! I never did hold with humans!'

'We aren't wicked, even if we are humans!' said John indignantly. 'And we didn't do anything!'

'It was Calidor's fault,' said Pergamond virtuously. 'We were hungry, and I only said I thought there might be sardines in the water at the bottom of the can, and he was looking to see, and he fell in. He was only doing this.'

She put her front paws on the rim of the can, and heaving her stumpy hind legs up the side, tried to stand on the rim. John's hand shot out again just in time to stop her from falling in as her brother had done. He set her firmly down on the ground.

'But there weren't any sardines,' said Calidor, who was beginning to revive. 'Only a lot of smelly water.' He sneezed violently. 'I think I've lost a life,' he went on with gloomy satisfaction. 'You'll catch it when father hears!'

'I'm hungry,' mewed Pergamond. 'I want my breakfast!'

'Regular meals they're used to, like any well brought-up kittens. There's some people takes on a job without so much as knowing the first thing about it.' Woppit looked sourly at John and Rosemary.

'Look here,' said John angrily, 'are you suggesting that Rosie and I aren't capable of looking after a couple of kittens?'

'Well then, which of you is going to lick my little princeling clean? And no licking round the corners, mind!'

'Lick him!' said Rosemary in horror, looking at the kitten's matted fur.

'That's what I said. You'll never get him clean without. Either I licks, or you licks, and if I stays and licks, I stays for good!' said Woppit. 'Which is it to be?'

'I should have thought a bath –' began Rosemary. But at the word 'bath' the kittens set up such a mewing, and Woppit's comforting was so noisy, that the children could not hear themselves speak. They slipped outside the greenhouse and shut the door behind them quite firmly.

'Whew!' said John. 'I'm beginning to see what Carbonel means about the kittens being "high spirited".'

'Look here,' interrupted Rosemary, 'I think we should find Woppit very useful. After all, we can't sit and hold their paws all day long.'

'Yes, but I refuse to have an old tabby cat ordering me around,' said John.

'I don't think she'll try if we make her see that we only want to do our best for the kittens.'

'Perhaps you're right,' said John. 'Suppose I run back upstairs and get them some milk, and you see what you can do with old Woppit.' John ran.

When Rosemary went back into the greenhouse, Woppit was already vigorously licking a sulky Calidor. She eyed Rosemary suspiciously, but she did not stop.

'Please, Woppit,' said Rosemary humbly, 'John and I want you to stay and show us how to look after Prince Calidor and Princess Pergamond, if you will.'

With a practised paw, Woppit rolled over a protesting Calidor and went on licking. She said nothing, but there was the faint suggestion of a purr.

'Please, Woppit!' pleaded Rosemary.

'I'll think about it!' said Woppit, as though it were a perfectly new idea of Rosemary's. 'I might do it, to oblige.' But she went on licking the unhappy Calidor so vigorously that Rosemary felt quite sorry for him, and her purring settled down to a deep, contented hum.

At that moment, John burst in at the door. 'Here's some milk, but I only just got out without being seen,' he said. 'I could hear your mother getting up. We'd better hurry.'

They put the saucer down, left Woppit in charge, closed the door of the greenhouse firmly and ran back to the house and breakfast.

Wild Wander

LILLIAN BECKWITH

For many years, Lillian Beckwith made her home in a tiny croft near the Hebridean village of Bruach. The rugged wind-blown crags of the island shore provide a home for the rarest of wild creatures . . .

I awoke with the first flurry of wind around the house and lay drowsily listening and wondering if this was just an exploratory thrust of a breeze attendant upon the turn of the tide or whether it was in the nature of a rehearsal for a gale which, gaining proficiency, would stampede the calm spell that had been lulling us during the past few days. The flurry died briefly then came again, still indecisive. I tried to guess at the time. It had been day bright when I had gone to bed at my usual time and it was day bright now and I felt as if I had slept no more than an hour. I gave up guessing and stretched out an arm to pick up the alarm clock. It was a crippled clock; both its feet had gone so that it had to lie prone and the minute hand had broken off, but as nearly all Bruach clocks were either crippled or wildly eccentric I saw no reason to waste money on a new one. Except for the postmistress, the schoolteacher and the bus driver 'mechanical time' was of little importance. In winter, day began with the very first glimmer of light which told the mothers of school-age children that there was time only for them to make a quick bowl of brose and murmur a bible reading before rushing the children off to school. It told the rest of us that though there might be time for a more leisurely breakfast this must be followed by a few brief hours crammed with disciplined comings and goings; carrying hay for the outwintered cattle; milking; mucking out and renewing bedding; bringing water from the well and peats from the stack; feeding hens, and yet more hay carrying until it was dark and we could recuperate with a long evening beside the fire until one decided for oneself that it was time for the day to end. During the spring and early summer when nights were transient enough to pass almost unnoticed the working day was not so easily definable. The children took their cue for school by the smoke which appeared from the schoolhouse chimney (the peat fire burned all the year round) and their mothers knew it was time to put on the potatoes for the evening meal when the returning scholars were sighted climbing the homeward path, but though these two daily events served as useful reminders to the rest of us no one appeared to notice the lack of them when the school was closed for the holidays. We would say, 'It is time to milk the cows', or, 'It is time to feed the hens', or, 'It is time to take my dinner', and even I, novice that I was, rarely glanced at a clock for guidance. Time became instinctive: a sense that developed with the constant observation of the sky and sun shadows and the behaviour of animals and birds whose promptings were less arbitrary and more reliable than clocks and watches.

Confused now by sleep I stared at the clock. The hour hand had crept fractionally past four showing me that it was some three hours before my usual waking time. My body felt as if it was roped to the bed with the need for sleep but nevertheless I continued listening, trying to gauge the strength of the wind and almost whimpering a prayer that it would die away for just three or four hours so that I could finish my rest when, I promised, it could blow for weeks and I should not grumble. Since coming to live in Bruach I had found I was inclined to sleep less deeply on nights of calm and quiet than on nights of bustling storm, wind and rain being the characteristic pattern of our weather and calm spells merely an interruption. Like everyone else I rejoiced in the respite from the interminable battles with the wind but I was conscious that if they lasted more than a day or two they became seductive, luring me into negligence. Perhaps into leaving an empty wheel-barrow out on the croft; into forgetting a feeding bowl or some garden tool that a strong gust could snatch up and hurl against a window; into omitting the extra tie on a barn door which, if the door were blown open, could result in the loss of the roof and though I might go to bed happily exhausted by all the extra work the calm spell had enabled me to accomplish there was always this subconscious awareness of more elementary chores neglected so that I was inclined to sleep fitfully, one ear alert for the first threatening rushes of a rising wind.

The flurries were undoubtedly gaining strength, punching at the windows and the roof. A pail rattled over the cobblestones and a tub went bumping after it reminding me of yesterday's big wash of sheets still on the clothes-line. I jumped out of bed and slid into some clothes. As soon as I opened the door I could hear the noise of the sheets cracking like whips as they streamed in the wind and I hastened to rescue them. Some of the pegs had gone and the hems were already beginning to fray with long cottons plagued into tangles but I was relieved to see they were still whole. Once before when I had been slow to take in sheets left out in a gale I had found only the top hems still pegged to the clothes-line; the rest were white remnants clinging to clumps of spiky heather and decorating the barbed wire and netting fence around the haystack. At that time it had been near disaster since my linen cupboard was not well stocked and I was expecting a succession of visitors. My only recourse had been to buy sheets from 'Aberdeen Angus' the cheerful Asian tinker, whose entire stock I discovered to have become stained along the folds with a most persistent brown dye which had leaked from the cheap and inevitably sodden portman-teaus in which he always carried round his wares.

As soon as I grasped the sheets the remaining pegs flew out and

I fought the wind for possession of my bundle, crushing it against me as I trotted back to the house. Dumping it on the table I sped back to the croft, retrieving anything that might be blown away: a bundle of potato sacks washed in the burn and left to dry on the stone dyke; odd pieces of driftwood; a half-gallon tin of paint which I had been using to paint the barn door; a shovel; a broom, and a couple of pails. Even a creel of peats had to be taken to the safety of the shed since it had already been nudged over and some of the peats scattered thus making the creel light enough to be tumbled about and perhaps become airborne should the wind increase to a gale. Satisfied at last I returned to the cottage and while I folded the sheets, cool and fresh-smelling as the dawn wind itself, I debated whether it was worth while going back to bed. My sorties into the brisk morning had driven away the yearning for sleep and I wondered whether after a quick cup of coffee I should turn my back on work and make the most of the enforced early rising by indulging in what I liked to call a 'wild wander'. Several times during the kindlier months of the year I liked to make these early-morning expeditions either along the shore or over the moors before there was much risk of other people being about and rarely did I return without the reward of having glimpsed some shy, wild creature or witnessed a thrilling example of animal behaviour the memory of which I knew would remain with me for the rest of my life. I had seen the elusive wild cat slinking among the bracken; I had observed at close quarters a family of otters playing like puppies at the mouth of a cave until, presumably winding me, they slid lithe as snakes across the rocks and into the sea. I had come at low tide within forty yards of a party of seals, lying out on the rocks and rolling and flopping their great bodies into first one position and then another while they expressed their satisfaction or otherwise by noises that were half belches, half groans. I had been puzzled by a gathering of weasels, I counted seven in all, which appeared to be playing a game of 'In and out of the bluebells' on a mossy bank near the shore, and I had watched enchanted while a magnificent stag had led his party of hinds across a swollen burn, turning every now and then it seemed to reassure the more apprehensive among them. At almost any time there was a variety of wild life to be observed in and around Bruach but in the early mornings when it felt as if the day itself had only just begun to breathe there was more chance of surprising the more wily or more timid creatures which, once discerning the slightest stir of human activity, speedily retreated to the security of the hills or took refuge on unscalable cliffs. Admittedly there were mornings when I saw nothing more unusual than a stag silhouetted against the skyline; a buzzard swooping on a rabbit, or a patient heron being attacked by a couple of gulls which coveted his fresh-caught breakfast but no matter how common the sight for me the wonder and the rapture were always there. I had come straight to Bruach from the town and though the ensuing years had moulded me into a countrywoman they had not lessened my excitement on seeing creatures of the wild. So far as they were concerned I knew I should remain in a perpetual state of wonder.

I opened the door and studied the great soft clouds that were moving serenely across the sky to join those already in ambush behind the hills. With this wind I should have expected them to be racing across the sky and I seemed to recollect that according to Bruach weather lore when there was 'more wind low than high' it was a sign that the wind would not last long. The morning was inviting. I made my cup of coffee and refused to think of work. As yet I could see no threat of rain in the sky but all the same I pulled on an oilskin, tied it round my waist with a length of rope and pushed a sou'wester into the pocket. In Bruach it was usually raining, had just ceased raining or was threatening to rain so it was as well to be prepared. In any case there was nothing so good as an oilskin for defence against the wind. Discarding my heavy workaday gumboots I slipped into a pair of shiny, thin-soled rubber boots, bought in an English town and kept exclusively for 'wild wanders'. Ordinary gumboots had to be heavyweight to withstand the rough stony ground and had to be several sizes too big to allow for heavy socks in winter which resulted in their clumping noisily as one walked, warning anything within a hundred yards of one's approach, but these lightweight boots, though

I could feel every pebble through the thin soles, were excellent in that they kept my feet dry and yet trod as quietly as a pair of tennis pumps. Slinging my binoculars round my neck I closed the door and stood once more to assess the weather and decide which way I should go. The tide was well in and throwing great plumes of spray, wetter than any rain, over the shore so I made for the moors. As I passed the hen-run the hens came racing towards me with an expectancy that changed to puzzled murmurings as I ignored them. A feed at this hour of the morning would have upset their routine and I might have affected their egg-laying. They would have to wait until I returned in about three hours' time. Crossing the stepping stones of the burn I climbed into the wind and followed one of the sheep-tracks that would take me around the shoulder of the hill and eventually into a small corrie where I could peer down into a vast chasm of tumbled rocks, reputed to be a favourite haunt of hill foxes. In all my years in Bruach I had never glimpsed a hill fox yet I was constantly hearing the shepherd grumbling at the number of sheep they took and hearing the gamekeeper boast of the number he had shot. The shepherd claimed that hill foxes were far wilier than other foxes and described almost with admiration how one of them had got the better of him at lambing time. The shepherd had gone to check up on his ewes and found one in a sheltered corrie all by herself with newly born twin lambs. He noticed that the ewe seemed agitated and looking round for the reason soon spotted the fox stealing towards her. The ewe turned to face her enemy, backing away and trying to keep her lambs behind her but it was obvious that one of the lambs was much weaker than the other. Before the shepherd could get near enough to do anything about it the fox had nipped in and taken the weaker lamb. The shepherd scrambled quickly down into the corrie, throwing stones and shouting at the fox until it dropped its catch and made off, but he was too late. When he reached the lamb it was already dead. Just as he made his discovery he heard a sharp bleat from the ewe and turning round was in time to see the same fox slinking rapidly out of sight with the remaining lamb in its jaws. It had merely circled the corrie and while his back was turned had swiftly taken the other lamb. 'If only,' the shepherd chided himself, 'I'd had the sense to let it get away with the weaker lamb I would have been able to get the strong one to safety, but ach, he was just too clever for me I doubt.'

The shepherd told too of his experience with an old dog fox. He had been out on the hills one day looking for white heather for some friends of his and feeling rather warm he took off his jacket and left it on a small knoll while he made his way down to the burn for a drink. Having refreshed himself he was about to retrace his path to the knoll when looking up he saw the old dog fox was there pawing at something. Realising it was his own jacket he shouted and waved his arms at the fox trying to scare it off but the animal only looked at him before resuming his attack on the jacket, pulling it about the knoll until the shepherd was afraid it would be torn. He hurried forward to rescue it and just as he reached the knoll he saw the fox extract a bar of chocolate from one of the pockets. It gave him another leisurely look before loping away with the chocolate still held in its mouth. 'The look that beast gave me as it went off with my chocolate was kind of uncanny,' he used to add when he told the story.

For another mile or so I trudged on, disturbing nothing more exciting than a flock of drowsy sheep and a trio of hill ponies contentedly grazing the short grass while the wind combed their long manes. The ponies pranced away, full of summer energy and sweet mountain grass. It was while I was negotiating a skintight little path between two bastions of cliff which led to a miniature plateau that I came upon the wild goats. Several times previously I had glimpsed the goats but never at such close quarters and from the concealment of the cliffs I was able to observe them without their seeing me. The herd was clustered around the entrance to a cave, the old grey billy to the fore but still fast asleep lying half curled with his nose resting on his flank like a dog. Behind him two young nannies stood steadily cudding and staring out at the sea with tranquil yellow eyes. Behind them again three more elderly nannies lay with the relaxed air of those who are enjoying a morning lie-in while two leggy kids sniffed at each other's ears and seemed to be consulting with each other as to whether they should lie down again with their elders or begin the day's gambolling.

It was said in Bruach that this herd of goats were the descendants of domesticated animals left behind by the crofters during the terrible evictions of the last century when homes and possessions were burned and pillaged by avaricious landlords but whatever their history the goats looked wild enough now with their strong horns and their long shaggy coats so matted and bramble-threaded that the wind could scarcely hustle a way through. I edged back along the path, not wishing to disturb them, and clambered up a rocky gully which brought me to an even loftier sheep-track so that when I came out at last above the corrie I had to slide and scramble down into it. I approached the rock edge cautiously expecting a snatch of wind to buffet me as I came into the open, but I was pleasantly surprised. I had been too engrossed to notice how the wind was dropping and now as I looked towards the sea I realised it was only a stiff breeze that was turning the white bellies of the waves towards the wink of silver above the mainland hills and that the gale I had prepared for would prove to be no more than a morning prank. I lay down, peering hopefully into the deep abyss, impressed as always by the sheer desolation and size of the havoc of barren rocks severed so cleanly from the rest of the land by steep, sharp cliffs that provided footholds for nothing larger than a raven. It was an eerie place and if it was true that there were many fox earths among the boulders I imagined the foxes would continue to live there without fear of molestation.

For about an hour I lay there enjoying the solitude and silence while ranging the abyss hopefully with my binoculars, without once detecting even a suggestion of movement. Any foxes were either still asleep or already out prospecting for their breakfast. I gave up, aware that I was hungry for my own breakfast and that even if I hurried by the time I reached home again my poultry would be protesting that their feed was overdue. Not wishing to risk meeting or disturbing the wild goats I began to climb, zigzagging my way towards the higher track through mossy gullies that provided easy footholds and over projecting boulders which did not. I was standing on a ledge of rock about to pull myself up and over it when glancing carelessly to my right something caught my eye. Instinctively I froze. For a fleeting second I imagined the tawny, gold shape perched on the plinth of rock above me to be headless but as my excited thoughts steadied I realised I was looking at an enormous golden eagle standing with its head turned away from me and tucked under its wing. It looked to be about three feet high and except for the golden feathers on its back which were being gently lifted by the breeze it was as still as a carving. I gaped at it, astounded by its size and by the great talons, bigger than my own hand, which gripped the rock and I think I forgot to breathe for so long that I must eventually have let out a gasp. At any rate, some noise I made disturbed the eagle which turned its head quickly and looked straight at me with piercing yellow eyes. 'You beauty!' I raved silently. 'You stupendous, unbelievable beauty!' My heart thumped as we stared at each other with what seemed like equal incredulity until the eagle spread its great wings, poised itself for a second and without haste allowed the wind to lift it from its perch. I wanted to cry out to it to stay but I could only stand dumbly watching its trance-like descent on the wind out towards the sea where, levelling off and still without discernible movement of its magnificent wings, it glided on and on until it merged into the mainland hills and no matter how much I peered I could see it no more.

I pulled myself on to the ledge and walked to where the eagle had stood. I counted only five of my paces. It was staggering! I had actually stood within five paces of a golden eagle and I wanted to scream the fact into the wind if only to convince myself it was really true. I stood leaning against the rock, overwhelmed by my phenomenal good luck and conscious of the deep soul-satisfying elation that filled me and would, I knew, surge through me whenever I recollected my morning's adventures. 'People will never believe me,' I thought and with something of a shock realised that this was perfectly true. No one would believe me. If I mentioned my experience to my neighbours they would undoubtedly appear

to accept my story but I knew myself it would sound too implaus-
ible. To have got within fifty paces of a resting golden eagle they
might just have accepted but a claim to have got within five they
would have regarded as pure exaggeration. It would be better to
say nothing, I thought, and tried to make the thought a resolution,
reminding myself that there were idiots with guns in Bruach who
were the avowed enemies of eagles because of their reputation for
taking new-born lambs. 'Say nothing,' I told myself firmly as I left
the place of the eagle's perch. 'Say nothing,' I repeated to myself
again and again. And all the time I was bursting with the urge to
tell somebody. Just one other person if only to see their reaction.

Once safely past the goats' cave I dropped down again to the
lower path and as I reached the corrie where I had encountered the
hill ponies I saw a figure in cap and oilskins seated comfortably on
a boulder and staring out to sea through binoculars. I recognised
Donald, Bruach's shyest bachelor, and would have skirted the
corrie so as to keep out of his way had he not appeared to sense my
presence the moment I spotted him. Perhaps for a space I had been
visible on the skyline while I was on the high path and he had
expected me to make for the corrie. He turned and we greeted
each other with stiff smiles.

'You're out early,' he observed.

I was surprised. He had always evaded addressing me directly
and I had gained the impression he resented me as an intruder in
Bruach. This morning, however, he appeared distinctly affable so
I told him what had led me to take such an early-morning walk.

'Ach, but that was what we call a tide wind, just,' he replied,
confirming what by this time I already knew. 'Even this bitty
breeze will be away before the tide's been gone back for more than
an hour.' He looked up at me. 'You'd best be tryin' to learn the
ways of the wind.'

I gave a rueful little laugh. 'I try,' I told him, 'and I know more
of its ways now than when I first came to Bruach but these, what
you call "tide winds", usually manage to fox me.' His expression
became faintly superior. 'You're out early yourself,' I observed.

'Aye.' He rose deliberately. 'I'd best be away back to my house or the cailleach will be shoutin' I'm starvin' her hens.' Donald lived with his testy, chair-bound old mother and did all the housework and cooking as well as the croft work. He seemed disposed to accept my company for the walk home and for once I was at a loss to know whether I should attempt to start a conversation or whether he would prefer it if we continued on our way virtually in silence. For a time I left the initiative to him although I wanted to talk to him very much. Apart from the fact that Donald was supposed to know more than anyone else about the wild life of the area I wanted to ask him why, when he had the reputation of being by far the best shot in the village, he had suddenly and without explanation put away his gun and taken to using binoculars and a camera to observe wild life rather than to destroy it indiscriminately as he once had. He bent, picked up a pebble, and aimed it at a clump of heather below the path. A surprised rabbit peered above the clump and loped unhurriedly away. Donald grunted.

'Did you know it was there?' I asked him.

'I didn't know for sure but I felt as if there should be one there.' He darted a glance at me. 'If you'd had a gun now that would have made a dinner for you.'

'I don't shoot,' I told him.

'No, I don't myself now.'

'Not at all?' I queried.

'Ach, I might get a rabbit if they're takin' too much of the corn or if the cailleach takes a fancy for one but I scarcely ever take the gun down from the wall now.'

'And yet people tell me you are easily the best shot in Bruach,' I encouraged.

'Aye, I believe I might have been once,' he acknowledged. He tweaked a stalk of grass from beside the path and stuck it in his mouth. I thought it signified the end of the subject but after we had walked another little distance in silence he turned to me, slowing his pace almost to a standstill.

'There was a time once when I'd shoot at almost anythin' that moved: rabbits, hares, grouse, hoodies, gulls, ach, any bird you'd name an' just think myself the fine fellow that I had the skill to do it but then the day came, an' it came all of a sudden, that I was brought to my senses. I grew up as you might say.'

He flushed and his yellow uneven teeth were bared in an embarrassed smile but he was still walking slowly. I reasoned that if he wanted me not to pursue the subject he would have quickened his pace again so I prompted:

'You say the day came quite suddenly?'

'Aye.' He took the stalk of grass from his mouth and started to pull it into tiny pieces between his fingers. 'Did you ever see a newly dead grouse?' he asked, looking at me searchingly.

'Yes.'

'An' did you ever notice the markings on its feathers; all its feathers, I mean, not just the wings an' the brighter coloured ones?' He moved his fingers as if he were riffling them through the feathers on a bird's breast.

'Not specially,' I confirmed.

He nodded. 'I'd shot this grouse one day an' I was just bendin' down to pick it up when suddenly the sun comes through the clouds like a pointing finger an' a wee breeze tickled at the bird's feathers, liftin' them so that it made me notice the markin's on them. Beautiful it was, beautiful just. No man could have made a thing like it. I've never been able to explain it, least of all to myself, but it was as though somethin' was behind my shoulder forcin' me to see what I'd been blind to before an' what a fearful waste it was to destroy it. I took home the grouse an' we ate it but for the first time in my life I didn't enjoy it an' when I came to put the feathers at the back of the fire an' I saw their lovely patterns goin' up in smoke I knew I didn't want to destroy another living creature. I cleaned the gun that night an' I put it up on the wall an' I doubt I've taken it down more than two or maybe three times since an' that's a good few years back.' His pace quickened. 'Ach, I daresay I was daft but that's the way of it just.'

I tried to give him an understanding smile but he kept his face averted. All the same I knew now that here was someone with whom I could safely share my secret.

'I don't suppose you'll believe me,' I began, trying to keep the excitement out of my voice, 'but up there on the crag I've just stood within five paces of a golden eagle. It was asleep with its head under its wing.'

He turned to face me. 'Why wouldn't I believe you?' he demanded. There was a wry twist to his mouth.

'Oh, it just sounds too impossible. I'd decided not to mention it at all but I was dying to tell someone. You won't let it go any further, will you?' I asked hastily. There was something about the tightening of his lips that made it unnecessary for him to answer.

'Indeed not long before you found me I was watchin' a golden eagle makin' over towards the mainland. Likely it would be the one you disturbed.'

'Oh, yes!' I exclaimed, glad of some corroboration of my story.

'You were lucky all the same,' he congratulated me. 'There's not more than one other person hereabouts that I mind ever got that close to an eagle.'

'You know of someone else?' I asked tensely.

'Aye, an' he was my own father.'

'Your father?'

'Indeed. He was salmon watchin' at the time, living in the bothy, an' he was comin' over to collect some fresh milk an' food. It was about midday, an' sunny an' calm. Seein' he was keepin' an eye open for his sheep at the same time he didn't stay on the path. He climbed up to a crag an' found himself almost on a level with the eagle an' so close he could touch it. Like the one you saw it had it's head under its wing so that it didn't see him. My father was a very honest man, you understand, Miss Peckwitt?' He looked at me and I nodded. 'There's nothin' that upset him more than bein' disbelieved but all the same he knew if he came back to the village tellin' nothin' but the truth about what he'd seen people wouldn't be able to bring themselves to believe him just. So, quick as a flash he slipped off his jacket an' threw it over the eagle an' held it in his arms. He lifted it an' carried it all the way down to the village an' there he started shoutin' for folks to come an' see what he had. When he thought there was enough witnesses he lifted his jacket off the eagle an' let it go.' He grinned. 'They had to believe him then.'

'He must have been even closer than I was,' I remarked.

'Aye, but I doubt you wouldn't have had the strength to carry it back even supposin' you were able to throw your jacket over it,' he replied. 'They're big birds with some weight in them.'

I laughed. 'It wouldn't have occurred to me to try,' I retorted. 'It looked enormous and its talons were really fearsome.'

He grunted again. 'You'd best be careful who you mention the eagle to,' he warned. 'There's one or two here would be out with the gun if they heard of it.'

'I've already decided I'm going to keep quiet about it,' I assured him. 'It's enough that I've seen it.'

We were coming in sight of the village now and he began to move away, gradually making for a track that would take him to the far moor gate. I guessed that he had no wish to be seen in my company.

'Aye, well,' he said, throwing the words over his shoulder, 'I'd best go an' make some breakfast.'

'D'you know,' I told him, 'I recall feeling quite hungry for my breakfast before I saw the eagle but since then the thought of food hasn't crossed my mind.'

He paused and looked at me with a gentle understanding smile.

'Ach, Miss Peckwitt,' he pronounced, 'when anyone has seen such a sight as you have seen this morning they have had food and drink for the day.' He turned his back on me and we went our separate ways.

Dogsbody

DIANA WYNNE JONES

Sirius the Dog Star is born as a real dog on earth to fulfil an important mission – to track down the mysterious Zoi. He is adopted by an animal-loving family, given the name Leo and forced to face the everyday – but to him incomprehensible – problems of family life . . .

Now, in those days, Sirius's whole world was the house and the yard behind it. The shop left very little of the world downstairs over, so he was naturally curious to see into this shop. He was naturally curious anyway. Kathleen often said, 'I know they say *Curiosity killed the cat,* but it ought to be *killed the dog.* Get your nose out, Leo.' Sirius made a number of attempts to poke his blunt inquiring nose round the door that led to the shop. Duffie always stopped him. Mostly she kicked at him with a sandalled foot. Sometimes she hit him with a broom. And once, she slammed the door against his nose, which hurt him considerably. But he kept on trying. It was not that the dusty, clayey smell from beyond the door was particularly pleasing, or that he wanted to be with Duffie. It was that he felt he was being cheated of the greater part of his world. Besides, the cats were allowed inside, and he was rapidly becoming very jealous of those cats.

By this time, it would have been hard to say whether the cats were more jealous of Sirius than he of them. He envied the cats their delicacy and disdain, the ease with which they leapt to places far out of his reach, and the way they came and went so secretly. He could not go anywhere or do anything without somebody noticing. The cats, on their part, disliked him for being a dog, for being new, and for taking up everyone's attention.

They were three rather neglected cats. Until Kathleen came no one except Duffie had taken any notice of them at all. Duffie, from time to time, took it into her head that she loved cats. When this happened, she would seize a struggling cat, hold it against her smock and announce, 'Diddums diddy, Mother loves a pussy then!'

Romulus and Remus, who were twin tabbies, both escaped from this treatment as soon as they could fight loose. But Tibbles bore it. She had an affectionate nature, and even this seemed better to her than total neglect. Tibbles was an elegant cat, mostly white, with a fine tabby patch on her back, and worthy of better treatment.

All three welcomed Kathleen with delight. She fed them generously, knew Romulus and Remus apart from the first, and gave Tibbles all the affection she wanted. Then Sirius came. Kathleen still fed the cats generously, but that was all Sirius would let her do. The day Sirius found Tibbles sitting on Kathleen's knee was the first time he barked. Yapping in a furious soprano, he flung himself at Kathleen and managed to get his front paws almost above her kneecaps. Tibbles arose and spat. Her paw shot out, once, twice, three times, before Sirius could remove himself. He was lucky not to lose an eye. But he continued to bark, and Tibbles, very ruffled, escaped on to the sideboard, furious and swearing revenge.

'Oh Leo!' Kathleen said reproachfully. 'That's not kind. Why shouldn't she sit on my knee?'

Sirius did not understand the question, but he was determined that Tibbles should sit on Kathleen's knee only over his dead body. Kathleen was *his*. The trouble was, he could not trust Kathleen to remember this. Kathleen was kind to all living things. She fed birds, rescued mice from the cats, and tried to grow flowers in a row of cracked cups on her bedroom window-sill. Sirius slept in Kathleen's bedroom, at first in the basket, then on the end of her bed when the basket grew uncomfortably tight. Kathleen would sit up in bed, with a book open in front of her, and talk to him for hours on end. Sirius could not understand what she was saying, but he darkly suspected she was telling him of her abounding love for all creatures.

One night, when it was spitting with rain, Romulus forgot about Sirius and came in through Kathleen's bedroom window to spend the night on her bed as he had done before Sirius came. That was the first time Sirius really growled. He leapt up rumbling. Romulus growled too and fled helterskelter, knocking over Kathleen's flower-cups as he went.

'You mustn't, Leo,' said Kathleen. 'He's *allowed* to. Now look what you've made him do!' She was so miserable about her broken flowers that Sirius had to lick her face.

After that, Sirius knew the cats were putting their heads together to get revenge. He did not care. He knew they were clever, Tibbles especially, but he was not in the least afraid of them. He was at least twice their size by now and still growing. His paws, as Kathleen remarked, were as big as tea-cups, and he was getting some splendid new teeth. Robin, who was always reading books about dogs, told Kathleen that Leo was certainly half Labrador. But what the other half of him was, neither of them could conjecture. Sirius's unusually glossy coat was a wavy golden-cream, except for the two red-brown patches, foxy red, one over each ear. Then there were those queer green eyes.

'Red Setter, perhaps?' Robin said doubtfully. 'He's got those feathery bits at the backs of his legs.'

'Mongrel,' said Basil. 'His father was a white rat and his mother was a fox.'

'Vixen,' Robin corrected him.

'I thought you'd agree,' said Basil.

Kathleen, who seldom argued with Basil, said nothing and went away upstairs to make the beds, with Sirius trotting after. 'I think you're really a Griffin,' she said. 'Look.' She opened the door of Duffie's wardrobe so that Sirius could see himself in the long mirror.

Sirius did not make the mistake of thinking it was another dog. He did not even go round the back of the mirror to see how his reflection got there. He simply sat himself down and looked, which impressed Kathleen very much. 'You *are* intelligent,' she said.

Sirius met his own strange eyes. He had no means of knowing they were unusual, but, all the same, just for a moment, he seemed to be looking at immeasurable distances down inside those eyes. Then he saw people and places so different from Duffie's bedroom that they were almost inconceivable. That was only for an instant. After that, they were only the green eyes of a fat curly puppy. Annoyed by something he could not understand, Sirius yawned like a crocodile, showing all his splendid new teeth.

'Come, come!' said Kathleen, laughing. 'You're not that boring!'

Those splendid teeth had Sirius in trouble the next day. The urge was on him to chew. And chew and chew. He chewed his basket into a kind of grass skirt. Then he went on to the hearthrug. Kathleen tore the hearthrug out of his mouth and gave him an old shoe, imploring him not to chew anything else but that. Sirius munched it threadbare in half an hour and looked round for something else. Basil had left a box of fossils on the floor. Sirius selected a piece of petrified wood out of it, propped it between his front paws, and was settling down to some glorious gritty grating when Basil found him. Basil kicked him, rolling and howling, across the room.

'Stinking Rat! Do that again and I'll kill you!'

Sirius dared not move. He wagged his tail apologetically and looked round for something else to bite on. Nicely within reach trailed a black chewy wire from a shelf above. He had his head up and the wire across the corners of his mouth in an ecstasy of chew, when Robin descended on him and put a stop to that.

'Kathleen! He's eaten the telephone wire now!'

'I'll go and buy a rubber bone,' said Kathleen. She went out.

Robin, rapidly and furtively, dreading Duffie coming, wrapped black sticky tape round the telephone wire. Basil was anxiously making sure none of his fossils had been eaten. No one attended to Sirius, crouched under the sideboard. He lay there, nose on paws, and there it came to him what it was he really wanted to chew. The ideal thing. With a little ticker-tack of claws, he crept to the door and up the stairs. He nosed open the door of the main bedroom without difficulty and, with a little more trouble, succeeded in opening the wardrobe too. Inside were shoes – long large leather shoes, with laces and thick chewable soles. Sirius selected the juiciest and took it under the bed to enjoy in peace.

The thunderous voice found him there and chased him round the house with a walking-stick. Duffie spoke long and coldly. Kathleen wept. Robin tried to explain about teething. Basil jeered. And throughout, Tibbles sat thoughtfully on the sideboard, giving the inside of her left front leg little hasty licks, like a cat seized with an idea. Sirius saw her. To show his contempt and to soothe his feelings, he went into the kitchen and ate the cats' supper. Then he lay down glumly to gnaw the unsatisfactory rubber thing Kathleen had bought him.

'That settles it,' said Duffie. 'That Creature is not going to spend all day in the house when you go back to school. He's going to be tied up in the yard.'

'Yes. Yes, all right,' Kathleen said humbly. 'I'll take him for walks when I get home. I'll start getting him used to it today.'

She had bought something else besides the bone. There was a red jingly strap, which she buckled round Sirius's neck. He did not like it. It was tight and it itched. But, twist as he might, he could not get it off. Then Kathleen hitched another strap with a loop at one end to the red one, and, to his great delight, opened the side door on the outside world, where he had never been before.

Sirius set off down the side of the house in a delighted rush. He was brought up short with a jerk and a jingle. Something seemed to be pulling his neck. He strained. He dragged. He made hoarse choking-noises to show Kathleen what was wrong. He stood on his hind legs to be free.

'No, Leo,' said Kathleen. 'You mustn't pull.'

But he went on pulling. The indignity was too much. He was not a slave, or a prisoner. He was Sirius. He was a free luminary and a high effulgent. He would not be held. He braced his four legs, and Kathleen had to walk backwards, towing him.

Being towed is hard on the paws, let alone the legs and ears. But Sirius was stiff with shock, and Kathleen had to drag him right down the passage. He was not what he seemed. He felt as if the world had stopped, just in front of his fore-feet, and he was looking down into infinite cloudy green depths. What was down in those depths frightened him, because he could not understand it.

'Really, Leo!' said Kathleen, at the end of the passage.

Sirius gave in and began to walk, absently at first, trying to understand what had happened. But he had no leisure to think. As soon as they were in the street, half a million new smells hit his nose simultaneously. Kathleen was walking briskly, and so were other legs around her. Beyond, large groaning things shot by with a swish and a queer smell. Sirius pulled away sideways to have a closer look at those things and was distracted at once by a deliciously rotten something in the gutter. When Kathleen dragged him off that, there were smells several dogs had left on a lamp-post, and, beyond that, a savoury dustbin, decaying fit to make his mouth water.

'No, Leo,' said Kathleen, dragging.

Sirius was forced to follow her. It irked his pride to be so small and weak when he knew he had once been almost infinitely strong. How had he come to be like this? What had happened to reduce him? But he could not think of the answer when something black was trickling on the pavement, demanding to be sniffed all over at once.

'Leave it,' said Kathleen. 'That's dirty.'

It seemed to Sirius that Kathleen said this to everything really interesting. It seemed to Kathleen that she had said it several

He was very happy

hundred times before they came to the meadow by the river. And here more new smells imperiously wanted attention. Kathleen took off the lead and Sirius bounded away, jingling and joyful, into the damp green grass. He ranged to and fro, rooting and sniffing, his tail crooked into a stiff and eager question-mark. Beautiful. Goluptious scents. What was he looking for in all this glorious green plain? He was looking for something. He became more and more certain of that. This bush? No. This smelly lump, then? No. What then?

There was a scent, beyond, which was vaguely familiar. Perhaps that was what he was looking for. Sirius galloped questing towards it, with Kathleen in desperate pursuit, and skidded to a stop on the bank of the river. He knew it, this whelming brown thing – he dimly remembered – and the hair on his back stood up slightly. This was not what he was looking for. And surely, although it was brown and never for a second stopped crawling past him, by the smell it was only water? Sirius felt he had better test this theory – and quickly. The rate the stuff was crawling, it would soon have crawled right past and away if he did not catch it at once. He descended cautiously to it. Yes, it was water, crawling water. It tasted a good deal more full-bodied than the water Kathleen put down for him in the kitchen.

'Oh, no!' said Kathleen, panting up to find him black-legged and stinking, lapping at the river as if he had drunk nothing for a week. 'Come out.'

Sirius obligingly came out. He was very happy. He wiped some of the mud off his legs on to Kathleen's and continued his search of the meadow. He still could not think what he was looking for. Then, suddenly, as puppies do, he got exhausted. He was so tired that all he could do was to sit down and stay sitting. Nothing Kathleen said would make him move. So she sat down beside him and waited until he had recovered.

And there, sitting in the centre of the green meadow, Sirius remembered a little. He felt as if, inside his head, he was sitting in a green space that was vast, boundless, queer, and even more alive than the meadow in which his body sat. It was appalling. Yet, if he looked round the meadow, he knew that in time he could get to know every tuft and molehill in it. And, in the same way, he thought he might come to know the vaster green spaces inside his head.

'I don't understand,' he thought, panting, with his tongue hanging out. 'Why do those queer green spaces seem to be me?'

But his brain was not yet big enough to contain those spaces. It tried to close itself away from them. In doing so, it nipped the green vision down to a narrow channel, and urgent and miserable memories poured through. Sirius knew he had been wrongly accused of something. He knew someone had let him down terribly. How and why he could not tell, but he knew he had been condemned. He had raged, and it had been no use. And there was a Zoi: he had no idea what a Zoi was, but he knew he had to find it, urgently. And how could he find it, not knowing what it was like, when he himself was so small and weak that even a well-meaning being like Kathleen could pull him about on the end of a strap? He began whining softly, because it was so hopeless and so difficult to understand.

'There, there.' Kathleen gently patted him. 'You *are* tired, aren't you? We'd better get back.'

She got up from her damp hollow in the grass and fastened the lead to the red collar again. Sirius came when she dragged. He was too tired and dejected to resist. They went back the way they had come, and this time Sirius was not interested in all the various smells. He had too much else to worry about.

As soon as Robin set eyes on Sirius, he said something. It was, 'He's pretty filthy, isn't he?' but of course Sirius could not understand. Basil said something too, and Duffie's cold voice in the distance said more. Kathleen hastily fetched cloths and towels and rubbed Sirius down and, all the while, Duffie talked in the way that made Sirius cower. He suddenly understood two things. One was that Duffie – and perhaps the whole family – had power of life and death over him. The other was that he needed to understand what they said. If he did not know what Duffie was objecting to, he might do it again and be put to death for it.

After that he fell asleep on the hearthrug with all four paws stiffly stretched out, and was dead to the world for a time. He was greatly in the way. Robin shoved him this way, Basil that. The thunderous voice made an attempt to roll him away under the sofa, but it was like trying to roll a heavy log, and he gave up. Sirius was so fast asleep that he did not even notice. While he slept, things came a little clearer in his mind. It was if his brain was forced larger by all the things which had been in it that day.

He woke up ravenous. He ate his own supper, and finished what the cats had left of the second supper Kathleen had given them. He looked round hopefully for more, but there was no more. He lay sighing, with his face on his great clumsy paws, watching the family eat their supper – they always reserved the most interesting food for themselves – and trying with all his might to understand what they were saying. He was pleased to find that he had already unwittingly picked up a number of sounds. Some he could even put meanings to. But most of it sounded like gabble. It took him some days to sort the gabble into words. And when he had done that he found that his ears had not been picking up the most important part of these words.

He thought he had learnt the word *walk* straight away. Whenever Kathleen said it, he sprang up, knowing it meant a visit to the green meadow and the crawling water. In his delight at what that word meant, his tail took a life of its own and knocked things over, and he submitted to being fastened to the strap because of what came after. But he thought these pleasures were packed into a noise that went *ork*. Basil discovered this, and had great fun with him.

'Pork, Rat!' he would shout. 'Stalk! Cork!'

Each time, Sirius sprang up, tail slashing, fox-red drooping ears pricked, only to be disappointed. Basil howled with laughter.

'No go, Rat. Auk, hawk, fork!'

In fact, Basil did Sirius a favour, because he taught him to listen to the beginnings of words. By the end of a week, Sirius was watching for the noise humans made by pouting their mouth into a small pucker. It looked a difficult noise. He was not sure he would ever learn to make it himself. But he now knew that when *ork* began with this sound, it was real, and not otherwise. He did not respond to *fork* or *talk* and Basil grew quite peevish about it.

'This Rat's no fun any more,' he grumbled.

Kathleen was relieved that Leo had almost stopped chewing things. Sirius was too busy learning and observing to do more than munch absently on his rubber bone. He ached for knowledge now. He kept perceiving a vast green something in himself, which was always escaping from the corner of his eye. He could never capture it properly, but he saw enough of it to know that he was now something stupid and ignorant, slung on four clumsy legs, with a mind like an amiable sieve. He had to learn why this was, or he would never be able to understand about a Zoi.

So Sirius listened and listened, and watched till his head ached. He watched cats as well as humans. And slowly, slowly, things began to make sense to him. He learnt that animals were held to be inferior to humans, because they were less clever, and smaller and clumsier. Humans used their hands in all sorts of devious, delicate ways. If there was something their hands could not do, they were clever enough to think of some tool to use instead. This perception was a great help to Sirius. He had odd, dim memories of himself using a Zoi rather as humans used tools. But animals could not do this. That was how humans had power of life and death over them.

Nevertheless, Sirius watched, fascinated, the way the cats, and Tibbles in particular, used their paws almost as cleverly as humans. Tibbles could push the cover off a meat-dish, so that Romulus and Remus could make their claws into hooks and drag out the meat inside. She could pull down the catch of the kitchen window and let herself in at night if it was raining. And she could open any door that did not have a round handle. Sirius would look along his nose to his own great stumpy paws and sigh deeply. They were as useless as Duffie's feet. He might be stronger than all three cats put together, but he could not use his paws as they did. He saw that this put him further under the power of humans than the cats. Because of their skill, the cats lived a busy and private life outside and inside the house, whereas he had to wait for a human to lead him about. He grew very depressed.

Then he discovered he could be clever too.

It was over the smart red jingly collar. Kathleen left it buckled round his neck after the first walk. Sirius hated it. It itched, and its noise annoyed him. But he very soon saw that it was more than an annoyance – it was the sign and tool of the power humans had over him. One of them – Basil for instance – had only to take hold of it to make him a helpless prisoner. If Basil then flipped his nose or took his bone away, it was a sign of the power he felt he had.

So Sirius set to work to make sure he could be free of that collar when he wanted. He scratched. And he scratched. And scratched. Jingle, jingle, jingle went the collar.

'Make that filthy creature stop scratching,' said Duffie.

'I think his collar may be on too tight,' said Robin. He and Kathleen examined it and decided to let it out two holes.

This was a considerable relief to Sirius. The collar no longer itched, though in its looser state it jingled more annoyingly than before. That night, after a little manoeuvring under Kathleen's bed, he managed to hook it to one of Kathleen's bedsprings and tried to pull it off by walking away backwards. The collar stuck behind his ears. It hurt. It would not move. He could not get it off and he could not get it on again. He could not even get it off the bedspring. His ears were killing him. He panicked, yelping and jumping till the bed heaved.

Kathleen sat up with a shriek. 'Leo! Help! There's a ghost under my bed!' Then she added, much more reasonably, 'What on earth are you *doing*, Leo?' After that, she switched on the light and came and looked. 'You silly little dog! How did you get into that pickle? Hold still now.' She unhooked Sirius and dragged him out from under the bed. He was extremely grateful and licked her face hugely. 'Give over,' said Kathleen. 'And let's get some sleep.'

Sirius obediently curled up on her bed until she was asleep again. Then he got down and started scratching once more. Whenever no one was near, he scratched diligently, always in the same place, on the loops of loose skin under his chin. It did not hurt much there and yet, shortly, he had made himself a very satisfactory raw spot.

'Your horse has its collar on too tight,' the thunderous voice told Kathleen. 'Look.'

Kathleen looked, and felt terrible. 'Oh, my poor Leo!' She let the collar out three more holes.

That night, to his great satisfaction, Sirius found he could leave the collar hanging on the bedspring, while he ambled round the house with only the quiet ticker-tack of his claws to mark his progress. It was not quite such an easy matter to get the collar on again. Kathleen woke twice more thinking there was a ghost under her bed, before Sirius thought of pushing his head into the collar from the other side. Then it came off the bedspring and on to his neck in one neat movement. He curled up on Kathleen's bed feeling very pleased with himself.

This piece of cunning made Sirius much more confident. He began to suspect that he could settle most difficulties if he thought about them. His body might be clumsy, but his mind was quite as good as any cat's. It was fortunate he realized this, because, one afternoon when Kathleen, Robin and Basil were all out, long before Sirius had learnt more than a few words of human speech, Tibbles did her best to get rid of him for good.

Sirius, bored and lonely, drew himself quietly up on to the sofa and fell gingerly asleep there. He liked that sofa. He considered it unfair of the humans that they insisted on keeping all the most comfortable places for themselves. But he did not dare do more than doze. Duffie was moving about upstairs. It seemed to be one of the afternoons when she did not shut herself away in the shop and, Sirius had learnt by painful experience, you had to be extra wary on those days.

He had been dozing there for nearly an hour, when Romulus jumped on him. He hit Sirius like a bomb, every claw out and spitting abuse. Sirius sprang up with a yelp. He was more surprised than anything at first. But Romulus was fat and determined. He dug his claws in and stuck to Sirius's back and Sirius, for a second or so, could not shake him off. In those seconds,

Sirius became furiously angry. It was like a sheet of green flame in his head. How dared Romulus! He hurled the cat off and went for him, snarling and showing every pointed white tooth he had. Romulus took one look. Then he flashed over the sofa arm and vanished. Sirius's teeth snapped on empty air. By the time he reached the carpet, Romulus was nowhere to be seen.

A bubbling hiss drew Sirius's attention to Remus, crouched in the open doorway to the shop. Remus bared his teeth and spat. At that, Sirius's rage flared vaster and greener still. He responded with a deep rumbling growl that surprised him nearly as much as it surprised Remus. A great ridge of fur came up over his back and shoulders and his eyes blazed green. Remus stared at this nightmare of eyes, teeth and bristle, and his own fur stood and stood and stood, until he was nearly twice his normal size. He spat. Sirius throbbed like a motorcycle and crept forward, slow and stiff-legged, to tear Remus to pieces. He was angry, angry, angry.

Remus only waited to make sure Sirius was indeed coming his way. Then he bolted without courage or dignity. He had done what his mother wanted, but not even for Tibbles was he going to face this nightmare a second longer than he had to. When Sirius reached the door of the shop, there was no sign of Remus. There was only Tibbles, alone in the middle of a dusty floor.

Sirius stopped when his face was round the door. In spite of his rage, he knew something was not right here. This door should have been shut. Tibbles must have opened it. She must be trying to tempt him inside for reasons of her own. The prudent thing would be not to be tempted. But he had always wanted to explore the shop, and he was still very angry. To see what would happen, he pushed the door further open and let out another great throbbing growl at Tibbles.

At the sight and sound of him, Tibbles became a paper thin archway of a cat, and her tail stood above in a desperate question-mark. Was this a puppy or a monster? She was terrified. But she stood her ground because this was her chance to get rid of it.

Her terror gave Sirius rather an amusing sense of power. Slow and stiff-legged, he strutted into the room. Tibbles spat and drifted away sideways, so arched that she looked like a piece of paper blowing in the wind. Sirius saw she wanted him to chase her. Just for a moment, he did wonder how it would feel to take her arched and narrow back between his teeth and shake his head till she snapped, but he was sure she would jump out of reach somewhere before he could catch her. So he ignored her. Instead, he swaggered across the dusty floor to look at the objects piled by the walls and stacked on the shelves.

He sniffed at them cautiously. What were these things? As curiosity gained the upper hand in him, his growl died away and the hair on his back settled down into glossy waves again. The things had a blank, muddy smell. Some were damp and pink, some pale and dry, some again shiny and painted in ugly grey-greens. They were something like the cups humans drank out of, and he thought they might be made of the same stuff as the dish labelled DOG in which Kathleen gave him his water. But Sirius could not have got his tongue into most of them. No human could have drunk out of any. Then he remembered the thing on the living-room mantelpiece Kathleen had smashed that morning when she was dusting. It had held one rose. Duffie had been furious.

Sirius understood now. These things were rose-holders and they broke. Let a dog chase a cat among them and the result would be spectacular. Duffie would certainly carry out all her cold threats. It was clever of Tibbles.

Cautiously, carefully, walking stiff-legged in order not to knock anything, Sirius explored the two rooms thoroughly. He sniffed at rows of hand-thrown pottery. He nosed glaze. He investigated damp new clay. He put his feet on a stool to examine the pink and dusty wheel on which Duffie made the things, and snuffed at the oven where she fired them. That was a better smell than most. It brought a queer tinge of homesickness. He went into the shop itself, where rows of shiny pots in dull colours waited for people to buy them. He did not find it very interesting. In fact, the whole place was rather a disappointment. It astonished him that even

Duffie could find things like this important. But he was sure she did. The cold dusty smell of the place matched her personality.

Tibbles followed him about like a drifting outraged shadow. How could the creature resist chasing her to go sniffing about like this? But Sirius took no notice of her at all. When he had seen enough, he turned carefully and carefully pit-patted towards the open door. He was going back to the sofa.

It was too much for Tibbles. Determined to carry out her plan, she dashed at Sirius and clawed his face. Then she leapt for a high shelf in the place where pottery was stacked thickest.

That was her undoing. She was in too much of a hurry to judge her jump properly, or perhaps she was simply confident that Sirius would be blamed for anything that broke. She missed the space she was aiming for and collided with a mighty purple vase. Slowly and imposingly, the vase tipped over, knocked Tibbles sideways and fell into a heap of pots beneath. Tibbles just managed to hook her claws into the very end of the shelf, where she hung, scrabbling underneath the shelf for a foothold. Sirius bolted, with the smash ringing in his ears. He had a last sight of Tibbles desperately hanging and scrabbling, and the other end of the shelf tipping sharply upwards.

The Badgers of
Bearshanks

'B.B.'

The misty golden day was done, the sun was down, the tall lime trees along the avenue stood like the masts of windjammers with all sails furled. Their tops and cross-trees were bare, save for a few circular yellow leaves which hung bravely on.

The October winds had recently been at work, and the resulting harvest lay in rustling drifts, six inches deep, in the hollows up the avenue. Through this golden carpet the keeper's two small children sometimes scuffled, pretending they were ships ploughing a golden sea, the bow wave of coloured leaves foaming before their little worn boots with a dry rustling sound.

There was nobody about now: it was late. The owls were awake and calling from Bearshanks Wood, faint musical hoorooings, bird answering bird – if birds indeed they were! To the scolding finches and jays, who discovered their hiding places in the light of day, they appeared to be striped, fluffy, tabby cats, and not birds at all; and that is why they swore at them.

One of the yellow leaves at the very top of the highest lime parted gently from its twig, which had held it securely for over twenty weeks. It began a slow voyage, down, down, down, rocking like a little yellow boat. It took the leaf nearly half a minute to descend from eighty feet, and it alighted with a caress, softer than an angel's kiss, on the grey hairs of a sow badger, who was trotting below. It remained on her broad rough back until she trundled in under the box bushes which bordered the keeper's paths.

Sally Bawson knew very well where she was going; the path she followed was as well known to her as the keeper's path was to him. She had work to do, for she felt the breath of winter close upon her. Soon these nightly wanderings would be less frequent. There would be long cosy periods down in the ancient set close by (though badgers do not hibernate in the true sense).

This set had been the home of badger families for over five hundred years. You may find this hard to believe, but it is true; indeed, they may have been there much longer. It had been inherited by each succeeding generation, just as the Great House in the park had been passed from father to son down the centuries. There had been badgers in Bearshanks when Richard III died on Bosworth Field. The set was in the steep bank above the Great Pond, which at one time had served the monastery with fish for the Friday dinners. Long, long ago, in the summer evenings, when the shadows lay cool and lengthening across the green grass, forebears of Sally had glimpsed the sober-clad monks, with their shaven heads, sitting upon their small oak stools, fishing for carp. Descendants of those very carp still inhabited the deep black waters of the Great Pond, just as old Sally Bawson and her mate inhabited the set under the thick box bushes hard by. Monks and monastery had gone; badgers and carp remained.

Sally Bawson pushed up the bank under the sooty black box bushes, with their tough, green stems. A blackbird chinked in alarm: chink! chink! chink! A real winter evening sound. Chaffinches and greenfinches, which roosted nightly in the tight mass of the box, hopped about nervously, peering down at Sally's broad back as she passed under them. She moved forward at a brisk jog-trot, her stern wagging to and fro like a Victorian lady's bustle. Now and again she would stop in her tracks to smell and listen, turning her striped head this way and that, secrecy and caution in every movement. No wild animal has a keener sense of smell; it was her greatest protection, and her hearing was almost as acute. It is difficult for us to imagine how powerful was this sense of smell.

The October night seemed calm, but that wandering breeze, which had dislodged the single lime leaf up the avenue, showed there was some movement in the air. Sally could identify a number of things. There was, of course, the damp smell of fallen leaves and earth, and mingled with it the strong taint of sheep droppings from the sward in the avenue. Down in the black muddy margin of the Great Pond lay the remains of a ten-pound carp, whose back had been bitten out by an otter. Though this was over three hundred yards away, Sally could smell it. It did not interest her: badgers will never eat decomposed creatures, only freshly-killed meat. She could smell the faint wild reek of the wood smoke. This came from the walled gardens by the grey stone Ducal mansion in the park, where the gardeners had been busy all day burning rubbish.

She could hear the minute stirrings of the restless birds up in the black box bushes, the rustlings of mice among the leaves. Sally ate mice when she could get them, but usually the tiny furred creatures were far too quick for her, and, unlike the cat, the badger has poor eyesight. But whenever she found a nest of baby mice she ate them.

There was one rustling sound which interested her more than the sound of the mice. It was a rustling which was louder, and there was a smell with it, a most appetising smell!

She sat down on top of the bank studying it, looking very like a cosy bear. Just above her, beyond the bushes, the dying bracken formed a thick carpet under the trees. The sound and smell was wafting from there. Sally walked forward out of the shadow and on into the red bracken fronds. The rustling stopped. A foot away a hedgehog had rolled into a ball, his little snout tucked in, several oak leaves impaled upon his ashy pointed spines. Here was supper, supper without hunting for it! A lucky one too, for with the approach of winter the hedgehogs were seeking out their hibernation quarters, and soon they would all be hidden and snug. The badger moved noisily through the golden fronds. The hedgehog heard her coming, and rolled into a tighter ball, and closed its eyes. Sally wasted no time; she hooked one strong black claw under the spiny ball and rolled it out of the bracken . . . When she had finished her meal (which took about twenty minutes), there was nothing left of poor Mr Prickles but a neatly cleaned-out, spiny jacket. Her strong black claws and terrible teeth had opened up the little animal as easily as a man opens an oyster, and you may be sure it tasted just as good to Sally. But the old sow badger had not come up the bank to eat hedgehogs. She had come for a very different purpose. There was hard work ahead of her, and she set about it at once.

Much of the bracken was brittle and broken. She began to rake this in towards her with her strong black forefeet with their sharp, curved claws. Before long she had amassed a sizeable roll of the dead fronds, and she pulled this after her, scooping it towards and under her, as an old woman carries a mattress. She grunted as she worked. Some of the bracken arranged itself in a wreath around her neck; but she was soon at the set, under the roots of the huge beeches.

Here on the sloping bank was a considerable mound of trampled clay tinged with the golden orange of the ironstone, a colour that had dyed the coats of all the badgers who had lived there down the centuries. Framed in the dark cavern of the hole, which was quite three feet across, was the black-and-white striped face of old Brock Bawson, her husband, her mate of the past nine years.

He was eleven years old, and much bigger than Sally. He weighed thirty-eight pounds, which is very large for a badger. He had a heavier, coarser coat, and his head was more masculine. In his time old Brock Bawson had killed a Hunt terrier, and his rump and muzzle bore honourable scars of battle. When he saw Sally coming down the well-beaten path under the box bushes he made a strange little purring noise deep in his throat, and stirred his tail from side to side. Sally trotted forward, leaving her bundle of bedding, and they rubbed noses (which is the way a badger kisses its mate). Then both animals began to take the bedding down into the set. They moved backwards, pulling the bracken after them with their curved forefeet. There was something quite human in the way they did this.

A few days before, their two cubs of the spring, who had been living with them in the set, had left and set up on their own in Gun Wood, a mile away; so now they had the place to themselves.

Soon all the bedding was taken down into the warm darkness. The black mouth of the hole became even darker, as night setled over the wood. The owls were calling continuously now, and a gibbous moon rode between the naked, sweeping traceries of the huge beeches.

The sides of these towering trees were stained dark where the rains had drained down their smooth grey-green skins, and among their knotted roots were little natural ponds full of moisture; for the bark of the beech is not porous. The water was foul and black, and was never drunk by either bird or animal.

The ancient citadel of the badgers under the roots of the great beeches in Bearshanks was a fortress indeed. Many a siege had been laid to it when badger digging was a favourite sport. Those massive inner roots, which roofed and floored the intricate passage-ways, still bore the scars of mattock and spade; just as a castle wall is scored by the marks of cannon ball and mangonel.

The badgers regarded man as their only enemy; for, though the owner of the estate had forbidden his keepers to disturb them, there were others, outside Bearshanks, who would have liked to see every fox, badger, every bird even, banished from their land. Chief of these was a 'go-ahead', modern farmer called Marney. He cut down all the trees in his hedgerows, because they shaded his corn crops; he uprooted the hedges themselves, because he regarded the cutting and laying of them as a shocking waste of labour and money; he dressed his corn with the new, deadly weed dressings which killed off the finches in their thousands (Bearshanks was littered with diminutive corpses). He would have no rookeries in his fields; and certainly, if the Bawsons had been upon his land, he would have gassed them long ago. He employed a shepherd-cum-bailiff who bore the curious name of 'Fiddler' Dean. His real name was James Dean. 'Fiddler' was a nickname, for he had the reputation, well justified, of being crafty and dishonest. Everyone knew him as Fiddler; even the farmers called him by his nickname. He was a sworn enemy of old Head, the keeper on the Bearshanks estate. The latter had caught him poaching several times, and he had had to go to court.

Of course old Head knew all about the Bawsons. Sometimes, on favourable nights, when on his rounds, he would hide up in the box bushes and watch them come out and play. Unlike many keepers he was an observant naturalist, and he knew every bird that flew, or sang, on the estate. That very summer he had seen a rare and exotic crested bird digging in the lawns by the Great House. It was a Hoopoe, and it had stayed about the park for several days.

If the intricate winding tunnels of the set had been laid in a straight line, they would have extended for close on one hundred yards. There were two storeys, an upper set of galleries and a lower, with connecting holes. The Bawsons kept to one end (that nearest the Great Pond), and another family sometimes moved into the other half. On these occasions everybody got on with everybody else, for badgers are by no means quarrelsome. Some years even rabbits and foxes shared the set. This may seem strange to us, but it was as if a truce was observed, though an occasional slip would occur, some 'little accident': a fox cub would disappear in a mysterious fashion, or a nest of young rabbits would vanish overnight – and perhaps old Sally or Brock Bawson would know something about it. In the main, however, they had the set to themselves.

Inside, beyond the great mound of excavated earth, the main entrance was cunningly constructed, and fortified – though no one looking at it would have guessed it. From the main heap at the entrance the floor of the tunnel, beaten hard by generations of heavy animals coming and going, sloped downwards at an angle for three feet or so and then levelled out, branching to right and left: right to the Bawson's apartments, left to the 'spare accommodation', sometimes occupied, but more often not. The roof of the burrow at this parting of the ways was composed of a huge, hawser-like root of beech, fully three feet thick, deeply gashed by an old mattock scar. Directly above it was a large and roomy chamber, large enough to hold two badgers lying side by side. It was, if you like, akin to a portcullis to a castle. When siege was laid and the terriers were sent in, the defenders could then take up positions up above, where they could grip the invading enemy by the back of the neck. Not even the hardiest, pluckiest terrier could live for a moment if squarely gripped by those interlocking jaws; for the badger has a terrible bite.

In one of the far recesses in this labyrinth of tunnels the badgers had made their winter bed of dried bracken fronds, moss, chestnut leaves, and grass; sweet-smelling woodland growth which had been dried by the autumn winds. All the old bedding had been cleared out a week previously. Sally Bawson had had a thorough autumn clean (as opposed to a spring clean); for it is in the late autumn and early winter that this most necessary work is undertaken. The old bedding had not been shuffled in a slovenly fashion up some side passage: it had been painstakingly transported, by pulling and rolling, to the main entrance, and there it had been pushed outside and spread down the clay bank under the box bushes. Some of it, when dried, could be used again when the winds and frosts had purified it.

In addition to all the autumn cleaning to be done, there was always work going on somewhere in the tunnel system – new corridors being dug, old ones being filled in. All the main digging is done with the powerful back claws. A dog steadies himself with his back legs to dig, but a badger uses his back legs as a man uses a shovel. When hard pressed by terriers he can move a lot of earth.

A cold night wind was blowing through Bearshanks. It whirled the red beech leaves up the slope of the bank, where they danced together in spirals as if they were alive. It ruffled the surface of the

Great Pond, until the steel grey ripples talked and clucked among the dead boughs of a huge pine which had fallen into the pond ten years before; it was here the moorhens built their nests in the spring of the year.

Brock Bawson came cautiously out of his front door and sat on his haunches like a little bear, trying the wind. Beyond the Great Pond, whose pale glimmering surface he could see between gaps in the dark, wind-tossed bushes, the ash poles rocked and clattered together. Up above, somewhere in the tall beeches, a bough creaked and squeaked at intervals; it was a plaintive, eerie noise, but the badgers had long ago become used to it.

Brock Bawson sat listening and sniffing for quite five minutes, slowly turning his black-and-white face this way and that. Then, deciding that all was safe, he settled down to a luxurious *scratch*. Down in the confined space of the set this was never possible; here on the threshold of their fortress he could really let himself go. You would have thought by the vigorous way he scratched that he was infested with vermin. But badgers are, in fact, cleanly creatures, and are not nearly so verminous as foxes; it was only one little flea which was bothering him.

He sat back now, scratching his tummy with his powerful back claws, his striped head held skywards with almost a grin on his grizzled old face. This operation took him more than six minutes. Finally he trundled down the bank to his 'smallest room', which was under the box bushes some forty yards from the set. He had dug a pit there and always used it, scratching earth over when he had finished. Then he climbed the steep bank and had a good roll in the bracken, all four feet in the air.

This exercise had made him hungry: he was ready for anything. After giving himself a vigorous shake, which started at his nose and finished with a final ecstatic shiver at his bob tail, he set off down the well-trodden hunting path, which wound away through the wood to where a fallen beech, covered with fungi, marked the point where several paths divided like the spread fingers of a hand.

He took the left track, which led into the oak wood and the ash pole spinney at the head of the pond. He spent some time there, rooting about among the ash stoles, digging for the roots which formed a large part of his winter diet. Above him the ash poles swayed and clattered; and fat wood pigeons roosting there, tossing like fishing smacks in a rough sea, opened their topaz eyes and saw the hunched, grey form busy below.

As he worked there came to him in one subtle puff of eddying wind, the overpowering 'gamey' smell of pheasant. It came from a cock bird which had gone to roost in the top of a hawthorn bush higher up the slope, near the crest of the bank. It sat hunched, its scaly claws locked securely round its perching branch, its long pointed tail drooped downwards, its head sunk deep in the glorious tinted mail of its chest. In that dark windy light the bird was as black as a crow, and you would never have guessed at the glorious golden colours upon its feathers which, in the winter sun, were so wondrously beautiful, like coloured chain mail or goldfish scales.

It was safe enough, far out of reach of the foxes, and sleeping deeply after a somewhat anxious day. The Duke had been shooting Bearshanks; all day long the shots had cracked and echoed: sharp, dry thunder claps on the frosty air, sounds which had roused the badgers from their sleep under the high bank. Empty orange-coloured cases lay all about the ridings close to the slender hazel wands, in the tops of which little numbered tickets told of where the 'guns' had stood.

This old cock had given them all the slip. Twice he had crouched in the bracken, listening to the 'tap tap' of the beaters' sticks and the sinister rustlings of hunting spaniels. Twice he had lain low, and they had passed him by; and he had run like a swift greyhound under the branching fronds, until he had got back through the beaters' line. But all was peace now, save for the clack and wheeze of the uneasy wind-tossed trees.

Brock Bawson left off digging for bluebell bulbs. Perhaps there was a fallen pheasant up there in the bracken. Always, after a shoot, there were dead and wounded birds which had been missed in the 'pick-up'; indeed, the badgers had come to associate the distant muffled popping of guns with the chance of a free meal.

This knowledge, perhaps, was in the back of his mind as he trundled upwards between the mossy ash stoles.

At that very instant, just as he was threading his way between two mossy stumps twenty yards from the hawthorn, a man was coming stealthily up the bank opposite. He was thickset, with a round, red, bad-tempered face. He wore a ragged coat, and had a khaki muffler round his neck. He held a rusty, double-barrelled gun at the ready. It was a stumpy weapon, for the barrels had been shortened ten inches so that the gun, when taken apart, could be concealed down his trousers in case of emergency. It was, of course, Fiddler Dean, who had poached these woods for years, and fared almost as well as the Duke himself in the matter of game (without the heavy cost of preserving, feeding, and guarding the tasty 'long tails'). Around his shoulders was slung a large canvas bag which already contained two warm bodies with their long, barred tails well crumpled and tucked out of sight.

At his heels, creeping forward step by step, was his valiant little rough-haired fox terrier, Chopper, who had nailed many a rabbit, hare, and wounded runner for his master, and who had the heart of a lion. He had been so well trained that if, as often happened, he was pursued, or confronted with a keeper, he would run away home all by himself. Fiddler had only to give a certain whistle, and off he would go under the briers and bracken, licketty split; and when Fiddler reached home, usually much out of breath but with plenty in the bag, Chopper would be waiting by the little white gate to his cottage.

Fiddler's small sharp eyes, set in his round, red, bad-tempered face, were quietly roving round the trees and bushes. He could see as well as an owl in the half darkness, far better indeed than Brock Bawson. He noted the swaying ash poles, the dark smudges of old pigeons' and rooks' nests, and the darker, smaller, more compact blobs of roosting birds – blackbirds, crows, and pigeons. Now and again he would stop, just as old Brock Bawson stopped, to listen and look; though his hearing was not a quarter as good as the badger's, and his sense of smell, in comparison, was non-existent.

In a moment he saw the familiar dark shape of the roosting pheasant in the hawthorn bush.

It was these lower bushes he searched with the greatest care. Pheasants favour them particularly as roosting places in winter, and prefer them to the taller trees, even to the thick firs. As soon as Fiddler saw the still, black, familiar shape, he stiffened and crept a foot or two nearer. Chopper only moved when his master moved; he knew the drill.

Now, whereas Fiddler had his eyes on the pheasant, he could not, of course, smell it; nor could he smell the musky odour of old Brock Bawson, who was at that instant trundling up the slope towards him. But Chopper smelt him. His hackles began to creep erect like the spines of a perch.

Slowly the sawn-off shot gun came to Fiddler's shoulder. In the dim light he saw the half-visible, swaying stems of the ash poles, and the hawthorn bush which, though much stouter, was moving a little in the wind. He was taking aim. Now his black-nailed finger crooked the trigger: he had the sleeping bird in his sights.

A dagger of orange flame, a desperate fluttering in the top of the hawthorn, and a body falling heavily to the bank below in a cloud of feathers!

As Fiddler ran forward to pick up his victim he was brought up sharp in astonishment. Not ten yards away, just below the bank, was Brock Bawson, his black-and-white striped head framed between two ash butts. Instinctively Fiddler raised his gun again. He had, so he thought, many a score to pay, not only to old Head the keeper, who, he knew, guarded and protected the badgers, but also to the badgers themselves, whom he blamed, quite mistakenly, for killing lambs at lambing time. A fox he would have spared, but a badger . . . Besides, the skin would be worth something! Just as he was about to fire, the white form of Chopper went flying down the bank.

Fiddler Dean swore loudly at the dog who, unable to restrain himself, had disappeared like a white bullet into a thick patch of briers beyond the thorn bush. Horrible sounds came from that bush: grunts, agonised yelps, a threshing of undergrowth! Fiddler ran forward just in time to see Chopper come backing out, barking furiously, with a dark streak of blood down one side of his face. Dodging away between the grey ash poles was the dimly-seen form of Brock Bawson. With a curse, the man raised his gun and let fly his second cartridge.

Brock Bawson felt a violent, numbing impact on his rump, which knocked him sideways. One single number six shot had struck him, but it was only a glancing blow and the range was over sixty yards.

Before Chopper could gather himself for pursuit (for not even so fearsome an opponent as a badger could daunt him), Fiddler made a grab at his collar and held him clear off the ground, choking, writhing, and growling. Then he picked up the dead pheasant and thrust it into his sack. 'Blast that badger, I'll get him one of these days!'

The Hour of Triumph

E.B. WHITE

**Wilbur, the white pig, is rescued from the usual fate
of his species by the farmer's daughter, Fern. Accompanied by his faithful friend, the spider Charlotte A.
Cavatica, he travels to the Fair to take part in a Grand
Pig Contest ...**

'Special announcement!' said the loud speaker in a pompous
voice. 'The management of the Fair takes great pleasure in
presenting Mr Homer L. Zuckerman and his famous pig. The
truck bearing this extraordinary animal is now approaching the
infield. Kindly stand back and give the truck room to proceed! In
a few moments the pig will be unloaded in the special judging ring
in front of the grandstand, where a special award will be made.
Will the crowd please make way and let the truck pass. Thank
you.'

Wilbur trembled when he heard this speech. He felt happy but
dizzy. The truck crept along slowly in low speed. Crowds of
people surrounded it, and Mr Arable had to drive very carefully
in order not to run over anybody. At last he managed to reach the
judges' stand. Avery jumped out and lowered the tailgate.

'I'm scared to death,' whispered Mrs Zuckerman. 'Hundreds of people are looking at us.'

'Cheer up,' replied Mrs Arable, 'this is fun.'

'Unload your pig, please!' said the loud speaker.

'Altogether, now, boys!' said Mr Zuckerman. Several men stepped forward from the crowd to help lift the crate. Avery was the busiest helper of all.

'Tuck your shirt in, Avery!' cried Mrs Zuckerman. 'And tighten your belt. Your pants are coming down.'

'Can't you see I'm busy?' replied Avery in disgust.

'Look!' cried Fern, pointing. 'There's Henry!'

'Don't shout, Fern!' said her mother. 'And don't point!'

'Can't I *please* have some money?' asked Fern. 'Henry invited me to go on the Ferris wheel again, only I don't think he has any money left. He ran out of money.'

Mrs Arable opened her handbag. 'Here,' she said. 'Here is forty cents. Now don't get lost! And be back at our regular meeting-place by the pigpen very soon!'

Fern raced off, ducking and dodging through the crowd, in search of Henry.

'The Zuckerman pig is now being taken from his crate,' boomed the voice of the loud speaker. 'Stand by for an announcement!'

Templeton crouched under the straw at the bottom of the crate. 'What a lot of nonsense!' muttered the rat. 'What a lot of fuss about nothing!'

Over in the pigpen, silent and alone, Charlotte rested. Her two front legs embraced the egg sac. Charlotte could hear everything that was said on the loud speaker. The words gave her courage. This was her hour of triumph.

As Wilbur came out of the crate, the crowd clapped and cheered. Mr Zuckerman took off his cap and bowed. Lurvy pulled his big handkerchief from his pocket and wiped the sweat from the back of his neck. Avery knelt in the dirt by Wilbur's side, busily stroking him and showing off. Mrs Zuckerman and Mrs Arable stood on the running board of the truck.

The Hour of Triumph

'Ladeez and gentlemen,' said the loud speaker 'we now present Mr Homer L. Zuckerman's distinguished pig. The fame of this unique animal has spread to the far corners of the earth, attracting many valuable tourists to our great State. Many of you will recall that never-to-be-forgotten day last summer when the writing appeared mysteriously on the spider's web in Mr Zuckerman's barn, calling the attention of all and sundry to the fact that this pig was completely out of the ordinary. This miracle has never been fully explained, although learned men have visited the Zuckerman pigpen to study and observe the phenomenon. In the last analysis, we simply know that we are dealing with supernatural forces here, and we should all feel proud and grateful. In the words of the spider's web, ladies and gentlemen, this is some pig.'

Wilbur blushed. He stood perfectly still and tried to look his best.

'This magnificent animal,' continued the loud speaker, 'is truly terrific. Look at him, ladies and gentlemen! Note the smoothness and whiteness of the coat, observe the spotless skin, the healthy pink glow of ears and snout.'

'It's the buttermilk,' whispered Mrs Arable to Mrs Zuckerman.

'Note the general radiance of this animal! Then remember the day when the word "radiant" appeared clearly on the web. Whence came this mysterious writing? Not from the spider, we can rest assured of that. Spiders are very clever at weaving their webs, but needless to say spiders cannot write.'

'Oh, they can't, can't they?' murmured Charlotte to herself.

'Ladeez and gentlemen,' continued the loud speaker, 'I must not take any more of your valuable time. On behalf of the governors of the Fair, I have the honour of awarding a special prize of twenty-five dollars to Mr Zuckerman, together with a handsome bronze medal suitably engraved, in token of our appreciation of the part played by this pig – this radiant, this terrific, this humble pig – in attracting so many visitors to our great County Fair.'

Wilbur had been feeling dizzier and dizzier through this long, complimentary speech. When he heard the crowd begin to cheer and clap again, he suddenly fainted away. His legs collapsed, his mind went blank, and he fell to the ground, unconscious.

'What's wrong?' asked the loud speaker. 'What's going on, Zuckerman? What's the trouble with your pig?'

Avery was kneeling by Wilbur's head, stroking him. Mr Zuckerman was dancing about, fanning him with his cap.

'He's all right,' cried Mr Zuckerman. 'He gets these spells. He's modest and can't stand praise.'

'Well, we can't give a prize to a *dead* pig,' said the loud speaker. 'It's never been done.'

'He isn't dead,' hollered Zuckerman. 'He's fainted. He gets embarrassed easily. Run for some water, Lurvy!'

Lurvy sprang from the judges' ring and disappeared.

Templeton poked his head from the straw. He noticed that the end of Wilbur's tail was within reach. Templeton grinned. 'I'll tend to this,' he chuckled. He took Wilbur's tail in his mouth and bit it, just as hard as he could bite. The pain revived Wilbur. In a flash he was back on his feet.

'Ouch!' he screamed.

'Hooray!' yelled the crowd. 'He's up! The pig's up! Good work, Zuckerman! That's some pig!' Everyone was delighted. Mr Zuckerman was the most pleased of all. He sighed with relief. Nobody had seen Templeton. The rat had done his work well.

And now one of the judges climbed into the ring with the prizes. He handed Mr Zuckerman two ten-dollar bills and a five-dollar bill. Then he tied the medal around Wilbur's neck. Then he shook hands with Mr Zuckerman while Wilbur blushed. Avery put out his hand and the judge shook hands with him, too. The crowd cheered. A photographer took Wilbur's picture.

A great feeling of happiness swept over the Zuckermans and the Arables. This was the greatest moment in Mr Zuckerman's life. It is deeply satisfying to win a prize in front of a lot of people.

As Wilbur was being shoved back into the crate, Lurvy came charging through the crowd carrying a pail of water. His eyes had a wild look. Without hesitating a second, he dashed the water at Wilbur. In his excitement he missed his aim, and the water splashed all over Mr Zuckerman and Avery. They got soaking wet.

'For goodness' sake!' bellowed Mr Zuckerman, who was really drenched. 'What ails you, Lurvy? Can't you see the pig is all right?'

'You asked for water,' said Lurvy meekly.

'I didn't ask for a shower bath,' said Mr Zuckerman. The crowd roared with laughter. Finally Mr Zuckerman had to laugh, too. And of course Avery was tickled to find himself so wet, and he immediately started to act like a clown. He pretended he was taking a shower bath; he made faces and danced around and rubbed imaginary soap under his armpits. Then he dried himself with an imaginary towel.

'Avery, stop it!' cried his mother. 'Stop showing off!'

But the crowd loved it. Avery heard nothing but the applause. He liked being a clown in a ring, with everybody watching, in front of a grandstand. When he discovered there was still a little water left in the bottom of the pail, he raised the pail high in the air and dumped the water on himself and made faces. The children in the grandstand screamed with appreciation.

At last things calmed down. Wilbur was loaded into the truck. Avery was led from the ring by his mother and placed on the seat of the truck to dry off. The truck, driven by Mr Arable, crawled slowly back to the pigpen. Avery's wet trousers made a big wet spot on the seat.

Charlotte and Wilbur were alone. The families had gone to look for Fern. Templeton was alseep. Wilbur lay resting after the excitement and strain of the ceremony. His medal still hung from his neck; by looking out of the corner of his eye he could see it.

'Charlotte,' said Wilbur after a while, 'why are you so quiet?'

'I like to sit still,' she said. 'I've always been rather quiet.'

'Yes, but you seem specially so today. Do you feel all right?'

'A little tired, perhaps. But I feel peaceful. Your success in the ring this morning was, to a small degree, *my* success. Your future is assured. You will live, secure and safe, Wilbur. Nothing can harm you now. These autumn days will shorten and grow cold.

The leaves will shake loose from the trees and fall. Christmas will come, then the snows of winter. You will live to enjoy the beauty of the frozen world, for you mean a great deal to Zuckerman and he will not harm you, ever. Winter will pass, the days will lengthen, the ice will melt in the pasture pond. The song sparrow will return and sing, the frogs will awake, the warm wind will blow again. All these sights and sounds and smells will be yours to enjoy, Wilbur – this lovely world, these golden days . . .'

Charlotte stopped. A moment later a tear came to Wilbur's eye. 'Oh, Charlotte,' he said. 'To think that when I first met you I thought you were cruel and bloodthirsty!'

When he recovered from his emotion, he spoke again.

'Why did you do all this for me?' he asked. 'I don't deserve it. I've never done anything for you.'

'You have been my friend,' replied Charlotte. 'That in itself is a tremendous thing. I wove my webs for you because I liked you. After all, what's a life anyway? We're born, we live a little while, we die. A spider's life can't help being something of a mess, with all this trapping and eating flies. By helping you, perhaps I was trying to lift up my life a trifle. Heaven knows anyone's life can stand a little of that.'

'Well,' said Wilbur, 'I'm no good at making speeches. I haven't got your gift for words. But you have saved me, Charlotte, and I would gladly give my life for you – I really would.'

'I'm sure you would. And I thank you for your generous sentiments.'

'Charlotte,' said Wilbur. 'We're all going home today. The Fair is almost over. Won't it be wonderful to be back home in the barn cellar again with the sheep and the geese? Aren't you anxious to get home?'

For a moment Charlotte said nothing. Then she spoke in a voice so low Wilbur could hardly hear the words.

'I will not be going back to the barn,' she said.

Wilbur leapt to his feet. 'Not going back?' he cried. 'Charlotte, what are you talking about?'

'I'm done for,' she replied. 'In a day or two I'll be dead. I

He tied the medal around Wilbur's neck

haven't even strength enough to climb down into the crate. I doubt if I have enough silk in my spinneret to lower me to the ground.'

Hearing this, Wilbur threw himself down in an agony of pain and sorrow. Great sobs racked his body. He heaved and grunted with desolation. 'Charlotte,' he moaned. 'Charlotte! My true friend!'

'Come now, let's not make a scene,' said the spider. 'Be quiet, Wilbur. Stop thrashing about!'

'But I can't *stand* it,' shouted Wilbur. 'I won't leave you here alone to die. If you're going to stay here I shall stay, too.'

'Don't be ridiculous,' said Charlotte. 'You can't stay here. Zuckerman and Lurvy and John Arable and the others will be back any minute now, and they'll shove you into that crate and away you'll go. Besides, it wouldn't make any sense for you to stay. There would be no one to feed you. The Fair Grounds will soon be empty and deserted.'

Wilbur was in a panic. He raced round and round the pen. Suddenly he had an idea – he thought of the egg sac and the five hundred and fourteen little spiders that would hatch in the spring. If Charlotte herself was unable to go home to the barn, at least he must take her children along.

Wilbur rushed to the front of his pen. He put his front feet up on the top board and gazed around. In the distance he saw the Arables and the Zuckermans approaching. He knew he would have to act quickly.

'Where's Templeton?' he demanded.

'He's in that corner, under the straw, asleep,' said Charlotte.

Wilbur rushed over, pushed his strong snout under the rat, and tossed him into the air.

'Templeton!' screamed Wilbur. 'Pay attention!'

The rat, surprised out of a sound sleep, looked first dazed then disgusted.

'What kind of monkeyshine is this?' he growled. 'Can't a rat catch a wink of sleep without being rudely popped into the air?'

'Listen to me!' cried Wilbur. 'Charlotte is very ill. She has only a short time to live. She cannot accompany us home, because of her condition. Therefore, it is absolutely necessary that I take her egg sac with me. I can't reach it, and I can't climb. You are the only one that can get it. There's not a second to be lost. The people are coming – they'll be here in no time. Please, please, *please*, Templeton, climb up and get the egg sac.'

The rat yawned. He straightened his whiskers. Then he looked up at the egg sac.

'So!' he said, in disgust. 'So it's old Templeton to the rescue again, is it? Templeton do this, Templeton do that, Templeton please run down to the dump and get me a magazine clipping, Templeton please lend me a piece of string so I can spin a web.'

'Oh, hurry! said Wilbur. 'Hurry up, Templeton!'

But the rat was in no hurry. He began imitating Wilbur's voice.

'So it's "Hurry up, Templeton", is it?' he said. 'Ho, ho. And what thanks do I ever get for these services, I would like to know? Never a kind word for old Templeton, only abuse and wisecracks and side remarks. Never a kind word for a rat.'

'Templeton,' said Wilbur in desperation, 'if you don't stop talking and get busy, all will be lost, and I will die of a broken heart. Please climb up!'

Templeton lay back in the straw. Lazily he placed his forepaws behind his head and crossed his knees, in an attitude of complete relaxation.

'Die of a broken heart,' he mimicked. 'How touching! My, my! I notice that it's always me you come to when in trouble. But I've never heard of anyone's heart breaking on *my* account. Oh, no. Who cares anything about old Templeton?'

'Get up!' screamed Wilbur. 'Stop acting like a spoiled child!'

Templeton grinned and lay still. 'Who made trip after trip to the dump?' he asked. 'Why, it was old Templeton! Who saved Charlotte's life by scaring that Arable boy away with a rotten goose egg? Bless my soul, I believe it was old Templeton. Who bit your tail and got you back on your feet this morning after you had fainted in front of the crowd? Old Templeton. Has it ever occurred to you that I'm sick of running errands and doing favours? What do you think I am, anyway, a rat-of-all-work?'

Wilbur was desperate. The people were coming. And the rat was failing him. Suddenly he remembered Templeton's fondness for food.

'Templeton,' he said, 'I will make you a solemn promise. Get Charlotte's egg sac for me, and from now on I will let you eat first, when Lurvy slops me. I will let you have your choice of everything in the trough and I won't touch a thing until you're through.'

The rat sat up. 'You mean that?' he said.

'I promise. I cross my heart.'

'All right, it's a deal,' said the rat. He walked to the wall and started to climb. His stomach was still swollen from last night's gorge. Groaning and complaining, he pulled himself slowly to the ceiling. He crept along till he reached the egg sac. Charlotte moved aside for him. She was dying, but she still had strength enough to move a little. Then Templeton bared his long ugly teeth and began snipping the threads that fastened the sac to the ceiling. Wilbur watched from below.

'Use extreme care!' he said. 'I don't want a single one of those eggs harmed.'

'Thith thtuff thticks in my mouth,' complained the rat, 'It'th worth than caramel candy.'

But Templeton worked away at the job, and managed to cut the sac adrift and carry it to the ground, where he dropped it in front of Wilbur. Wilbur heaved a great sigh of relief.

'Thank you, Templeton,' he said. 'I will never forget this as long as I live.'

'Neither will I,' said the rat, picking his teeth. 'I feel as though I'd eaten a spool of thread. Well, home we go!'

Templeton crept into the crate and buried himself in the straw. He got out of sight just in time. Lurvy and John Arable and Mr Zuckerman came along at that moment, followed by Mrs Arable and Mrs Zuckerman and Avery and Fern. Wilbur had already decided how he would carry the egg sac – there was only one way possible. He carefully took the little bundle in his mouth and held it there on top of his tongue. He remembered what Charlotte had told him – that the sac was waterproof and strong. It felt funny on his tongue and made him drool a bit. And of course he couldn't say anything. But as he was being shoved into the crate, he looked up at Charlotte and gave her a wink. She knew he was saying good-bye in the only way he could. And she knew her children were safe.

'Good-bye!' she whispered. Then she summoned all her strength and waved one of her front legs at him.

She never moved again. Next day, as the Ferris wheel was being taken apart and the race horses were being loaded into vans and the entertainers were packing up their belongings and driving away in their trailers, Charlotte died. The Fair Grounds were soon deserted. The shed and buildings were empty and forlorn. The infield was littered with bottles and trash. Nobody, of the hundreds of people that had visited the Fair, knew that a grey spider had played the most important part of all. No one was with her when she died.

The Animals of Farthing Wood

COLIN DANN

A group of animals, exiled from their natural home by the invasion of bulldozers, are striving to reach the safety of the distant White Deer Park. Danger is at its height as the company needs to cross town in a violent rainstorm . . .

The animals spent the remaining few hours before darkness out of sight under the thick hedge. When it was dark enough, they set off singly, or in small groups, to forage and satisfy their ravenous hunger. Fox told them they could have all the time they wanted to accomplish this very necessary and enjoyable task, as they were to have a day's complete rest before continuing their journey through the nearby town. Only Kestrel and Whistler were left in the meadow, intermittently chatting and dozing through the night. Their needs had been satisfied while the daylight held out; Kestrel had hunted from the air, while Whistler had flown a considerable distance before finding a stream where he could indulge his favourite pastime of fishing.

Mole, too, had no need to leave the meadow. He merely looked

256

for a soft piece of ground, and with a speed greatly accelerated by his hunger, dug himself towards his dinner.

On the animals' return, they went straight to sleep in the thickest part of the hedge and slept the clock round until dusk the following day.

They woke in stages, completely refreshed, and with healthy appetites again. This time Fox told them to eat enough to last them for the next stage of the journey only, and to be as quick as they could about it, as their route now ran through the town, which they could only risk crossing at the dead of night.

When they were ready to leave, the night had become several degrees cooler, and a gusty breeze was blowing. Toad had told them that if they were careful there was not a lot to worry about, as it was quite a small town and had been very quiet when he had passed through it before during the night hours. At his direction Fox avoided the main street, but led the animals along a series of lanes and alleys, each of which was bordered by high brick walls.

The party kept close against these walls, on the darker side of the alleys, and were really quite inconspicuous as the passages were very murky and badly lit. When they came out of the last lane some spots of rain began to fall. This increased very quickly to a heavy shower, but the animals felt it was to their advantage, as the few humans who might be abroad would be looking for shelter.

'The next bit's the worst,' said Toad. 'We have to cross the town square. But don't worry; it should be deserted at this time of night.'

They crossed the road that lay in front of them and entered the square from one corner via an empty shopping colonnade. This square contained an island of flagstones and trees, surrounded on all sides by roads, pavements and shops.

They quickly crossed to the island, and at once froze. Under a pair of lime trees, whose thick foliage afforded excellent shelter from the rain, a group of about a dozen humans, mostly courting couples, was standing.

'No use stopping, Fox,' whispered Toad, 'You must go on. They're not likely to do anything.'

Fox and Vixen broke into a trot, and the other animals followed suit as they passed the lime trees, and made their way to the far end of the island. Luckily the dim lighting in the square and the hard rain combined to screen the column of animals from detection.

They left the square and the hard rain combined to screen the column of animals from detection.

They left the square and, turning a corner, found themselves in a market-place. Empty crates and boxes and small heaps of straw, paper and squashed fruit and cabbage-leaves lined the sides of this deserted spot, normally so crowded with eager, jostling shoppers.

'Ugh, what filth these humans make,' growled Adder, as he slithered across the muddy cobbles.

The rain fell harder and harder, and the wind dashed it against their faces in squalls, almost blinding them.

'We can't take much more of this, Fox,' Fieldmouse called from the midst of the soaked, struggling mass of mice.

'It's not much further now,' Toad encouraged them. 'Once we're out of the town we can stop.'

The animals made the best progress they could, and eventually the last shop, the last pavement, the last house was passed. Now that they were able to stop for a rest, they did not at all want to do so. There was absolutely no shelter from the stinging rain. They were surrounded by open playing-fields, devoid of trees or any kind of wind-break.

'This is dreadful,' wailed Squirrel. 'Our fur is so drenched and matted together, we'll all catch our deaths.'

'We came through a storm before,' Hedgehog observed. 'I don't think any casualties were suffered.'

'Nevertheless, it's no less uncomfortable the second time,' Squirrel insisted.

'What about us?' said Vole. 'We voles, and the fieldmice, will be drowned if we stay here in the open.'

Fox looked all round, his brow furrowed as he strained to make out some object in the vicinity where they could take shelter.

'I can't see *anything*,' he said in despair to Toad.

'I can,' said Vixen. 'It looks like a church. At any rate, it's a big building – on the other side of these fields – look!'

Fox could just make out a dark mass looming in the near distance.

'Come on, my gallant little friends,' he urged. 'One last effort and we're home and dry.'

'Just to be dry would be something,' Squirrel muttered.

'Supposing it's shut?' said the pessimistic Vole.

'If it *is* a church there's sure to be a porch we can shelter under,' said Fox, trying to sound confident.

'Well, don't let's waste time,' said Squirrel, in a weary sort of whine.

Fox started off across the fields, Vixen at his side, with Badger, the hares, Weasel and the rabbits close behind. The squirrels, their usually busy tails plastered with wet, were a sorry sight as they ran nimbly in their wake. The hedgehogs, whom rain did not bother very much, and the soaked voles and fieldmice were last, save for Adder.

There was a second hazard for the mice, for, because of their size, the heaviness of the drops was an additional hardship. Yet the sight of the church looming nearer and nearer drove them on, with its promise of eventual comfort and shelter.

So the animals arrived beneath the building's towering dark walls, tired, cold, soaked and shivering. The mice were the last to arrive, uttering piteous little cries of misery.

Fox looked at them with a forlorn expression. 'I . . . I'm afraid there's no porch,' he told them hesitantly.

Some of the voles and fieldmice broke down at the news. To have come through all they had, and then to find no relief, was too hard to bear. They huddled together on the muddy ground and sobbed heartbreakingly.

'But just a minute, my little friends,' said Fox, 'perhaps we can get inside. We're not beaten yet. Badger, look after them. I'll have a scout round.' After shaking his saturated coat with a single vigorous movement, Fox began inspecting the walls.

The animals watched him despairingly, while the cruel rain relentlessly lashed down as if it were trying to beat them into the ground. Tawny Owl flew up to the steeple and took up a perch in the belfry, where it was dry. Kestrel joined him, but Whistler remained on the ground standing with his great wings extended as an umbrella over the cowering mice.

Fox disappeared round the other side of the church.

'How much longer will this rain continue?' groaned Rabbit. 'I'm sure we shall all end up being drowned.' He looked with distaste at the Toad who, alone amongst the animals, was enjoying every minute of the rainfall, and was busy splashing about in a large puddle.

'Extraordinary habits he has,' Rabbit muttered to Hare.

'Yes,' Hare replied, 'water is certainly a tonic to Toad. Just look how his skin glistens – as if he had put on a new one.'

A shout from Fox made them all prick up their ears.

'Quickly! Round here!' he was calling from round the corner. 'We're in luck!'

In one mass the party of animals scurried round to the other side. Fox proudly indicated a greyish shape that was draped against the brickwork.

'Well, what is it?' Badger asked, almost irritably.

'It's a hole!' said Fox triumphantly.

'There's no hole there,' said Rabbit peevishly. 'What have you . . .?'

'Of course, you can't see the hole,' Fox interrupted him. 'They've covered it with this material' – he indicated the greyish shape which in fact was canvas – 'but we can soon get behind that!'

He at once began to paw an opening, tugging the material away from the wall.

'Ooh, there *is* a hole!' cried one of the fieldmice.

Fox climbed over the broken brickwork that framed the hole and looked back at the animals, all of whom were still watching him, except Vixen who had at once followed him inside.

'What are you waiting for?' Fox asked. 'It's dry in here. It smells strongly of humans, but it's as dark as Badger's set. There's no one about.'

The animals needed no second bidding, and they scrambled together through the hold, Whistler stepping awkwardly after them in his upright gait. Adder was the last to slither between the canvas and the bricks.

'I think Tawny Owl and Kestrel ought to be with us,' Fox said. 'Whistler, will you fetch them?'

The heron cheerfully stepped back into the rain, and soon the three birds appeared together on the threshold.

'Are we complete?' asked Fox, beginning to see through the gloom.

'No,' Adder drawled. 'It seems that Toad finds the rain preferable to our company.'

'Oh, drat the fellow!' exclaimed Fox. 'All right, I'll go this time. Vixen dear, would you help Badger look for a suitable hiding-place? We want somewhere dry and inconspicuous, and free from draughts.'

'But I can't see anything, Fox,' she protested mildly.

'We could do with your glow-worms now, Badger,' chuckled Weasel.

'Leave it to me,' pleaded Mole. 'Darkness is nothing to me. I'm used to it. I prefer it to sunlight really, you know,' he added, trying to impress. 'Oh yes, the darker the better.'

'No wonder he's as blind as a bat,' said Adder maliciously, under his breath.

'He's just trying to be helpful,' said Badger pointedly, rounding on the snake. 'But, of course, *you* wouldn't understand that.'

Adder remained unabashed.

Mole led the party, at a necessarily slow pace, down one of the side aisles. The animals' feet produced a variety of clipping and padding noises against the worn stone floor, while Adder's scaly body made a dry, swishing rasp as he writhed along behind them. In the almost total darkness the animals had no idea where they were going, and followed the confident Mole quite blindly.

The little velvet-coated animal went forward purposefully,

using his instinct to find the darkest corner of a thoroughly dark building. He turned a few corners, and threaded the line of animals between pews, and eventually stopped in the narrow space behind the organ. Here it really was pitch-dark, but in its musty seclusion it was as dry as dust and completely sheltered from any unwelcome draughts.

'Where have you brought us, Mole?' asked Badger.

'I don't know,' Mole replied, 'but it ... um ... *seems* all right.'

Fox, in the meantime, had brought Toad into the church, and was sniffing and groping about for a sign of his friends.

'Do you see anything?' Toad asked him.

'No,' he replied, 'but I can smell their damp bodies.'

An unexpected flapping of wings above them made them both jump, but Tawny Owl had appeared to guide them to the hiding-place.

'Good old Owl,' said Fox, trying to mask his momentary fright. 'Well, we should all get a good rest tonight.'

'I'm not so sure I approve of sheltering in a place that seems to have such a magnetic influence over humans,' Tawny Owl remarked. 'But I suppose there is no choice.'

'It's certainly better than being out in the rain,' Fox laughed.

'Personally, I don't like these very dry spots,' Toad said, shaking his head. 'I always wonder if my skin might crack.'

'Nonsense,' Fox told him. 'Anyway, it's only for a day. I should have thought you were tired.'

'I am,' admitted Toad, as Tawny Owl alighted on the back of a pew and then fluttered to the ground.

When all the animals were together, they began to ask Toad in sleepy voices how far away they now were from their destination.

'About a day's travelling, I should think,' he answered. 'However,' he added, as assorted squeals of delight and excitement were heard, 'I can't be absolutely sure, because we've gone a little bit out of the way in our search for shelter. I didn't ever come past this church before, but I do know that, having come through that town, the Park is now very, very close.'

'Do you think we'll have any difficulty in getting back on the correct route?' asked Hedgehog.

'Of course not,' Toad said cheerfully. 'It only needs Kestrel to do a little flying some time tomorrow, provided this rain has stopped. Why, I'm sure he could see the Park from here.'

'As soon as it's light enough ...' murmured Kestrel, as he tucked his head under his wing.

When he emerged from the building early the next morning, leaving his friends sleeping, Kestrel was pleased to see the countryside looking so clear and fresh. The air was cool and crisp, and the sky blue again, as if washed clean of clouds. The wet grass gleamed and sparkled in the sunlight.

Kestrel flew lazily aloft and stretched his wing muscles. After enjoying a series of swoops and dives, he began to look around him, at the landscape. Sure enough, in one direction, an area of parkland was easily discernible. Kestrel could see stretches of fencing and rolling grassy country, with dark patches that he recognized as bracken, and clusters of trees that were copses or woods. The Edible Frogs' pond was not visible from Kestrel's position, but he decided to fly and have a closer look. There was no longer any doubt as to the park's identity when, as he approached he saw several white blobs moving over the grass, which gradually took form and shape as the very white deer that gave the park its name. As he drew near this place that the party of animals and birds had been struggling to reach for so long, Kestrel felt that their arrival, which now seemed inevitable, should be suitably memorable, and a plan began to form in his mind.

Back in the church, his friends were not feeling so confident of finally reaching their new home or even of getting safely away from the building, for daylight had brought workmen along to continue their repair work on the broken wall. The sound of human tools banging and chipping at the very place they had expected to use as their exit and, worse still, raucous human voices, awoke and seriously alarmed the animals. In reply to a barrage of questions all more or less encompassing the one demand of what was to be done next, Fox replied grimly that for the present they should sit tight.

'That's all very well,' said Rabbit. 'But what if those men wall us in?'

'There are such things as doors in churches, you know,' Tawny Owl remarked testily.

Rabbit felt foolish, although he tried not to show it. In this he failed dismally. 'Anyway,' he said sullenly, 'there's no knowing when the doors will be opened.'

'Oh, it won't be long.' Fox tried to sound unconcerned. 'Somebody's bound to come sooner or later, with these workmen here.'

'Actually, Rabbit has got a point,' said Hare, surprising his distant cousin by siding with him for once. 'If a human *does* come to open one of the doors, we might well be too slow to get out before it's closed again, and in any case he's hardly likely to hold it open for us while we file through.'

Fox started to think and, as he had begun to do more and more, consulted Vixen.

'It's safer to stay here at the moment,' the animals heard her say to him in a low voice.

Fox looked round at his companions, studying every face. 'Does anyone want to make a dash for it now?' he asked.

No one replied, but there were sounds of shifting feet and one or two coughs.

'Vixen and I are quite ready to accompany any of you who wish to chance it now, rather than finding we might have left it too late,' Fox said.

'We'll probably have a better opportunity later,' said Badger in his soothing voice. 'I think an attempt to leave now might prove to be rather foolhardy.'

The concerted murmurs of the party seemed to express approval of Badger's opinion.

'Then it's decided,' said Fox. 'We wait.'

The noise of the workmen continued unabated, and the animals remained in their hiding-place, listening with sinking hearts to the ceaseless hammering and shouts, and wondering what Kestrel was doing. After some hours, during which time none of them spoke very much, the noise came to an end. Fox looked at each of his companions significantly, as if mentally warning them to be ready.

They waited for the voices of the workmen, who were obviously preparing to leave, to diminish. The light inside the church, filtering through the coloured panes, and striking straight through the clear glass, had moved gradually round the building. A shaft of sunlight, illuminating a thousand dancing motes of dust, now shone obliquely on to the organ pipes, in front of which the crouching animals were all geared for flight.

The rough voices were retreating; there seemed to be only a matter of seconds longer to wait, when a swooping form suddenly alighted in front of them. Kestrel had returned.

'It's no good,' he said immediately. 'Stay where you are. There's a throng of people on the way here, and two of them are just about to open the main door.'

Even as he finished speaking the noises of a handle being turned, followed by creaking hinges, reached their ears. Instinctively they all cowered closer to the floor. New, quieter human voices could be heard.

'What about the wall?' whispered Fox. 'Surely we could still make a dash for it before any more arrive?'

'No, it's hopeless.' Kestrel shook his head. 'They've bricked up the lower part of the hole completely. There's only a small gap left now, about four feet from the ground.'

'Oh no!' Fox groaned. 'We're stuck fast.'

'But we can't remain here,' protested Hedgehog, in an agitated voice. 'It's not dark any more. We'll be discovered in no time.'

'On the contrary,' Fox told him. 'We're as safe as we can be under the circumstances. We're screened all round pretty well, and there is no room for any humans to come close to us. And don't forget, they don't know we're here. They won't come looking for us.'

'I'm sorry I didn't leave with you now, Kestrel,' said Whistler, who always slept well and had not woken as early as the hawk.

'You needn't have come back,' Fox remarked. 'Now you're stuck with us.'

'Kestrel's a good friend,' said Mole.

'Well, I didn't want you to move from here,' the hawk said, smiling in a pleased way. 'I thought I might have been too late to stop you.'

More voices came through the open door, and more steps echoed on the stone floor. There was a scraping of chairs, and one set of footsteps came nearer and nearer to the animals and then stopped just the other side of the organ which sheltered them. A sound of rustling papers and the varied noises of someone settling himself into a seat were then audible, so that they knew one of the humans was very close.

'Just when we're so close to home,' muttered Toad.

His unconscious use of the word 'home' to describe somewhere none of his companions, except Kestrel, had ever seen, acted as a tonic on the whole party. It reminded them all with a peculiar force that not only was their long journey nearly over, but that in a matter of hours their lives would no longer be governed by the factors of how far they could walk in one day, or how to negotiate some difficult obstacle. They all realized that their escape from the church represented the very last of the obstacles which they had to surmount, before they could begin to enjoy a normal and peaceful life again – something they had almost forgotten how to do. So the thought of that home, and all it meant to each weary creature in his own particular way, produced a resolve, stronger than at any time on their journey, that they would not be stopped now from reaching it by any power, human or otherwise. Each animal sensed this fresh upsurge of moral strength in his companions, and felt his confidence rise.

'We can wait a little longer,' said Weasel philosophically.

'It's only a matter of time,' remarked Mole, who was already feeling pleased at Fox's indirect compliment on the hiding-place he had found them.

'As far as I can see it's a *waste* of time,' whispered Adder. But the party settled down silently, while the echoing footsteps and the low-pitched human voices increased in number.

Finally the shuffling of feet, and the creaking and scraping of pews and chairs, and even the whispering voices subsided, and it seemed as if the church and its people had entered a period of quiet, of expectancy.

The animals had all begun to think that their ordeal might, after all, not be so grim when, with a deafening, blaring shock, the organ pipes behind them suddenly pealed forth.

The noise was so terrifying and sudden that the whole party of animals leapt up, panic-stricken, and scattered all over the church in a sort of zoological eruption.

The birds flew up to the rafters where the terrible sounds of the organ reverberated tremendously, causing them to fly in every direction in their efforts to escape the noise.

Fox and Vixen dashed straight down the nave in blind terror, and more by luck than judgement found themselves at the open door. The voles and fieldmice, the rabbits and hares and the squirrels scurried to every corner, some of them getting under chairs, producing shrieks and screams of alarm from the female congregation. The men, no less astounded, uttered gruff shouts and exclamations, while the Vicar, who was about to perform a wedding ceremony, dropped his book as Badger lumbered against his legs. Weasel, Mole, Toad and the hedgehogs made for the opposite end of the church, each taking a different and completely motiveless route, their only thought being to get away from that horrifying machine. Only Adder, fortunately for him, was not noticed as he slid his slender body along every hidden crevice and crack he could find to reach the door.

For a few moments pandemonium held sway, but with the ceasing of the wedding music by the astonished organist, the animals' panic was calmed sufficiently, to turn their flight towards the one safe direction.

With the gradual disappearance of the swifter-running animals, the congregation's initial amazement changed to excitement, and soon a general buzz of chatter filled the church.

As Fox and Vixen hurtled forth from the doorway, the bride, with her escorting father, and bridesmaids, were just approaching it. They stopped dead, speechless, only to see, after a short interval, a badger, an assortment of rabbits, squirrels and hares and a weasel gallop out of the door and race off in the direction the two foxes had taken.

The bride looked towards her father, as if silently asking him if this were some sort of omen for her imminent marriage, but his amazement prevented him from forming any words and he merely stammered incoherently. Eventually he seemed to recall their reason for being there, and he began to lead his daughter forward again.

As they were about to enter the church, two birds shot past like bullets, and a third one, of huge proportions, flew directly at their faces, flapping its wings frantically in the confined space, and only veered upward at the last minute, making a rhythmical whistling as it soared higher and higher.

The poor bride shrieked with fright, and four sympathetic echoes came from the bridesmaids. The father's alarm now turned to anger. Telling them to wait on the threshold, he entered the church to discover who was behind the production of what he deemed a very bad effort at a wedding prank. No sooner was he inside than his legs were assailed by a group of scuttling hedgehogs who managed to scramble past him into the open. He began to call out furiously for the member of the congregation whom he thought was responsible for perpetrating such an outrage on his daughter's wedding day. Of course nobody replied, and the Vicar came forward, wringing his hands, and with a soothing voice tried to calm the irate gentleman.

After a minute or two the bride and bridesmaids could no longer bear being kept in ignorance of the matter, and they entered the church in their turn, unaccompanied by the expected strains of the organ.

While the humans stood around and debated, some heatedly

and others more calmly, the cause of such an extraordinary occur-
rence, the smaller animals still inside the building were able, one
by one, to make their escape unnoticed. Mole was the last to reach
the door, but just outside he found Toad and Adder, trying to look
inconspicuous by the wall.

'They went that way,' Toad said, indicating the direction the
swifter animals had taken. 'They'll probably wait for us
somewhere.'

'I can't see anyone,' said Mole, peering ahead.

'Of course you can't,' said Adder impatiently. 'I'm surprised
you could even see your way to the door.'

'Oh, Adder, don't be unkind,' said Mole, badly hurt at the
reference to his purblindness. 'Let's . . . let's go on together, shall
we?'

'Not much else we can do,' muttered the snake, who felt Mole
was to blame for their present position by choosing their hiding-
place by the organ pipes.

'I'm sure when they've recovered themselves, Fox will send
someone back to help us,' said Toad confidently. 'It'll probably
be Kestrel.'

A little further on they caught up with some of the mice, who
had been constantly looking back over their shoulders in dire fear
of being pursued.

The humans, however, were far too busy arguing and talking
inside the church for any of them to think of looking for the cause
of the disturbance outside, and pretty soon all the animals had put
enough distance behind them for the renewed sounds of the organ
not to reach their ears.

Tarka the Otter

HENRY WILLAMSON

When the bees' feet shake the bells of the heather, and the ruddy strings of the sap-stealing dodder are twined about the green spikes of the furze, it is summertime on the commons. Exmoor is the high country of the winds, which are to the falcons and the hawks: clothed by whortleberry bushes and lichens and ferns and mossed trees in the goyals, which are to the foxes, the badgers, and the red deer: served by rain-clouds and drained by rock-littered streams, which are to the otters.

The moor knew the sun before it was bright, when it rolled red and ragged through the vapours of creation, not blindingly rayed like one of its own dandelions. The soil of the moor is of its own dead, and scanty; the rains return to the lower ground, to the pasture and cornfields of the valleys, which are under the wind, and the haunts of men.

The moor is to the deer, the badgers, the foxes, the otters, the falcons, and the hawks, pitiless despoilers of rooted and blooded things, which man has collected and set apart for himself; so they are killed. Olden war against greater despoilers began to end with the discoveries of iron and gunpowder; the sabre-toothed tigers, the bears, the wolves, all are gone, and the fragments of their bones lie on the rock of the original creation, under the lichens and grasses and mosses, or in the museums of towns. Once hunted himself, then hunting for necessity, man now hunts in the leisure of his time; but in nearly all those who through necessity of life till fields, herd beasts, and keep fowls, these remaining wildlings of the moors have enemies who care nothing for their survival. The farmers would exterminate nearly every wild bird and animal of prey, were it not for the landowners, among whom are some who care for the wildlings because they are sprung from the same land of England, and who would be unhappy if they thought the country would know them no more. For the animal they hunt to kill in its season, or those other animals or birds they cause to be destroyed for the continuance of their pleasure in sport – which they believe to be natural – they have no pity; and since they lack this incipient human instinct, they misunderstand and deride it in others. Pity acts through the imagination, the higher light of the world, and imagination arises from the world of things, as a rainbow from the sun. A rainbow may be beautiful and heavenly, but it will not grow corn for bread.

Within the moor is the Forest, a region high and treeless, where sedge grasses grow on the slopes to the sky. In early summer the wild spirit of the hills is heard in the voices of curlews. The birds fly up from solitary places, above their beloved and little ones, and float the wind in a sweet uprising music. Slowly on spread and hollow wings they sink, and their cries are trilling and cadent, until they touch earth and lift their wings above their heads, and poising, loose the last notes from their throats, like gold bubbles rising into sky again. Tall and solemn, with long hooped beaks, they stalk to their nestlings standing in wonder beside the tussocks. The mother-bird feeds her singer, and his three children cry to him. There are usually but three, because the carrion-crows rob the curlews of the first egg laid in each nest. Only when they find the broken empty shell do the curlews watch the crows, black and slinking, up the hillside.

Soon the curlew lifts his wings and runs from his young, trilling with open beak; his wings flap, and up he flies to fetch song from heaven to the wilderness again.

A tarn lies under two hills, draining water from a tussock-linked tract of bog called The Chains. The tarn is deep and brown and still, reflecting rushes and reeds at its sides, the sedges of the hills, and the sky over them. The northern end of the tarn is morass, trodden by deer and ponies. Water trickles away under its southern bank, and hurries in its narrow course by falls, runnels, pools, and cascades. One afternoon Tarka climbed out of the rillet's bed, scarcely wider than himself, and looked through green hart's-tongue ferns at the combe up which he had travelled. Nothing moved below him except water. He walked up the hill, and saw the tarn below him. He heard the dry croaking of frogs, and ran down the bank that dammed the dark peat-water. A yard down the slope he stopped.

A hen-raven, black from bristled beak to toes, hopped along the edge of the tarn when she saw him. Tarka heard small plopping sounds and saw ripples in the water, where bull-frogs had dived off the bank. The raven took three hops to a pile of dead frogs, then stopped, crouched down, poked out her head with flattened feathers, and gazed at Tarka. Her small eyes flickered with the whitish-grey membranes of the third eyelids. The raven was not afraid of an otter.

She had been fishing for frogs by dapping the water with her beak. Hearing the noises, the bull-frogs swam to the surface and turned with bulging eyes towards the dapping. The raven made a dry and brittle croak. When the frogs heard it, the skin swelled under their necks, and they croaked a challenge, mistaking the noises for the struggle of a choking female. They swam within a few inches of the raven's beak. One, perhaps two, would leap out of the water, and then the raven opened her beak and caught one, perhaps two. She was very quick. She hopped with them to her pile, spiked them through the head, and walked quietly to another fishing-place. She could carry eight or nine frogs in her craw at once to her nest of young in a rocky clitter near the head of the river Exe. When loaded, she flew with gaping beak. Tarka lifted his head and worked his nostrils. The steadfast glance of the small eyes along the black beak pointed at him. He smelled the frogs, took three quaddling steps towards the raven, and stopped again. The raven did not move, and he did not like her eyes. He turned away. She hopped after him, and nipped the tip of his rudder as he slipped into the tarn.

Krok-krok-krok! said the raven, cocking an eye at the sky. Tarka lay in the water and watched her picking up frog after frog and pouching them, before she jumped off the bank and flew over the eastern hill.

When she returned her mate was with her. They soared above the tarn. Sometimes the cock raven shut his wings, rolled sideways, and twirled on open wings again. *Krok-krok!* he said to the hen, seeing below the form of the swimming otter, darker than the dark tarn. The raven opened his beak wide, set his wings for descent, and croaked *kron-n-n-nk* during the slow, dipping swoop, in the curve of a scythe, from one green-lined margin to the other. Then he tumbled and twirled, alighting on the slope of the hill, and walked down to the water to catch frogs.

Several times each day the two ravens flew to the tarn. The cockbird talked to Tarka whenever he saw him, and pestered him when he was sunning himself on the bank. He would hop to within a few feet of him with a frog in his beak, and drop it just to windward of Tarka's nose. Once, when Tarka was playing with a frog and had turned his back on it for a moment, the raven picked it up and threw it to one side. Bird and otter played together, but they never touched one another. The raven, who was one of the three hundred sons of Kronk, would drop a stick into the tarn and Tarka would swim after it, bringing it to the bank and rolling with it between his paws. Occasionally the raven slyly pinched his rudder, and Tarka would run at him, tissing through his teeth. With flaps and hops the raven dodged him, flying up out of his way only when driven to water.

Day after day Tarka slept in the rushes in the morass at the north end of the tarn. Unless he was tired after the nightly prowl, the *kron-n-n-n-k* of the zooming raven would always wake him, and he would either run along the bank or swim by the reeds to play with the bird. One morning five ravens flew over the tarn, the hen leading three smaller ravens in line and the father behind them – black constellation of Orion. They lit on the turf of the dam. The youngsters sat on the bank and watched their mother dapping for frogs. Tarka ran along the bank, amid guttural squawks and cronks, to play with them, but the parents stabbed at him with their beaks, beating wings in his face and hustling him back to water. They flew over him when he bobbed for breath, and worried him so persistently that he never again went near a raven.

When the wind had blown the seeds of the cotton grass and the sedge drooped tawny under the sun, the curlews flew again to the seashore and the rivers. Little jerky flights of pipits crossed over the hollow in the hills, their twittering passed on, and the tarn lay silent as the sky. One afternoon in early September the silence stirred, and along the tawny hillcrest moved something like a leafless top of an oak branch. It became a stag hastening with tongue a-loll to the wooded valleys of the south. Silence settled on the moor until the hill-line was broken by a long and silent file of staghounds running down from The Chains on the line of a deer. Tarka stood on his bed of rushes and watched them until they loped into the sky. When he had settled again a blackcock hurtled down the western hill and flew over the tarn, followed by a grey hen with her two heath poults. Two horsemen in red coats slanted down the side of the hill; and after them came a young farmer riding bare-back a stallion with blown mane and flying tail. Then came a grey hunter, carrying a man with a face nearly as red as his coat. Others followed singly, and at long intervals, on weary horses.

That evening Tarka quitted the tarn, and journeyed over The Chains to water that hastened in a bright thread out of the bog. It entered a narrow goyal, and the moon was hid by the hill before him. After a mile the water turned north, under the hill whose worn grey feet it had broken for its bed. The goyal widened by the Hoar Oak, whose splintered stump, black as its shadow with the moon behind, glistered with the tracks of slugs. Near the Hoar Oak stood a sapling, caged from the teeth and horns of deer, a little tree by the grave of its father.

And Tarka went down the Hoar Oak Water which, under ridge and common, shattered the moon into shards and lost them under the trees which grew together in the lower valley. Its voice passed from leaf to leaf, up through the woods where badgers were seeking mice and black slugs, and to the night over the autumn hills.

Where two waters met, to seek the sea together, Tarka walked over the trail of otters, and recognizing the scent of White-tip, he followed up the water the otter had travelled. Near the end of the night, while he was swimming in a pool scooped in the rock below a fall, he saw an otter-shape before him. It moved slowly with the sway of water, its head lolled on a stone. It had been drowned some hours. The whistles of otters playing at the fall during the previous night had been heard by the water-owner, who had set a gin under the wash of the fall, on a sunken ledge of rock where otters touched after the joyful pounding of the plunge. The otters had come back again.

Iron in the water sinks, and however long cubs call her, a bitch-otter cannot swim with three legs for ever.

Tarka heard the clink of the chain as the swollen body rolled; and his bubbles blown of fear rose behind him.

At sunrise he had crossed two miles of woods and fields – stubble with lines of sheaves, stacked in sixes and tied in fours, fields of mangel and sweet turnip, where partridge crouched, and pasture given over to sheep – and found other water below Beggars' Roost hill. Ducks were paddling by a farm as he walked upstream, passing under a bridge, by which grew a monkey-tree with leaves as sharp as magpies' beaks. Cottages by the waterside and a mill were left behind, and he came to quiet meadows where only robins were singing. He crossed from side to side looking for a place to hide during the sunlight. Half a mile above the mill he found a rock in the left bank of the stream, with a wide opening half under water. Hazels grew on the bank above. Their leaves took on the golden-green of spring in the beams of the low autumn sun as Tarka crept under the rock.

He was awakened by the tremendous baying of hounds. He saw

feet splashing in the shallow water, a row of noses, and many flacking tongues. The entrance was too small for any head to enter. He crouched a yard away, against the cold rock. The noise hurt the fine drums of his ears.

Hob-nailed boots scraped on the brown shillets of the waterbed, and iron-tipped hunting-poles tapped the rocks.

Go'r'n leave it! Leave it! Go'r'n leave it! Deadlock! Harper! Go'r'n leave it!

Tarka heard the horn and the low opening became lighter.

Go'r'n leave it! Captain! Deadlock! Go'r'n leave it!

The horn twanged fainter as the pack was taken away. Then a pole was thrust into the holt and prodded about blindly. It slid out again. Tarka saw boots and hands and the face of a terrier. A voice whispered, *Leu in there, Sammy, leu in there!* The small ragged brown animal crept out of the hands. Sammy smelled Tarka, saw him, and began to sidle towards him. *Waugh-waugh-waugh-wa-waugh.* As the otter did not move, the terrier crept nearer to him, yapping with head stretched forward.

After a minute Tarka could bear the irritating noises no more. Tissing, with open mouth, he moved past the terrier, whose snarly yapping changed to a high-pitched yelping. The men on the opposite bank stood silent and still. They saw Tarka's head in sunlight, which came through the trees behind them and turned the brown shillets a warm yellow. The water ran clear and cold. Tarka saw three men in blue coats; they did not move and he slipped into the water. It did not cover his back, and he returned to the bankside roots. He moved in the shadows and under the ferns at his ordinary travelling pace. One of three watching men declared that an otter had no sense of fear.

No hound spoke, but the reason of the silence was not considered by Tarka, who could not reason such things. He had been awakened with a shock, he had been tormented by a noise, he had left a dangerous place, and he was escaping from human enemies. As he walked upstream, with raised head, his senses of smell, sight, and hearing were alert for his greatest enemies, the hounds.

The stream being narrow and shallow, the otter was given four minutes' law. Four minutes after Tarka had left he heard behind him the short and long notes of the horn, and the huntsman crying amidst the tongues of hounds *Ol-ol-ol-ol-ol-ol-over! Get on to'm! Ol-ol-ol-ol-over!* as the pack returned in full cry to the water. Hounds splashed into the water around the rock, wedging themselves at its opening and breaking into couples and half couples, leaping through the water after the wet and shivering terrier, throwing their tongues and dipping their noses to the wash of scent coming down.

Deadlock plunged at the lead, with Caroline, Sailoress, Captain, and Playboy. They passed the terrier, and Deadlock was so eager that he knocked him down. Sammy picked up his shivery body and followed.

Tarka sank all but his nostrils in a pool and waited. He lay in the sunlit water like a brown log slanting to the stones on which his rudder rested. The huntsman saw him. Tarka lifted his whiskered head out of the water, and stared at the huntsman. Hounds were speaking just below. From the pond the stream flowed for six feet down the smooth side up which he had crept. When Deadlock jumped into the pool and lapped the scent lying on the water, Tarka put down his head with hardly a ripple, and like a skin of brown oil moved under the hound's belly. Soundlessly he emerged, and the sun glistened on his water-sleeked coat as he walked down on the algae-smeared rock. He seemed to walk under their muzzles slowly, and to be treading on their feet.

Let hound, hunt him! Don't help hounds or they'll chop him!

The pack was confused. Every hound owned the scent, which was like a tangled line, the end of which was sought for unravelling. But soon Deadlock pushed through the pack and told the way the otter had gone.

As Tarka was running over shillets with water scarcely deep enough to cover his rudder, Deadlock saw him and with stiff stern ran straight at him. Tarka quitted the water. The dead twigs and leaves at the hedge-bottom crackled and rustled as he pushed through to the meadow. While he was running over the grass, he

Deadlock . . . threw his tongue before the pack

could hear the voice of Deadlock raging as the bigger black-and-white hound struggled through the hazel twigs and brambles and honeysuckle bines. He crossed fifty yards of meadow, climbed the bank, and ran down again on to a tarred road. The surface burned his pads, but he ran on, and even, when an immense crimson creature bore down upon him he did not go back into the meadow across which hounds were streaming. With a series of shudders the crimson creature slowed to a standstill, while human figures rose out of it, and pointed. He ran under the motor-coach, and came out into brown sunshine, hearing above the shouts of men the clamour of hounds trying to scramble up the high bank and pulling each other down in their eagerness.

He ran in the shade of the ditch, among bits of newspaper, banana and orange skins, cigarette ends and crushed chocolate boxes. A long yellow creature grew bigger and bigger before him, and some men rose out of it and peered down at him as he passed it. With smarting eyes he ran two hundred yards of the road, which for him was a place of choking stinks and hurtful noises. Pausing in the ditch, he hearkened to the clamour changing its tone as hounds leaped down into the road. He ran on for another two hundred yards, then climbed the bank, pushed through dusty leaves and grasses and briars that would hold him, and down the sloping meadow to the stream. He splashed into the water and swam until rocks and boulders rose before him. He climbed and walked over them. His rudder drawn on mosses and lichens left a strong scent behind him. Deadlock, racing over the green shadowed grassland, threw his tongue before the pack.

In the water, through shallow and pool, his pace was steady, but not hurried; he moved faster than the stream; he insinuated himself from slide to pool, from pool to boulder, leaving his scent in the wet marks of his pads and rudder.

People were running through the meadow, and in the near distance arose the notes of the horn and hoarse cries. Hounds' tongues broke out united and firm, and Tarka knew that they had reached the stream. The sun-laden water of the pools was spun into eddies by the thrusts of his webbed hindlegs. He passed through shadow and dapple, through runnel and plash. The water sparkled amber in the sunbeams, and his brown sleek pelt glistened whenever his back made ripples. His movements in water were unhurried, like an eel's. The hounds came nearer.

The stream after a bend flowed near the roadway, where more motor-cars were drawn up. Some men and women, holding notched poles, were watching from the cars – sportsmen on wheels.

Beggars' Roost Bridge was below. With hounds so near Tarka was heedless of the man that leaned over the stone parapet, watching for him. They shouted, waved hats, and cheered the hounds. There were ducks above the bridge, quacking loudly as they left the stream and waddled to the yard, and when Tarka came to where they had been, he left the water and ran after them. They beat their wings as they tried to fly from him, but he reached the file and scattered them running through them and disappearing. Nearer and nearer came Deadlock, with Captain and Waterwitch leading the pack. Huntsmen, whippers-in, and field were left behind, struggling through hedges and over banks.

Hounds were bewildered when they reached the yard. They ran with noses to ground in puzzled excitement. Captain's shrill voice told that Tarka had gone under a gate. Waterwitch followed the wet seals in the dust, but turned off along a track of larger webs. The line was tangled again. Deadlock threw his belving tongue. Other hounds followed, but the scent only led to a duck that beat its wings and quacked in terror before them. A man with a rake drove them off, shouting and threatening to strike them. Dewdrop spoke across the yard and the hounds galloped to her, but the line led to a gate which they tried to leap, hurtling themselves up and falling from the top bar. A duck had gone under the gate, but not Tarka.

All scent was gone. Hounds rolled in the dust or trotted up to the men and women, sniffing their pockets for food. Rufus found a rabbit skin and ate it; Render fought with Sandboy – but not seriously, as they feared each other; Deadlock went off alone. And hounds were waiting for a lead when the sweating huntsman, grey pot-hat pushed back from his red brow, ran up with the two whippers-in and called them into a pack again. The thick scent of Muscovy ducks had checked the hunt.

Tarka had run through a drain back to the stream, and now he rested in the water that carried him every moment nearer to the murmurous glooms of the glen below. He saw the coloured blur of a kingfisher perching on a twig as it eyed the water for beetle or loach. The kingfisher saw him moving under the surface, as his shadow broke the net of ripple shadows that drifted in meshes of pale gold on the stony bed beneath him.

While he was walking past the roots of a willow under the bank, he heard the yapping of the terrier. Sammy had crept through the drain, and was looking out at the end, covered with black filth, and eagerly telling his big friends to follow him downstream. As he yapped, Deadlock threw his tongue. The stallion hound was below the drain, and had refound the line where Tarka had last touched the shillets. Tarka saw him ten yards away, and slipping back into the water, swam with all webs down the current, pushing from his nose a ream whose shadow beneath was an arrow of gold pointing down to the sea.

Again he quitted the water and ran on land to wear away his scent. He had gone twenty yards when Deadlock scrambled up the bank with Render and Sandboy, breathing the scent which was as high as their muzzles. Tarka reached the waterside trees again a length ahead of Deadlock, and fell into the water like a sodden log. Deadlock leapt after him and snapped at his head; but the water was friendly to the otter, who rolled in smooth and graceful movement away from the jaws, a straight bite of which would have crushed his skull.

Here sunlight was shut out by the oaks, and the roar of the first fall was beating back from the leaves. The current ran faster, narrowing into a race with twirls and hollows marking the sunken rocks. The roar grew louder in a drifting spray. Tarka and Deadlock were carried to where a broad sunbeam came down through a break in the foliage and lit the mist above the fall. Tarka went over in the heavy white folds of the torrent and Deadlock was hurled over after him. They were lost in the churn and pressure of the pool until a small brown head appeared and gazed for its enemy in the broken honeycomb of foam. A black-and-white body uprolled beside it, and the head of the hound was thrust up as he tried to tread away from the current that would draw him under. Tarka was master of whirlpools; they were his playthings. He rocked in the surge with delight; then high above he heard the note of the horn. He yielded himself to the water and let it take him away down the gorge into a pool where rocks were piled above. He searched under the dripping ferny clitter for a hiding-place.

Underwater he saw two legs, joined to two wavering and inverted images of legs, and above them the blurred shapes of a man's head and shoulders. He turned away from the fisherman into the current again, and as he breathed he heard the horn again. On the road above the glen the pack was trotting between huntsman and whippers-in, and before them men were running with poles at the trail, hurrying down the hill to the bridge, to make a stickle to stop Tarka reaching the sea.

Tarka left Deadlock far behind. The hound was feeble and bruised and breathing harshly, his head battered and his sight dazed, but still following. Tarka passed another fisherman, and by chance the tiny feathered hook lodged in his ear. The reel spun against the cheek, *re-re-re* continuously, until all the silken line had run through the snake-rings of the rod, which bent into a circle, and whipped back straight again as the gut trace snapped.

Tarka saw the bridge, the figure of a man below it, and a row of faces above. He heard shouts. The man standing on a rock took off his hat, scooped the air, and holla'd to the huntsman, who was running and slipping with the pack on the loose stones of the steep red road. Tarka walked out of the last pool above the bridge, ran over a mossy rock merged with the water again, and pushed through the legs of the man.

Tally-ho!

Tarka had gone under the bridge when Harper splashed into the water. The pack poured through the gap between the end of the parapet and the hillside earth, and their tongues rang under the bridge and down the walls of the houses built on the rock above the river.

Among rotting motor tyres, broken bottles, tins, pails, shoes, and other castaway rubbish lying in the bright water, hounds made their plunging leaps. Once Tarka turned back: often he was splashed and trodden on. The stream was seldom deep enough to cover him, and always shallow enough for the hounds to move at double his speed. Sometimes he was under the pack, and then, while hounds were massing for the worry, his small head would look out beside a rock ten yards below them.

Between boulders and rocks crusted with shellfish and shaggy with seaweed, past worm-channered posts that marked the fairway for fishing boats at high water, the pack hunted the otter. Off each post a gull launched itself, cackling angrily as it looked down at the animals. Tarka reached the sea. He walked slowly into the surge of a wavelet, and sank away from the chop of old Harper's jaws, just as Deadlock ran through the pack. Hounds swam beyond the lines of waves, while people stood at the sea-lap and watched the huntsman wading to his waist. It was said that the otter was dead-beat, and probably floating stiffly in the shallow water. After a few minutes the huntsman shook his head, and withdrew the horn from his waistcoat. He filled his lungs and stopped his breath and was tightening his lips for the four long notes of the call-off, when a brown head with hard eyes was thrust out of the water a yard from Deadlock. Tarka stared into the hound's face and cried *Ic-yang!*

The head sank. Swimming under Deadlock, Tarka bit on to the loose skin of the flews and pulled the hound's head under water. Deadlock tried to twist round and crush the otter's skull in his jaws, but he struggled vainly. Bubbles blew out of his mouth. Soon he was choking. The hounds did not know what was happening. Deadlock's hindlegs kicked the air weakly. The huntsman waded out and pulled him inshore, but Tarka loosened his bite only when he needed new air in his lungs; and then he swam under and gripped Deadlock again. Only when hounds were upon him did Tarka let go. He vanished in a wave.

Long after the water had been emptied out of Deadlock's lungs, and the pack had trotted off for the long uphill climb to the railway station, the gulls were flying over something in the sea beyond the mouth of the little estuary. Sometimes one dropped its yellow webs to alight on the water; always it flew up again into the restless, wailing throng, startled by the snaps of white teeth. A cargo steamer was passing up the Severn Sea, leaving a long smudge of smoke on the horizon, where a low line of clouds billowed over the coast of Wales. The regular thumps of its screw in the windless blue calm were borne to where Tarka lay, drowsy and content, but watching the pale yellow eyes of the nearest bird. At last the gulls grew tired of seeing only his eyes, and flew back to their post; and turning on his back, Tarka yawned and stretched himself, and floated at his ease.

The New Horse

R. M. BALLANTYNE

Young Charley Kennedy grows up in the frozen wastes of Hudson's Bay, during the early days of fur trading. Here Charley attempts, somewhat rashly, to break a new horse, and learns the hard way the advantages of caution . . .

During the long winter that reigns in the northern regions of America, the thermometer ranges, for many months together, from zero down to 20, 30, and 40 degrees *below* it. In different parts of the country the intensity of the frost varies a little, but not sufficiently to make any appreciable change in one's sensation of cold. At York Fort, on the shores of Hudson's Bay, where the winter is eight months long, the spirit-of-wine (mercury being useless in so cold a climate) sometimes falls so low as 50 degrees below zero; and away in the regions of Great Bear Lake, it has been known to fall considerably lower than 60 degrees below zero of Fahrenheit. Cold of such intensity, of course, produces many curious and interesting effects; which, although scarcely noticed by the inhabitants, make a strong impression upon the minds of those who visit the country for the first time. A youth goes out to walk on one of the first sharp, frosty mornings. His locks are brown and his face ruddy. In half-an-hour he returns with his face blue, his nose frost-bitten, and his locks *white* – the latter effect being produced by his breath congealing on his hair and breast, until both are covered with hoar-frost. Perhaps he is of a sceptical nature, prejudiced, it may be, in favour of old habits and customs, so that, although told, by those who ought to know, that it is absolutely necessary to wear moccasins in winter, he prefers the leather boots to which he has been accustomed at home, and goes out with them accordingly. In a few minutes the feet begin to lose sensation. First the toes, as far as feeling goes, vanish; then the heels depart, and he feels the extraordinary, and peculiar, and altogether disagreeable sensation of one who has had his heels and toes amputated, and is walking about on his insteps. Soon, however, these also fade away, and the unhappy youth rushes frantically home on the stumps of his ankle-bones – at least so it appears to him – and so in reality it would turn out to be, if he did not speedily rub the benumbed appendages into vitality again.

The whole country, during this season, is buried in snow, and the prairies of Red River present the appearance of a sea of the purest white, for five or six months of the year. Impelled by hunger, troops of prairie wolves prowl round the settlement, safe from the assault of man in consequence of their light weight permitting them to scamper away on the surface of the snow, into which man or horse, from their greater weight, would sink, so as to render pursuit either fearfully laborious, or altogether impossible. In spring, however, when the first thaws begin to take place, and commence that delightful process of disruption which introduces this charming season of the year, the relative position of wolf and man is reversed. The snow becomes suddenly soft, so that the short legs of the wolf, sinking deep into it, fail to reach the solid ground below, and he is obliged to drag heavily along, while the long legs of the horse enable him to plunge through and dash aside the snow at a rate which, although not very fleet, is sufficient, nevertheless, to overtake the chase and give his rider a chance of shooting it. The inhabitants of Red River are not much addicted to this sport, but the gentlemen of the Hudson Bay

The New Horse

Service sometimes practise it; and it was to a hunt of this description that our young friend Charley Kennedy was now so anxious to go.

The morning was propitious. The sun blazed in dazzling splendour in a sky of deep unclouded blue, while the white prairie glittered as if it were a sea of diamonds rolling out in an unbroken sheet from the walls of the fort to the horizon, and on looking at which one experienced all the pleasurable feelings of being out on a calm day on the wide, wide sea, without the disagreeable consequence of being very, very sick.

The thermometer stood at 39° in the shade, and 'everythin*k*,' as Tom Whyte emphatically expressed it, 'looked like a runnin' of right away into slush.' That unusual sound, the trickling of water, so inexpressibly grateful to the ears of those who dwell in frosty climes, was heard all around, as the heavy masses of snow on the house-tops sent a few adventurous drops gliding down the icicles which depended from the eves and gables; and there was a balmy softness in the air that told of coming spring. Nature, in fact, seemed to have wakened from her long nap, and was beginning to think of getting up. Like people, however, who venture to delay so long as to *think* about it, Nature frequently turns round and goes to sleep again in her icy cradle for a few weeks after the first awakening.

The scene in the court-yard of Fort Garry harmonised with the cheerful spirit of the morning. Tom Whyte, with that upright solemnity which constituted one of his characteristic features, was standing in the centre of a group of horses, whose energy he endeavoured to restrain with the help of a small Indian boy, to whom, meanwhile, he imparted a variety of useful and otherwise unattainable information.

'You see, Joseph,' said he to the urchin, who gazed gravely in his face with a pair of very large and dark eyes, 'ponies is often skittish. Reason why one should be, an' another not, I can't comprehend. P'r'aps its nat'ral, p'r'aps not, but howsomediver so 'tis, an' if its more nor above the likes o' *me*, Joseph, you needn't be surprised that it's somethin*k* haltogether beyond *you*.'

It will not surprise the reader to be told that Joseph made no reply to this speech, having a very imperfect acquaintance with the English language, especially the peculiar dialect of that tongue in which Tom Whyte was wont to express his ideas, when he had any.

He merely gave a grunt, and continued to gaze at Tom's fishy eyes, which were about as interesting as the face to which they belonged, and *that* might have been mistaken for almost anything.

'Yes, Joseph,' he continued, 'that's a fact. There's the noo brown 'oss now, *it's* a skittish 'un. And there's Mr Kennedy's gray mare, wot's a standin' of beside me, she aint skittish a bit, though she's plenty of spirit, and wouldn't care hanything for a five-barred gate. Now, wot I want to know is, wot's the reason why?'

We fear that the reason why, however interesting it might prove to naturalists, must remain a profound secret for ever; for, just as the groom was about to entertain Joseph with one of his theories on the point, Charley Kennedy and Harry Somerville hastily approached.

'Ho, Tom!' exclaimed the former, 'have you got the miller's pony for me?'

'Why, no, sir; 'e 'adn't got his shoes on, sir, last night –'

'Oh! bother his shoes,' said Charley, in a voice of great disappointment. 'Why didn't you bring him up without shoes, man, eh?'

'Well, sir, the miller said 'e'd get 'em put on early this mornin', an' I 'xpect 'e'll be 'ere in 'alf a hour at farthest, sir.'

'Oh, very well,' replied Charley, much relieved, but still a little nettled at the bare possibility of being late. 'Come along, Harry, let's go and meet him. He'll be long enough of coming if we don't go to poke him up a bit.'

'You'd better wait,' called out the groom, as the boys hastened away. 'If you go by the river he'll p'r'aps come by the plains, and if you go by the plains he'll p'r'aps come by the river.'

Charley and Harry stopped and looked at each other. Then they looked at the groom, and as their eyes surveyed his solemn, cadaverous countenance, which seemed a sort of bad caricature of the long visages of the horses that stood around him, they burst into a simultaneous and prolonged laugh.

'He's a clever old lamp-post,' said Harry, at last; 'we had better remain, Charley.'

'You see,' continued Tom Whyte, 'the pony's 'oofs is in an 'orrible state. Last night w'en I see'd 'im, I said to the miller, says I, "John, I'll take 'im down to the smith d'rectly." "Very good," said John. So I 'ad him down to the smith –'

The remainder of Tom's speech was cut short by one of those unforeseen operations of the laws of nature, which are peculiar to arctic climates. During the long winter, repeated falls of snow cover the house-tops with white mantles upwards of a foot thick, which become gradually thicker and more consolidated as winter advances. In spring, the suddenness of the thaw loosens these from the sloping roofs, and precipitates them in masses to the ground. These miniature avalanches are dangerous, people having been seriously injured and sometimes killed by them. Now, it happened that a very large mass of snow, which lay on, and partly depended from, the roof of the house near to which the horses were standing, gave way, and just at that critical point in Tom Whyte's speech when he ' 'ad 'im down to the smith,' fell with a stunning crash on the back of Mr Kennedy's gray mare. The mare was not 'skittish' – by no means – according to Tom's idea, but it would have been more than an ordinary mare to have stood the sudden descent of half-a-ton of snow without *some* symptom of consciousness. No sooner did it feel the blow, than it sent both heels with a bang against the wooden store, by way of preliminary movement, and then, rearing up with a wild snort, it sprang over Tom Whyte's head, jerked the reins from his hand, and upset him in the snow. Poor Tom never *bent* to anything. The military despotism under which he had been reared having substituted a touch of the cap for a bow, rendered it unnecessary to bend; prolonged drill, laziness, and rheumatism made it at last impossible. When he stood up, he did so after the manner of a pillar; when he sat down, he broke across at two points, much in the way in which a foot-rule would have done, had *it* felt disposed to sit down, and when he fell, he came down like an overturned lamp-post. On the present occasion, Tom became horizontal in a moment, and from his unfortunate propensity to fall straight, his head, reaching much farther than might have been expected, came into violent contact with the small Indian boy, who fell flat likewise, letting go the reins of the horses, which latter no sooner felt themselves free, than they fled, curvetting and snorting round the court, with reins and manes flying in rare confusion.

The two boys, who could scarce stand for laughing, ran to the gates of the fort to prevent the chargers getting free, and in a short time they were again secured, although evidently much elated in spirit.

A few minutes after this, Mr Grant issued from the principal house, leaning on Mr Kennedy's arm, and followed by the senior clerk, Peter Mactavish, and one or two friends who had come to take part in the wolf-hunt. They were all armed with double or single barrelled guns or pistols, according to their several fancies. The two elderly gentlemen alone entered upon the scene without any more deadly weapons than their heavy riding whips. Young Harry Somerville, who had been strongly advised not to take a gun lest he should shoot himself, or his horse or his companions, was content to take the field with a small pocket-pistol, which he crammed to the muzzle with a compound of ball and swan-shot.

'It won't do,' said Mr Grant, in an earnest voice, to his friend, as they walked towards the horses – 'it won't do to check him too abruptly, my dear sir.'

It was evident that they were recurring to the subject of conversation of the previous day, and it was also evident that the father's wrath was in that very uncertain state when a word or a look can throw it into violent agitation.

'Just permit me,' continued Mr Grant, 'to get him sent to the Saskatchewan or Athabasca for a couple of years. By that time he'll have had enough of a rough life, and be only too glad to get a berth at headquarters. If you thwart him now, I feel convinced that he'll break through all restraint.'

'Humph!' ejaculated Mr Kennedy, with a frown. 'Come here,

Acknowledgements

The publishers would like to extend their grateful thanks to the following authors, publishers and others for kindly granting permission to reproduce the extracts and stories included in this anthology.

THE SMALL MIRACLE by Paul Gallico. Excerpt reprinted by permission of the author, Hughes Massie Ltd. and Doubleday & Co., Inc. Copyright 1950 by Paul Gallico.

BAMBI'S DISCOVERY from *Bambi* by Felix Salten, translated by Whittaker Chambers. Reprinted by permission of the Executors of the Felix Salten Estate, the translator and the publishers, Jonathan Cape Ltd. and Simon & Schuster, Inc., a Division of Gulf & Western Corporation. Copyright © 1928, 1956 by Simon & Schuster, Inc.

PETER, THE WHITE CAT OF TRENARREN from *Three Cornish Cats* by A. L. Rowse. Reprinted by permission of the author and the publishers, Weidenfeld (Publishers) Ltd.

TUCKER'S LIFE SAVINGS from *The Cricket in Times Square* by George Selden. Reprinted by permission of the author, Laurence Pollinger Ltd. and Farrar, Straus & Giroux, Inc. Copyright © 1960 by George Selden.

THE MALTESE CAT by Rudyard Kipling. Reprinted by permission of the National Trust and Macmillan London Ltd.

MRS PUMPHREY'S PEKINGESE from *If Only They Could Talk* by James Herriot. Reprinted by permission of the author, Michael Joseph Ltd. and St. Martin's Press, Inc. Macmillan & Co., Inc. Copyright © 1972 by James Herriot.

A SPOT OF DECORATING from *More About Paddington* by Michael Bond. © Michael Bond 1959, published Collins. Reprinted by permission of Collins Publishers and Houghton Mifflin Company. Copyright © 1959 by Michael Bond.

EGGBERT from *The Drunken Forest* by Gerald Durrell. Reprinted by permission of the author, Granada Publishing Ltd. and Curtis Brown Ltd.

KYM from the book of the same name by Joyce Stranger. Reprinted by permission of the author and the publishers, Michael Joseph Ltd.

CUB LIFE from *Born Free* by Joy Adamson. Reprinted by permission of the author, Collins Publishers and Pantheon Books, a Division of Random House, Inc. Copyright © 1960 by Joy Adamson.

HIS FIRST FLIGHT from *The Short Stories of Liam O'Flaherty* and *Spring Sowing* by Liam O'Flaherty. Reprinted by permission of the author and the publishers, Jonathan Cape Ltd. and Harcourt Brace Jovanovich, Inc.